THE SIOUX

THE SIOUX

IRENE HANDL

JONATHAN CAPE
THIRTY BEDFORD SQUARE LONDON

First published 1965
Reprinted 1966
Reissued 1984
Copyright © Irene Handl 1965
Jonathan Cape Ltd, 30 Bedford Square, London WC1B 3EL

British Library Cataloguing in Publication Data

Handl, Irene
The sioux.——2nd ed.
I. Title
823'.914[F]   PR6058.A564

ISBN 0-224-02243-1

Printed in Great Britain by
St Edmundsbury Press, Bury St Edmunds, Suffolk

For

LIANE AND DENNIS

CONTENTS

I

The Voice from Paris

'What's up, darling?' Castleton wants to know.

She makes a quick gesture for silence with her hand. It seems there is some hold-up about getting the boy over. Marguerite's brother, Armand Benoir, has been on the telephone from Paris every night for the last week of their honeymoon to report on her invalid son, Georges-Marie Benoir.

The boy is Mim's son by her first marriage at sixteen to her cousin, Georges Benoir.

It is about twenty-five minutes past six on Sunday night when Armand rings up. They are supposed to be going out for drinks.

'Mon dieu, Vincent,' says Marguerite, instantly apprehensive for her child.

Armand says at once: 'It's about little Benoir. Let Vince listen, Mimi. It concerns him too.'

Castleton takes up the special attachment he has had fitted to every telephone in the house at Marguerite's request. These extra earphones are considered indispensable to civilised telephone users

I

by the Benoirs who certainly use the telephone in a big way. Castleton has known Mim and her brother to talk to each other over the telephone for more than two hours at a stretch.

He hears his brother-in-law's pleasant voice saying: 'It's this. There is no question of flying puss over at the moment.' Puss is Armand's name for George.

'Ah, non,' calls out Marguerite. 'Ah, non, Armand! Pourquoi?'

Castleton can measure her alarm from the way she has lapsed into French.

'But what has happened? Is moumou ill?' Moumou is Mim's pet name for her son.

He is not ill. Nothing has happened. 'Courvoisier is against it, voilà tout.' Benoir says: 'Don't let her ruin what's left of your honeymoon for you, Vince.'

Marguerite cries: 'But it is quite ridiculous, moumou has always flown everywhere! Why is Courvoisier against it suddenly?'

Her brother merely asks: 'Is Vince still around, Mimi? I want to speak to him.'

'Yes, he is here. But what has happened with moumou, Armand? His last tests were good.'

'Courvoisier wanted a new diagnosis made. Obviously he wasn't satisfied.'

'He is an imbecile!' exclaims Marguerite. Her brother doesn't bother to answer this. He merely says: 'Puss had to go into the Clinic for two days.'

'Mon dieu, what happened?'

'They got the tests done.' Armand says simply.

'Is he back at Auteuil?'

'Naturally he is back. Mammy has given him his dinner in bed. He chose champagne and oysters.'

'It's a disaster,' declares Marguerite.

'On the contrary, champagne and oysters are very good. He shows a very respectable taste already, your little Benoir. Let me have Vince a moment, will you?'

'Who went with him to the Clinic?' Marguerite wants to know.

'I did. Everyone else sent love and kisses but it was Benoir who had to immure himself for two days.'

'My poor Armand. As always, everything devolves on you!'

'I have survived. Be a good fellow, Mi, pass me Vince.'

2

'But what will you do?' persists Marguerite. 'How will you get him over, Armand?'

'We'll just have to store him,' her brother says, laughing. 'Don't worry, you'll get your property back all right. Hey, Vince!'

'Hullo,' says Castleton, taking over. He keeps hold of his wife's hand. She is listening intently by his side, her whole body tense.

'You heard that, Vince, I suppose?'

'Yes, it's a brute,' Castleton says. 'Can I do anything?'

'They are afraid of the altitude,' Armand says. 'I'll have to freight him over as best I can. How're you making out, fella?'

'I'm fine,' says Castleton, but Marguerite bursts out: 'It will take you six days by sea and train, Benoir. You will be bored to tears!'

He points out tranquilly: 'It can't be helped, my dear.'

'Ah! Bad moumou!' scolds Marguerite as if her son were in the room. 'You make so much trouble for my poor Armand, you bad moumou!' Her indignation with her treasure for being less than perfect strikes Castleton as being very funny. He asks his brother-in-law: 'Why can't I fetch George? I can meet you at Cherbourg and bring him back. Or I could fly direct to Paris and take the whole thing off your hands. It can't exactly be convenient for you to take time off just now.'

Armand's son Bienville is getting married in a month's time. From what Castleton has gathered from Mim, the wedding is to be *the* event of the Paris season.

'Ah, that!' Armand says laughing. 'Let the de Greniers worry about that. For once Marie and I are on the credit side. One of the few decent things Viv has ever done for his poor papa and maman is to have been born a boy.' Aside from that Armand says he will be quite glad of a few days' respite from the attentions of the Paris press. 'Poor Marie and I live in constant terror of reporters. They have practically taken over at Auteuil. Elaine and Viv of course are absolutely delighted. Their generation has been conditioned to finding photographers in their marriage bed.'

'Ah, non, be serious!' Marguerite says in a dissatisfied voice. 'What will you do about George, Benoir?'

'Paris-Cherbourg,' Armand says simply. 'Cherbourg-New York. Then, if the customs are not too anti-Benoir, we'll just be able to make the Gulf flyer in time for you to drink in your trésor with the apéritifs on Sunday night.'

3

'But moumou can't travel by train,' objects Marguerite, taking her hand away from Castleton's. 'Leave me, Vincent, please, it is getting on my nerves.'

'Moumou can't travel period,' Armand says. 'We will just have to do the best we can for him, my dear.'

She asks suddenly: 'Are all the results of the tests out?'

'No. They will be complete in two days.'

'Then you could still go by air,' his sister tells him, 'and save yourself this débâcle of a journey by sea and train.'

'I will not fly, chérie,' Armand says.

'Even if Courvoisier agrees, on the results of the tests?'

'Even if Courvoisier agrees,' Armand says. 'We talked it over. It appears that if he flies at all he would have to wear an oxygen mask.'

'Well?'

'I shall not ask it of him. It could affect his nerves.'

But since it would only be for a few hours?

The voice from Paris returns calmly: 'I have just said he will not fly, my dear.'

'You are completely mad!' Marguerite says. 'It is ridiculous just for a few hours.'

'Non, j'ai dit non,' Armand says. 'Terminé, Mi.'

She says no more, and Castleton is made aware of the absolute authority carried by his brother-in-law as head of Mim's family. She sits looking at her husband, her eyes full of a sombre discontent.

'Ah, ça, vous savez. Ça!'

'Never mind, darling,' Castleton comforts her. 'It'll only be a few days till you have your boy.' Six and a bit, says Castleton, to be exact.

'How d'you like being married to the Governor of Alcatraz, Vince?' enquires Armand. The Governor of Alcatraz is Armand's name for Marguerite in a certain mood.

'I like it,' Castleton says, 'very much.'

Armand says blandly: 'Wait till you get little Benoir on your neck—then you'll catch the full aroma of married life in your face.'

Marguerite says: 'If moumou is going by sea . . .'

'He is going by sea, my darling,' Armand says. 'We have already covered this subject.'

'Then you must tell Mammy to give him only his biscottes and

4

Vichy and a little cognac during the whole crossing. He is to remain in his suite, d'you hear me, Armand? I absolutely forbid him to eat in the dining-room.'

'D'accord, madame.'

And on the train it must be the same. 'Armand, are you listening to me? Vichy, biscottes and cognac. Nothing more.'

'D'accord, d'accord.'

At worst her son will become an alcoholic.

'I do not want moumou to leave his state-room. Mammy must keep him in bed. And she is to keep that child of hers, that stupid Dédé, away from him for the whole of the trip. D'you hear me, Benoir? I shall question moumou when I see him and you know he always tells the truth.'

'What a fool!' Armand says laughing. 'Can you imagine that fool stepson of yours, Vince? He's out of his shoes because he's going back to Alcatraz next week!'

Marguerite says: 'I don't want to hear from him that that imbecile has been with him even for half-an-hour! Moumou will be exhausted enough as it is with this ridiculous journey.' Marguerite says bitterly: 'It will probably bring on an attack.'

'Mimi,' says Armand, 'you're frightening Vince to death. He'll think he's getting the biggest confirmed invalid for a stepson.'

Marguerite says: 'If you want my opinion, I think Courvoisier is out of his mind.'

Armand calmly assures her: 'He will survive your opinion, ma chère. He has a reputation to consider.' She may not know it, but the world contains quite a few names besides Benoir. He changes the subject by asking Castleton what his sister is wearing tonight.

Castleton says that Mrs C. is wearing a black frock and looks particularly stunning in spite of being in a bit of a state about the boy.

Armand says coolly: 'I hope my sister has no intention of playing the eternal widow with you, Vince. Otherwise, as her nephew Bienville puts it, she will pretty soon bore the piss.'

Marguerite says briefly: 'Black is a Benoir colour. Black and white.'

All the same the British prefer colours. Floral prints. And blue. 'My God,' says Armand, 'those Merrick blues!' Miss Merrick is George's English governess.

Benoir is of the opinion that at least a gesture should be made

5

to compensate his luckless brother-in-law for what the Sioux have done to him. The Sioux is the Benoir name for the Benoirs. 'That lift and all those bidets, Vince—they are already installed, I suppose?'

Oh yes, the whole shooting match is in. Castleton says: 'I realise I have only been semi-civilised up till now.'

Armand says: 'She left that poor animal Davis in the middle of Mississippi with thirty bidets and a lift.'

Castleton smiles. Mim's second marriage, to Governor Davis of Mississippi, had only lasted three months and is still a bit of a joke.

His brother-in-law is saying: 'I couldn't get up much sympathy for Davis, but I refuse to let it happen to you. I shall instruct the Pope to withold special dispensation when the time comes for divorce. Your marriage must be kept together at all costs!'

'Ah, Armand!' calls out Marguerite. 'Petit frère chéri!' She is laughing at last. 'You are saint to your bad sister.' If only she could spare her adored brother this nightmare of a journey. The tedium and hardship of the crossing: 'That will be the worst.'

Armand points out drily: 'The *Égalité* isn't exactly a tramp steamer, ma chère. Oh, by the way'—he asks his brother-in-law—'has Mimi told you about pussy's harem, Vince?'

'Yes,' says Castleton.

'All of it?'

'I think so,' Castleton says.

''Bout Mammy and Albert and Dédé? And the type from the Agence Duval?'

'Yes,' Castleton says.

Armand says: 'I won't ask you what you think about it. I'm just delighted you know.'

'Who's Dédé?' Castleton asks.

Marguerite says: 'I have told you, Vincent, she is moumou's milk-sister. That little stupid Madeleine.'

'Oh yes, of course,' says Castleton.

Armand explains: 'Dédé's a kind of attachment, Vince, that goes all out with puss. Kind of a package deal. Puss got Mammy's milk and Benoirs got Dédé.'

Castleton says equably: 'That's only four.'

There is worse to come. Marcel and Maurice, Mimi's two chauffeurs.

Marguerite says at once: 'Marcel is indispensable, Benoir.'

6

Castleton knows that ever since her first husband's death in a car crash near Chantilly she is terribly nervous of letting her son go out in a car.

That's the list, then. Armand says: 'You should have had horse sense and not got yourself involved with the Sioux.'

Marguerite asks, what about Fräulein and Miss?

He is delighted to be able to inform her that neither lady will be making the journey with them. They have both got a mild case of varicelle. Armand says: 'I was keeping that as a bonne bouche for Vince to make up for the harem.'

'What's varicelle?' Castleton asks.

'Mon dieu, varicelle!' Marguerite calls out at once, 'has moumou got chicken pox, Armand?'

No, he has not got chicken pox. Nor has he any other kind of pox. But both puss and he are delighted that the two governesses have.

'I'm not too pleased with that Barnum and Bailey act, Mimi.' When he comes to Orleans they must have a little talk about Merrick and Weber.

And George's education?

That will be the subject of another little talk. 'I mean it, chérie.' In Armand's opinion there can be no advantage in it. 'They are pure Disney characters, those two.'

Marguerite says sharply: 'Has George been behaving himself badly towards Fräulein?' Her pronunciation of this word makes her sound very French.

'Well, he bit her,' Armand allows, 'but that was before she was infectious, so you may remain calm.'

'Moumou? Bit Fräulein?'

'I believe she enquired into the state of his bowels.'

'It is unbelievable!' exclaims Marguerite.

'I guess that's what puss thought,' Armand agrees.

Castleton bursts out laughing.

'I wish you could have been here, Vince,' his brother-in-law tells him. 'Viv and I laughed for a week.'

'And you did nothing?' Marguerite asks.

Yes. No. He has forgotten. They can hear him calling: 'Marie, Mimi wants to know what I did when puss bit Weber? She says I gave him panpan. Marie sends you a big kiss.'

'With a rolled up newspaper, I suppose?'

'With the *Figaro*. No. With the *Paris-Soir*. It makes a louder

7

noise. Little Benoir was very impressed, let me tell you. He re-
frained from biting Merrick on the strength of it.' Armand says:
'In any case she would have had to be tenderised first. My God,
what sinew!' Armand says, 'My God!'

'You are quite hopeless,' Marguerite tells him. 'And George
will be completely ruined.'

Armand says quietly: 'On the contrary, he has been very good,
your little Benoir.'

'Is he still shy?' It is a disaster with his shyness, she tells her
husband.

'Yes, he is still shy. (Hence comes the inquisition, Vince.) Marie
and I drive him from home periodically with loud cries and imprecations, but it has not been a success so far. We have got as far
as persuading him to visit with the de Chassevent boy.'

And that was not successful?

'Well, puss didn't bite him, in so far I suppose you could call it
a success,' Armand says. 'He is a Disaster, that de Chassevent kid.
He will not even make a good cuckold like his father. I can't
imagine how Liane and Yves could have dreamed up such a
dismal monster between them. Mimi, he looks exactly like une
tête de veau in spectacles.'

She is less interested in Paul de Chassevent than in her son. 'Did
he at least stay?'

'Oh yes, I said he must stay for one hour, so he stayed. But I
had the impression that Monsieur was pretty glad to see us all at
Auteuil again.' Armand says: 'I think Viv's best for him at the
moment, Mimi. He always seems to brisk up when Viv's around.'

'Mon dieu, there is always some fuss with that child. Have you
at least obliged him to talk French?'

There was no need to oblige him. 'Since it was your wish not a
single word of another language has passed his lips.' Her brother
says quite seriously: 'You underestimate the filial piety of little
Benoir, my dear.'

'And with his cousin? What does he speak with his cousin?' asks
Marguerite.

With his cousin he speaks Ol' Kintuck. 'Come on now, Mi, be
chic. Leave him his little comforts, will you? Puss will do what he
can to please you, be content with that. Don't push him beyond
his powers.' Armand says: 'Your wife is beautiful, Vince, but she
hasn't an atom of patience in her make-up, you noticed that?
Mimi, you are exactly, but exactly, like Papa.'

8

'Et quoi? Does he still cry so much, Armand?'

Does he still cry so much? Armand has to confess he is getting a little tired of this questionnaire. He says blandly: 'I don't think so, chérie. He refreshes himself with a little shower every morning when he wakes up and realises that his maman isn't there.' After that the household can be pretty certain that the rest of the day will be dry. 'There have been positively no Floods at the Delta if that is what you mean.' Floods at the Delta is the family's name for George's all too frequent and abundant tears.

'Thank God for that, at least,' Marguerite asks: 'How is he eating?'

'I am quite satisfied. My God, Mimi, you must be boring Vince to death. He is not yet conditioned to these telephone marathons— and now you subject him to your terrible quiz as well.'

She says: 'It is only because you excuse him from eating anything he doesn't like. I know you, Armand, so well!'

He is delighted that she should know him. 'But I assure you puss has a great enthusiasm for Joseph's cuisine.' Joseph is Armand's maître-chef. 'They see exactly eye-to-eye on all vital matters like tarte aux fraises and glace aux mandarines. It is an entente extrêmement cordiale.'

'Which means he practically lives on desserts, I suppose?'

'You suppose quite wrong. Little Benoir eats everything that is put before him exactly as you commanded him to. He certainly loves Joseph's entremets but he loves his maman more. His piety towards you, ma chère, leaves nothing to be desired. Mimi' —Armand says—'shall we change this conversation before Vince really passes out with ennui?'

One last question. 'Has he disturbed you and Marie at night again?'

Armand says briefly: 'Once.'

Marguerite says: 'Was it an attack?'

Of course. Armand says: 'It wasn't very bad. Viv wants to have a word with you, Mimi.'

'What happened?' Marguerite says quickly. 'Armand?'

'The usual,' Armand says. 'I took him in between us until his trembling stopped. Then I put him back in his own bed. Mimi, I beg of you not to alienate your husband any further with this abysmal conversation.'

'Oh God,' breathes Marguerite. 'Oh God.'

Castleton takes her hand in his again. He hears his brother-in-

9

law say clearly: 'She is not to worry about it, Vince. He dreams about his father sometimes. When he has you he will be better.' He tells his sister: 'I promise you, Mimi. Now have a word with Viv.'

'Armand,' begs Marguerite, 'tell me, how is his breathing? Armand?'

'Darling, don't upset yourself like this. Don't do it, Mim.' Castleton has put his arm round her waist, but she has freed herself again.

'How is his breathing, Armand?'

Benoir says in a cold formal voice: 'His breathing is bad, Marguerite.'

'Does he breathe through his mouth?'

'All the time. And I have not once corrected him or told him to breathe through his nose. Because'—says Armand—'I consider it more important that your son should get some air into his lungs n'importe comment. And now'—says Armand—'this conversation is really finished.' He, personally, refuses to die of ennui at the age of thirty-six. He passes the instrument to Bienville and goes away without another word.

Castleton hears the harsher voice of Bienville Benoir greeting his aunt in French. 'Bon soir, ma petite Tante-chérie. Benoir is exhibiting signs of displeasure. What has occurred?'

Castleton hangs up on him and pours himself a drink. He is unable to get up any great enthusiasm for his wife's young nephew who always seems so bloody full of himself and is inferior, in Castleton's opinion, to Armand in every way.

'Come on and dress, darling!' Castleton shouts out. 'It's nearly eight o'clock.'

'Is that your British chap?' young Benoir wants to know. 'You are still married to him, then? Tiens!' says Bienville in a surprised voice.

'Mim!' shouts out Castleton.

'Bienville,' says Marguerite, 'is your cousin asleep? I am coming, Vincent.'

'My cousin? I have two cousins,' Bienville says. 'I don't know if that infant monster of Beau's is asleep and I care even less.'

Baudouin Benoir is the younger of Marguerite's two brothers. A widower with one little girl.

'Bienville, be serious!' Marguerite says.

'My cousin Marie is asleep, if that is the question.' Bienville always calls George by his second name. 'He has been asleep since nine o'clock, sated with his triumphs at the Clinic Benoir. D'you wish to speak to him? I will wake him with pleasure. He will stagger about in an endearing way.' Bienville says, laughing: 'His derrière has been so punctured by the needles of the good profs at the Clinic that if we put it on a victrola I'm sure it would play a tune. I wanted to have a look at it but the Dauphin wouldn't let me. He is guarding it jealously with his chemise modestly pulled round his ankles. He is a prude, that Dauphin,' Bienville says.

'Darling, do come *on*!'

'I am coming. Tell Nicole she may prepare my bath. Bienville, did moumou stand it well?'

He is utterly colourless, Bienville says. 'We aren't at all certain whether he will last the night.' He himself is going to risk it and intends to go out dancing with Elaine at a new nightspot which only opened yesterday. It is quite splendid and there is every evidence of its remaining quite splendid for at least another three days.

'Try and persuade your father to go with you,' Marguerite says. 'He is utterly selfless, your papa.'

Unlike his son. Bienville says he will do his best to persuade Armand. 'The de Chassevent has probably persuaded him already. She has had a splendid new bosom tailored for her by a new plastic man which she is naturally eager to show the world.'

'My God!' Marguerite says. 'Has she anything left that is her own?'

Bienville says slyly: 'She has your brother's undying affection, Tante Mimi.'

Liane de Chassevent is Armand's latest mistress, and for Marguerite's liking the liaison has already been going on for far too long.

'Vincent, be sweet and tell Nicole to start undoing my hair.' says Marguerite. 'I don't know if she expects me to go out with it like this.'

'You couldn't blame her,' Castleton tells her. 'Mim, for God's sake do come away from that bloody phone!'

'What is he grumbling about?'

'I must go,' says Marguerite. 'Shall we see you here soon, mon chéri?'

But of course. He intends to fly himself over and land exactly at her feet. He makes a kissing noise. 'Au'voir, au'voir, ma p'tite tante-chérie. We will leave Maman to watch over your son with strict injunctions to telephone you if he croaks, so you may rest assured.' Bienville calls out: 'Good news. Benoir has made himself resplendent. He is coming with us. By the way, did he tell you about the Dauphin-Weber affair? I have never seen papa laugh so much. The good Boche was bellowing like a cow in calf: "Diss Dchildt he iss umbossible! He has gebitten me! I will invorm Madame, M'zieu Penoir!" Maman thought Weber had rabies. She wanted Armand to call in Ouistiti's vet. The Dauphin was splendid. His calm and dignity were irreproachable.' Bienville tells his aunt: 'You have a splendid kid, Mimi. He is for me,' says Bienville.

Marguerite prophesies: 'He will be quite ruined between my brother and you.'

'Oh, by the way, your brother and I have a bet on that you will find fault with your favourite on Sunday night before he has been restored to you for half-an-hour. Benoir is optimistic and gives you till Monday. It's quite a considerable sum,' says Bienville, 'so don't let me down.'

'Mim, tell that bloody nephew of yours to let you go. You've been on the phone for three bloody hours!'

'Do I hear British oaths?' enquires Bienville. 'I will return you to your endearing chap.' Bienville says: 'Au'voir, ma petite tante-chérie. Here comes papa to tell you goodnight.'

'Oh no!' says Castleton, half-pulling her off the bed. 'Your family is completely raving, Mim!'

'It is only to say goodnight.'

She has had her hair taken down and brushed out. Castleton comes and sits beside her again with both his arms round her waist under the beautiful warm hair. He smiles at the impassioned Benoir goodnights.

'Bonne nuit, ma p'tite soeur adorée, à bientôt!'

'Au'voir mon Armand, mon frère aimé.'

'Armand, for Christ's sake turn it in unless you want to start a Franco-British war.'

He has pulled his wife to her feet.

Armand says: 'I neglected to tell you, Vince. You have now been included in pussy's prayers. It appears the list is now so formidable it takes Pious Puss at least half-an-hour to get us all in. Mammy tells me the entire household is prayed for sans faute matin et soir. That should get us at least a few days' remission from purgatory, eh, Vince? Only Weber and Merrick will have to do their full stretch. I understand neither lady is even mentioned in little Benoir's prayers.' Armand is laughing uncontrollably.

'Thank him for me, will you?' says Castleton, whose loud British laughter is now blasting his brother-in-law's ear. 'Mim, I can't wait to see that kid of yours again!'

Marguerite says: 'Mon dieu, Armand, I hope this doesn't mean that George is embarking on a religious phase?' The religious fervour of the Dauphin is another family joke.

'Now Mim, you're not to start another conversation,' Castleton fends her off the phone with his leg. 'I categorically forbid it, as the Benoirs say.'

He's right. 'Let that poor animal of yours at least finish his honeymoon in peace,' Armand says. 'I must go too. Liane is exhibiting signs of extreme patience—that's always bad.'

'Au'voir, mon chéri,' says Marguerite, hanging up at last. She remains standing by the telephone.

'Go on, darling, have your bath. Nicole has drawn it for you three times. If we're supposed to be there at seven,' Castleton says, 'or don't you want to go? D'you want me to phone the de Courcelles, Mim?' asks Castleton.

'Mim?' Castleton asks.

She makes neither answer nor move. He is thunderstruck by the expression on her face.

'Mim, what's the matter?'

She says in a low voice: 'It is a disaster of the first order, my God.'

'Oh come off it, darling. How can you say that when you haven't even seen the medical report?'

It isn't that at all, Marguerite says impatiently. She is not in the least worried on that score. At least three doctors have assured her that the child's health will probably be normal by the time he is fourteen. It is this incessant, this never-ending disruption of her son's education that is driving her to despair. 'D'you realise, mon cher, that my son is completely uneducated at nine years of age? He can read and write and that is all. And now he will be obliged

13

to miss at least another month's schooling because those two imbeciles, Weber and Merrick, have chosen to get varicelle.'

Chosen to get!

'Oh, Mim, you're bliss,' says Castleton, giving her a hug. 'Anyway, I don't suppose your chap will lose any sleep.'

It was the wrong thing to say, of course. The Sioux are dead serious about education.

She bursts out angrily: 'Oh, Vincent, please! Spare me your English philosophy! Moumou is behind enough with his studies as it is without the benefit of these gratuitous holidays!'

The truth is one is completely surrounded by fools and her brother has married the biggest of them!

'Oh darling, do shut up.' He is kissing her neck.

She is certain that none of this would have happened if that fool of a Marie had any sort of control.

'She is quite incapable of supervising her household. It is the biggest miracle that moumou has not already got varicelle. He will probably develop it the minute he lands here.'

Marguerite says it never fails to astonish her that Bienville has turned out so well. It is certainly not thanks to that fool his mother who has never had the faintest idea of how to bring up a child. 'It has all fallen on my poor brother's shoulders. Always. Everything. And now, thanks to that imbecile Courvoisier, he is obliged to bring moumou over by ship. He will be bored to perdition for a week.'

Castleton says: 'I can still fetch him. I haven't got Armand's capacity for being bored.'

It's out of the question. Marguerite assures him neither she nor her brother would permit him to burden himself with their affairs.

'A sick child like that. Can you imagine what it would entail?'

Castleton teases: 'That's just a blind. You probably think I don't know the correct drill for shipping VIPs home. You're a very arrogant mum, aren't you, Mim?'

'Oh please, Vincent, don't start with those English expressions.' She can assure him: 'They have absolutely no meaning for me.'

All right. He is still smiling but his eyes look very grey. He says: 'I won't go on about fetching the boy any more, but once he's over here I hope you'll let me help you with him occasionally. Armand can't always be here, and anyway that's what you've got a husband for. I mean it, darling. I will do anything in the world for you and the boy.' Anything else is nonsense. 'Just A Big

14

Nonsense,' says Castleton, wiping her eyes. He is surprised at finding her in tears. It's the first time he has seen her cry.

'Oh, Poilu, you are so sweet to me,' whispers Marguerite. 'I love you so much, Poilu.'

That's more like it.

He likes her private name for him. It's a bit dotty because by normal standards he's not hairy at all, but Mim insists she's never seen hair on a man's chest before and that neither of her two brothers or her father had it. Nor had her first husband. 'Georges' whole body was completely smooth. It was like silk, Poilu.'

'Well, fancy,' says Castleton. He never knows what to say when Mim mentions her first husband.

She has inserted her hand under his shirt and is stroking his chest.

'What about Davis, then?'

She answers perkily: 'One doesn't count wild animals.'

He calls her maid. 'Have your bath, darling. Let the poor woman get on with it, Mim. I'm going to phone the de Courcelles we can't make it.'

She wants him to wash her. 'Poilu!'

In a tick. 'What'll I tell 'em, Mim?' shouts Castleton from the phone.

Ouf! Anything! Whatever he likes!

She calls out from the bath: 'It isn't necessary to let them know. We don't go, voilà tout.'

Toujours la politesse. 'Trust the French,' says Castleton. 'Hullo?'

2

A Fancy Artical

When she comes back from her bath she seems much happier and more relaxed. She says, smiling: 'My escritoire is here from Paris, Poilu. Shall we go and see how it looks? They have put it in the big salon provisionally.'

'Yes, rather, let's.'

They go together to see this desk Mim's fellow has such a pash for it follows them round wherever they go.

'It's his great love of the moment,' Marguerite declares. 'He would gape at it for hours if one gave him the chance. It will help to make him feel more at home. My little donkey,' says Marguerite.

Poor old Mim. She's bitterly disappointed at the delay. For himself he's delighted. It gives them six-and-a-bit more days together which is splendid because, of course, he's absolutely flipped over her.

'D'you like it, Poilu?'

It's a beautiful piece, circa 1797, in tulip-wood inlaid with palisander. Of native workmanship to a French design it has the most delightful medallions on it. There are seventeen of these altogether, five large and twelve small, oval in shape, of Sèvres porcelain, each framed and connected lightly by flying ribands of ormulu. These medallions depict scenes from West Indian life. The large ones show the domestic bliss of the young French planter and his newly imported bride with the great galleried house figuring prominently in the backgrounds.

The smaller ovals, which are the ones Castleton likes best, are very varied and lively. Some merely show plumed fields of maize, cotton, sugar, rice and indigo against an azure sky. Others show slaves garnering these crops or otherwise engaged in similar tasks of husbandry.

The male slaves are dressed in gaily striped pantaloons, their full white shirts neatly torn from neck to waist, exposing their brown backs or chests. The females are all completely naked, with lightly shackled limbs and rosy mantling cheeks and buttocks.

Also stark naked, except for their scarlet feathers, a solitary Carib or two lurks in the opal backgrounds where dagger-tailed parrots fly, and tiny apes swing in the tops of immensely high and French-looking trees.

The centre medallion, which is the most important, depicts the young couple, looking to Castleton's eyes the deadspit of Benoir and his Marie, walking hand in hand down a broad avenue of trees, clipped in the Versailles fashion but roped with slings of tropical creepers and interspersed with feathery knots of palms. The left hand of the young planter is laced boyishly in that of his child wife's, while in his right he carries a tiny whip, probably meant to control a small white dog with a plume of a tail, which is sporting round his feet.

The pair are attended by slaves bearing tiny goblets of negus on a golden tray and a scarlet parasol which is held over their little mistress's head against the setting sun.

A young wet-nurse, bearing the first fruit of the union on a cushion, brings up the rear. This sloe-eyed infant, surveying the scene unwinkingly from under an important and wholly fetching bonnet anod with ostrich plumes, reminds Castleton irresistibly of Mim's pretty beggar the few times he had met him during their short engagement in Paris.

Everyone had assured him that the Dauphin was even more terrified of Castleton than he was of the Dauphin, and that those haughty silences and withering looks from under sweeping eyelashes meant nothing more than a paralysing shyness, but that hadn't stopped Castleton from feeling like something that had just crawled out of the cheese.

Oh, lor', the Fambly, thinks Castleton. I hope he won't be too much of a pill. Aloud he says: 'Your desk's sheer heaven, darling. No wonder your chap's mad about it. I adore the way those little colons all look exactly like your family, Mim. Nobody a day over fifteen and all madly sophisticated with it. That terrifying infant in the hat could be the Dauphin, bonnet and all. Did you ever see such self-assurance in a baby!'

She says a little sadly: 'I wish my son had half as much aplomb.' It's an essential which, so far, has escaped him completely.

All the same, she's not surprised that Castleton should find a likeness. The desk was a commissioned work to commemorate the first union of the houses of Bienville and Benoir, and the medallions were painted especially for the occasion by l'Estoque and brought out to Martinique from Paris by special courier at great expense and with some difficulty owing to the blockade.

It was said that Napoleon, during the Consulate, had wanted the desk to make a present of to his Josephine, and had offered in the region of two thousand louis for it, but that his offer had been turned down by the Benoirs.

'My family, what fools!' shrugs Marguerite, who is not, Castleton has to admit, a particularly sentimental lady. She asks him carelessly: 'Do these old family histories interest you?'

Since they concern her family, very much.

Then these will probably amuse him for a short quarter of an hour. She has taken a bundle of old papers out of a drawer and is throwing them at him gaily. 'Here, catch! Now you'll see what kind of a camp you've walked into, my friend.'

He goes through the papers with Mim on his knee, already lightly bored with the whole business, taking stock of his features in an access of wifely affection.

'You have five different colours in your eyes, Poilu. I have just counted them. What an idea, to have five colours!' Her own are shining like liquid pitch.

The papers are nearly all receipted bills, records of slaves purchased for the newly acquired Benoir plantations on the Mississippi delta, or of house servants for the mansion in New Orleans. Mim's family had fled to Louisiana from Martinique during the slave insurrection.

'Oh, what a bore,' breathes Marguerite, kissing her husband's

18

nose. She has come to the end of his features. 'Show me your teeth, Poilu.'

There are two orders, written in French, for punishment at the Calaboose. One is for a dozen lashes to be applied with 'a certain severity, at the same time not excessive'. The other for fifty strokes 'to be laid on vigorously and without quarter'. Both orders are signed 'A-M. Benoir' in uncannily fresh-looking ink. The lively calligraphy, so characteristically Benoir, could be Mim's brother's.

Mim is clamouring to see his teeth. 'Show, show, Poilu!'

There is also what practically amounts to a slave catalogue, with price-lists, classifications and descriptions of merchandise in Spanish and French as well as in a peculiarly horrid, quasi-comic yankee-slaver jargon, very Simon Legree. It's a comprehensive compilation ranging from 'Direct Imports, Wild Niggers'. 'Unbroken Goldcoasts', 'Stud Zanzibars, Females, Heavy Breeders' and 'Advantageous Coffle Purchases for the Larger Plantation' to the most 'highly housetrained artical for the Elegant Town Establishment'.

'What's a coffle purchase?' Castleton wants to know.

She answers, yawning: 'A coffle purchase was when they bought a lot of blacks on the chain, just as they came off the ship.'

She can't imagine there would be any advantage in buying slaves in this way, or that the Benoirs ever did. 'There would be too many sick ones amongst them,' Marguerite says. 'A coffle could infect a whole plantation.'

Besides, the blacks would all be completely wild and savage and need quite special breaking in before they could be put to even the most unskilled labour in the fields. Marguerite says she's certain that the risk and annoyance carried with that type of transaction would have been out of all proportion to the few hundred dollars it might save.

It was a racket of the times, voilà tout. 'I like your teeth, by the way,' remarks Marguerite. 'They aren't bad at all, those wolf's fangs of yours.'

'You're a shocker, aren't you?' Castleton says. 'You just don't give a tinker's gob.'

Why should she? As far as she knows the whole business has been finished for almost a hundred years. 'What does it mean, a tinker's gob? Something uncomplimentary to me, I suppose?'

Certainly. 'Mim, listen to this!' He's come upon a special

announcement, boxed in heavy coal-black type, and liberally spiked with exclamation marks.

'By Private Negotiation Only!! Immediate Sale!!! A Fancy Artical specially raised for New Orleans Luxury Trade!!! Smart Lively Boy. Prime Condit. Vy LITE OCT. Approx. age 9 year. Unmarked. Positively no odor. Talks real pert. Train up 1st Chop Gents valet or amuse lady. Property prom. N.O. Family. Must Part. Write call Planters Bank St Felicien and Canal. Phew.'

What is he getting so excited about? That kind of advertisement wasn't at all unusual.

There is a question mark dashed against it, obviously put there by la plume de A-M. Benoir.

'I bet he bought the poor little sod.'

What if he did? Marguerite points out: 'If he was anything like my brother your little sod would have had nothing to complain about.'

What about those excursions to the Calaboose? Those fifty strokes point de quartier?

One had to make allowances for the times. She doesn't suppose his English were so soft-hearted either. 'Your Factory Kids et tout ce truc la. They weren't even black, your Factory Kids,' says Mim, who is not only a well read girl but logical to boot.

He shakes his head at her in mock despair, 'just a ruddy bunch of slave owners, your lot'.

Ouf! Pouf! Everyone who was anyone was a slave owner in those days. Except his stupid Castletons. 'Aren't you tired yet of that old rubbish, Vincent?'

Yes. Take 'em away, they're giving him the willies. The papers all smell very strong of sandalwood with which the desk is lined: so does a spry-looking little whip with a bright beadwork handle which has been hiding in amongst them all this while like a snake in a bunch of bananas and has now wriggled out on to the carpet.

'Hullo,' Castleton picks it up. 'Whose pretty thing is this?'

It's a fearsome-looking little instrument of rawhide plaited with a cynical artistry over a whalebone core.

Marguerite tells him: 'It's a soupir d'amour.'

'De what?'

'D'amour, mon amour. They were called that because the noise they make is supposed to resemble the sighs of a young girl in love.'

'Oh,' says Castleton. 'Nice.'

20

Fwt! Fwt! She makes it sigh for him a couple of times. 'D'you like it, Poilu? Shall I sigh like that when you make love to me?'

'Don't bother to specially,' Castleton says.

There is something disgusting about the way it fidgets in her hand. She says: 'It's over two hundred years old.' In point of fact it's the original of the whip in the big medallion on her desk.

There was a whole boring controversy about it when the desk was shown at the Paris Expo des Beaux Arts last year. At first many experts had believed the whip was for the dog, but afterwards it was proved to have been used exclusively for disciplining house servants or special slaves whom, for some reason, they didn't want disfigured at the Calaboose.

What a fuss! Who cares what it was used for, anyway? She asks him, giggling: 'Can you imagine the service one would get if one were still permitted to use these things by law?'

It's a jolly good job one isn't, then. 'Put it down, Mim. You look lousy with it.'

On the contrary she thinks it suits her very well, and it's a thousand pities one is debarred from using it. Without going further she could think of quite a few in this household in whom it would create a healthier attitude towards their work.

She really means it. Of course she's trying her damnedest to get a rise out of him, but she means it all right!

'You. You're a monster,' Castleton laughs.

And he's another Grand Romantic like her brother Benoir. 'He will be furious with me for not having long ago thrown all this rubbish away. Pass me your face, Poilu.'

She sets about polishing it off with great dispatch and gusto, explaining between each triumphant kiss: 'My noble brother is of the opinion that there is positively no room in the twentieth century for even one poor little innocent soupir d'amour. My noble brother considers such things should be relegated to museums of social history where they can serve to enlighten the more responsible section of the bourgeoisie on rainy Sunday afternoons. This is always supposing the bourgeoisie doesn't prefer making love on the bed on rainy Sundays, having first shown their responsibility by throwing their kids out on the street regardless of the rain. I give you the considered opinion of that noble ass my brother!' cries Marguerite, who has kissed herself to a standstill and is now surveying the result of her work with the utmost satisfaction.

21

'You have received exactly thirty kisses. One dozen for each cheek and six quite special ones for your mouth. Sign, please,' says Marguerite briskly.

While he is paying her back (You cheat! Those aren't my kisses at all! I want my kisses back! They were much nicer than those miserable unripe English things you have palmed off on me!) she confides that she suspects another member of her family of also harbouring these high-faluting notions. Her noble brat. Luckily he has been caught young. They still have time to knock it out of him.

'Fwt! Fwt!' cries Marguerite. Otherwise they will find themselves with a second Benoir on their hands. 'There are all the makings of it there already.'

What's wrong with that? 'Come to think, Armand's a damn sight nicer than you are.'

She quite agrees. All the same one saint in the family is enough. 'Oh, I don't put up with any nonsense from that one, you know. One word out of turn and fwt! fwt! Je lui fais cuire la peau!' cries Mim, who's in a sparky mood. She bursts out laughing, 'Oh, oh, your face, Poilu!'

'Come here, you bitch. I don't know why I love you, but I do.'

But she has turned suddenly serious. 'Will you love my poor moumou too, Poilu? He misses Georges so much. Please, will you love him for my sake?'

'I'll do my best, shall I?' says Castleton, smiling into her eyes.

'O, mon homme,' breathes Marguerite. 'Can you imagine, his cousin tells me those imbeciles at the Clinic have quite demolished his poor little behind? Pauv' p'tit bonhomme! It is quite marked with their stupid needles, Bienville says. What are you laughing at, Vincent?' She says quite seriously: 'He has a very pretty behind.'

He has inherited it from his ma.

She laughs. 'He has not inherited my digestion.' Marguerite says: 'He will be terribly sick on the ship. Armand will be in despair.'

He says: 'He's doing it for you, darling. He absolutely dotes on you and I suppose he's just as fond of your boy.'

'Oh, no,' says Marguerite. 'He isn't fond of him at all.'

He is so astounded by her cool reply he can't get over it. Mar-

22

guerite says: 'Armand is much too good to show it, but I know he will never suffer the child near him unless he must. You will notice it, Vincent, when they are here. He is too like Maman, my poor moumou. My brother loved our mother beyond all reason. I think his heart broke when she died.' She says, smiling: 'That little softie of mine has no idea. He loves his Uncle Benoir very dearly. He will love you too, Vincent,' she tells him. 'He has an infinite capacity for love.'

'Oh good, I like 'em friendly.' He's holding her so that he can catch the full contrast between the pert delicacy of her XVIIIème siècle features and the sombre brilliance of her West Indian eyes. It's quite his favourite view.

Mim is prattling happily on about her treasure. 'He will amuse you. He is a very unsophisticated child. He hasn't any reserve. Does it disturb you, my reserve, Poilu?'

'Let me see.' He kisses her face and decides: 'I've got used to it, I think.'

She says: 'Moumou is completely truthful, you know. Even if he knows he will get punished he will not tell a lie.'

'Fancy,' says Castleton who is still enjoying the view.

She says in an offended voice: 'You don't believe a word of what I'm saying.'

He does. That's just the trouble. Such virtues. He only hopes he will be able to live up to them. But she is not amused and says reproachfully: 'He is a very sweet-tempered child. Georges called him moumou when he was little because he was soft like a cat. Oh, he is good, Vincent,' Marguerite declares. 'There isn't any part of him that is ugly or bad.' Her whole being is informed with love as she speaks of her son. 'He is good like bread. D'you know what we mean, Vincent, when we say that in France, il est bon comme le pain?'

He does indeed. And he knows who's partial to a nice bit of crust.

'But I don't spoil him,' Marguerite says seriously. 'I love him far too much to let him make a nuisance of himself.' Of course George will be spoiled to death when he comes back from Paris. One can't expect anything else from that household over there. And naturally monsieur is only too delighted to be allowed his own way in everything. 'It is his one great fault,' says Marguerite, 'but I shall take it in hand.'

'I bet you will.'

She says: 'Oh, I'm not soft with him, you know. Armand has often reproached me with it.'

'Armand's a mug and you're another, but I love you very, very much.'

She says: 'I love you too, Poilu.'

She is holding his hands against her breast. 'When I have moumou back again . . .'

'Yes?'

'I will make you a little present just for you.'

'Really?'

Marguerite whispers: 'It will be only for you. A little present with grey eyes. Will you like that, Poilu?'

He will like it tremendously.

Then what is he laughing about?

'It's just a ruse to keep my hooks off your property.'

Oh, if he is going to start that nonsense again she is going up to dress. She finds his attitude too silly. She seems quite huffed about it, but when he tries to make it up to her by praising the boy, she answers snubbingly: 'It is not important to me whether my son is pretty or not. I am far more concerned that he should study hard and learn to behave himself.'

Well, well. She is a rum if very lovely girl. He joggles her on his knee to make her smile. 'What would you like to do tonight, you lovely thing?'

She answers promptly: 'I want to stop at home with you.'

He finds this answer mightily to his taste. 'Don't look now, but there's a ruddy great kiss coming up.'

She lies contentedly in his arms for a long time. 'Moumou will make big eyes when he sees you, Poilu.'

'He's seen me,' Castleton says. 'In Paris. Remember? We were engaged or something.'

'He has not seen you!' Marguerite insists. 'How many times has one to tell you that little donkey was too shy to lift his eyes from the ground?'

'He'll see me on Sunday, then,' says Castleton. 'I hope he will approve,' says Castleton who by this time has had the Dauphin slightly.

She murmurs dreamily: 'I shall make his favourite dessert for him. He will be in Heaven. He's a perfect little pig where sweet things are concerned. They could make it just as well in the kitchen, but if Maman has made it for him it will taste twice as good.' She says: 'I shall make it tomorrow, it is a dessert which should be made at least a day in advance.'

Tomorrow is only Monday. Castleton says firmly: 'George won't be here till Sunday, my duck.'

In case it interests her, he's counting the days as well.

3

The Dauphin

Two long white Rolls, flying the tricolour, flow into the courtyard and stop.

The second car, 'The Ambulance', as the Sioux call it, is the boy's. It has been fitted with a special seat that pulls out to make a bed.

Castleton's brother-in-law, Armand Benoir, is the first to jump out. A small Adonis with a vivacious smile, he greets his sister gaily: 'Mimi, your mob is here!' He embraces her tenderly, holding her in his arms. 'Where's that long-suffering animal, your husband?'

He salutes his brother-in-law on both cheeks. 'My poor Vince, can you stand it? There's still time to send them back.' Everybody is scrambling out of the cars at once. There seems to be no end to them. Mammy and Albert, George's coloured valet and nurse, and the skinny yellow child who is his foster sister, Dédé. A battered-looking individual in a short raincoat turns out to be the boy's detective, Deckers of the Agence Duval.

Maurice and Marcel, Marguerite's two French chauffeurs who

have ferried the cars across and who are to be included on her permanent staff at St Charles Street, start getting the luggage out of the boots.

Armand's two valets, Achille and Hippolyte, get out last. Achille is carrying Ouistiti, Armand's pet capuchin monkey, on his arm.

'Hey, Vince,' Armand says, 'here comes Mimi's flirt. Better watch your step now, fella!'

Marguerite's beautiful pale boy, Georges-Marie Benoir, escapes from the second car, ducks away from his nurse and flies up the gallery steps into his mother's arms like a bird released.

'Maman! Maman!'

His voice is very high and sweet. Castleton has never seen anyone quite so pale. His cap and the lining of his coat are of black sea otter. His eyes are a pure, incredible black. He seems very small for his age which is nine. To Castleton's English eyes he looks about seven.

Armand assures him: 'He'll grow. Mimi, Vince thinks we've short-changed him on puss.'

She is kissing her son, paying back kiss for kiss. 'Alors, are you so happy to be back? Are you really so pleased to see me, moumou?'

The little boy is holding so close to his mother he looks like a small extension of herself. Marguerite's servants are coping with the luggage, of which there seem to be vast amounts, despite the fact that the bulk of the boy's luggage is supposed to have been sent in advance.

They are separating piles of valises all marked G-M.B. or A-M.B.

Marguerite remarks coolly to her brother: 'I see they have forgotten to pack half of moumou's things again.'

Both men smile at the typical 'Mim' reaction to anything slapdash or disorganised. Even in the middle of her great joy at having her boy back the shiftlessness of her brother's household still annoys her. She dismisses the Auteuil staff as a bunch of incompetents, incapable of doing the simplest job.

'It is lucky for them they have Marie to deal with and not me.'

Armand agrees amicably. 'Puss and I were hoping love would be blind, but one can't walk anything past her, Vince.'

They all troop into the house together, Castleton bringing up the rear. Armand has got his arm round his sister's neck and she is

27

leading her pale boy by the hand. The salon is full of their light, upper-class French voices and the high sweet drawl of the child.

'Eh bien, moumou.'

She is smiling into her son's black eyes. 'Whatever else has been forgotten in Paris, it is certainly not your tongue.'

As usual her little silly is trying to tell her everything at once. 'O, mama, it has been so long,' calls out the little boy.

She questions him softly. 'Have you been good? Have you eaten well? Tell me, have you been obedient, moumou?'

O yes, he has remembered all these things. 'O, it has been for ever,' calls out George.

That is not very polite to Uncle Benoir. Marguerite says, smiling: 'You have given him so much trouble, you bad thing!'

Uncle Benoir will forgive the frankness. 'He's out of his shoes to be with you again, Mi.'

'O mama, I could die of pleasure,' calls out George who is sipping porto frappé out of his mother's glass.

She hopes he will defer his demise at least until he has said 'Bonjour' to his new stepfather. 'He will not have a very high opinion of your manners,' Marguerite says. 'Don't you see Mr Castleton, George?'

'Yes'm, mama. O look—he is drinking whisky-soda,' whispers George, who has been accommodated with, of all things, a glass of eau sucré. He calls out politely from his mother's side: 'Bonjour, Monsieur. I 'ope you 'ave enjoyed your how d'you say voyage de noces, maman-chérie?'

The men roar, but Marguerite says at once: 'No, please, you two, don't laugh at him. It would be fatal if George gets the idea that it is funny to be impolite.' She tells her son: 'Go and greet your stepfather properly. At once or I will put you outside.'

Castleton is surprised at the severity of her tone.

The little boy comes towards him like an elegant walking-doll.

'Well, what d'you say?' asks Marguerite.

'Bonjour, Monsieur,' says George, looking at his mother. Marguerite exclaims: 'Look at your stepfather, don't look at me!'

'Bonjour, Monsieur,' says George, and looks at Castleton's feet.

'Ah non! Not like that!' Marguerite calls out. 'It is a disaster with his shyness, Benoir.'

Armand says quietly: 'There's quite a lot of Vince for puss to take. Just let him get his breath, there's a sweet guy.'

28

The pale princeling steps forward and kisses Castleton's hand. 'Bonjour, petit-papa.'

'Bonjour, mon petit,' says Castleton.

'O, he speaks French!' exclaims the princeling. He is painfully, terrifically and paralysingly shy.

'What did I tell you?' Armand asks. 'I knew puss wouldn't let us down.'

'It's about time,' says Marguerite in a disgusted voice. 'Petit malhonnête!' She directs her son: 'Give papa a big kiss and disappear. Tell Albert to get you ready for dinner.'

'Yes'm.' He seems a little uncertain as to what is expected of him. He stands there smiling at his mother.

'Alors, embrasse-le!' calls out Marguerite.

He holds his mouth up for Castleton. 'George!' Marguerite is appalled. 'Not on the mouth! What are you thinking of? How many times has one to tell you one does not kiss people on the lips like that!'

Armand adds drily: 'That's reserved for grown-ups.'

George says shyly: 'I didn't think Mr Castleton was people, mama. I mean, I thought he was in the family.' He is blushing all over his face and neck.

'I should damn well think I am in the family,' says Castleton. He asks his stepson: 'Will you give me a kiss?'

The child submits a pale, vanilla-scented cheek. It is deliciously fresh and soft. He is still looking at his mother.

'Now you kiss me.'

The child returns his kiss with a shy enthusiasm, planting it firmly in the middle of Castleton's cheek. His extraordinary eyes are reflecting windows and bits of furniture. The expression in them is very shy and a little wild.

'I hope you're going to like it here.' Castleton lifts his stepson on to his knee. There is absolutely nothing to him; he weighs less than a normal child of five. 'D'you think you will?'

'Yes sir, I am fixing,' replies the creature in a weird accent Castleton recognises as Ol' Kintuck. He sits politely on the edge of Castleton's knee, his eyes fixed firmly on the whisky glass. Vivi done told him the British sold their children at birth and any that got left on their hands they beat up continually, but George knows from experience you can't believe the half of what Viv says.

'Mim, he's trembling,' Castleton says.

It is his second favourite occupation, Marguerite assures him. Crying is his first.

'Mim, did you tell him he can call me Vincent if he likes?'

No, she hasn't told him. 'It would serve no purpose,' Marguerite says. She tells her son: 'Be off and let Albert get you ready for dinner. Otherwise you will be late.'

'Yes'm,' he slides down happily from his stepfather's knee, but he has many tender messages from Paris to give his mother first. 'Tante Marie sends you a fat kiss. She is devastated she couldn't come with us, but unhappily she cannot go by sea, and to travel by air only with her maid would quite unnerve her, Tantan said.' He delivers the fat kiss faithfully. 'Mama, I threw up every single day on the train as well as on the ship.'

She quite believes it. 'Are those all the messages you have for me?'

O no, there are a thousand more. Everyone in the whole of Paris sends their love to her. Mlle Elaine and Marraine and Parrain and of course Mr Viv! 'Shall I see him soon, my cousin?' asks George, delivering the extra-specially fat kiss with which Bienville has entrusted him.

Yes, he will see his cousin very soon. Bienville is coming on Friday. 'Run along now. I will hear the rest of your news when I come up. Be quick. I shall not tell you again, moumou.'

But there are many more messages for her from the whole household at Auteuil. Joseph and Charles and Fernand send their respectful compliments. Fernand is Uncle Benoir's new sous-chef. His brioches are quite a dream. Then there are the chauffeurs and all the chambermaids and Rose and La Bossue who mends Tante's personal linen. All, but all, wish respectfully to be remembered to her. All, all are impatient for the day when Madame will honour them again with her presence in Paris.

O, but the best news of all, Fräulein and Miss have both got varicelle! 'O, mama, isn't it splendid!' George calls out.

'George,' says Marguerite. She is not smiling. 'I have said I would not tell you again.'

Armand says quietly: 'Run along, puss.'

'Yes sir.' George enquires shyly: 'Shall I see Mr Castleton again?'

Since it is his house it is more than likely they will meet. At dinner, for instance, says Marguerite.

'O, I am glad,' George says simply. 'Il est mignon, votre mari.'

She is glad he approves her choice. 'Get dressed,' says Marguerite, 'and try to avoid getting punished on your first day.' If he wishes to have dinner upstairs by himself, he is going the right way about it.

He turns at once and goes with Albert who has come down to fetch him and show him the way.

'Use the lift!' says Marguerite in a tone of command. 'You are not to use the stairs on any account, c'est bien compris?'

'Oui, maman.'

'Oui, Madame.'

Both boys are red in the face as they leave the room. She turns to her brother. 'So much for his obedience and his shyness. Nothing, but nothing, has changed.'

Armand says tranquilly: 'You went down a lump with him, Vince.'

'Darling, he's a smasher,' Castleton says.

That doesn't go down too well. 'A smasher—what is that?'

A smasher's something jolly splendid. She is a smasher and her boy's a smasher too. 'So now I've got two smashers,' Castleton says. 'Aren't I a lucky chap?' He can't resist it, Mim's too funny when she's being teased.

She gives him a coolish smile. 'If he pleases you I am glad.'

'Oh, Mim, you're heaven,' cries Castleton, hugging her to him.

He says he is utterly and completely sold on the Benoirs. She replies drily that for her part she is rather less than delighted with Monsieur Benoir. 'He has completely ruined my child for me. Many thanks, Armand!'

'Aw, come now, Mi, be chic,' Armand says. 'He was out of his shoes at seeing you again, that's all.'

Castleton says: 'I thought he behaved splendidly. What are you grousing at now, Mim?'

She makes no reply to either of them but goes upstairs to supervise her son.

'Poor girl. Her nerves aren't good,' observes Armand.

They chat together amicably, waiting for Marguerite. There is a great cordiality between the brothers-in-law who have actually not got a single point in common.

31

Castleton is astonished Mim hasn't made other arrangements about dinner now the boy is back. Nine o'clock seems fearfully late. As far as he can see, no special arrangements whatsoever have been made for George. Apparently the Sioux expect their children to adjust themselves.

Castleton says: 'I hope we'll be able to put a few roses into his cheeks. He's quite frightening he's so pale.'

Armand says: 'Only because you are used to seeing your English children with cheeks like peonies. They are nice,'—says Armand—'your English kids.' He is playing with Ouistiti who is whistling like a bird.

Castleton says: 'It knocked me for six.'

'I shouldn't voice that opinion to my sister, Vince,' Armand advises him, smiling. 'At least not tonight.'

Marguerite and the boy came back. He is resplendent but a little subdued in a white sailor suit. It seems his mother has been scolding his fourteen-year-old valet, Albert. 'George's dressing room looks like a Créole market. He is a disaster, that boy,' Marguerite says. 'I have no intention of putting up with his incompetence for Mammy's sake, if that is what you expect, Benoir.'

He says: 'I think we owe Madeleine a debt of gratitude, Mimi. If it had not been for her you'd have lost puss, and anyway this can't be amusing for Vince.'

'We shall see how Albert behaves himself,' returns Marguerite, 'after the dressing down he had tonight.' She tells Castleton: 'These people are all the same. Mammy has two good points. She is immaculately clean, and she has splendid milk. On every other count she is just as hopeless as the rest of them.'

George puts in anxiously: 'Albert was very good at Paris, mama. Tante Marie had no fault to find.'

'Trust puss to find le mot juste!'

'Did I ask your opinion, George?'

'No, ma'am.'

'Then remain silent.'

With that imbecile Dédé it will be just the same. That child has never been checked in her life. Marguerite says: 'These people have no idea of how to discipline their children.'

'Unlike my sister.' Armand points out: 'If it hadn't been for Dédé there would have been no milk for the Dauphin. You forget Madeleine had her solely for your convenience, ma chère. She didn't want another child.'

'Ouf, that! Just because it was you that asked it of her it has become the great thing of her life. It has made her feel important so of course she will never allow any of us to forget it. She thinks because she was your first mistress it has given her the right to dictate on household matters. She will find out her mistake,' says Marguerite. 'And very shortly.'

'My God,' says Armand. 'Vince's face! You have convinced the poor fellow that Dédé is my child, Mi.'

And also she has never noticed it was any great hardship for these people to bring children into the world. They breed like rabbits—'It's the usual emotional blackmail,' Marguerite says.

'Who are these people who breed like rabbits, Mimi?' Armand enquires. 'Can you see any rabbits in here, puss?'

George laughs delightedly as his uncle pretends to look. Marguerite tells him: 'Don't laugh at what you don't understand.'

Armand says calmly: 'You can't blame Madeleine for having special feelings for the child. To begin with it can't be easy for a nature like Madeleine's to deny her own child milk. That's why that Dédé's so skinny—puss lapped up all her milk.'

The child looks solemnly at him.

His mother exclaims: 'What are you mooning like that at Uncle Benoir for? You will put ideas into his head, Armand.' Marguerite says: 'I have told Mammy this evening that unless there is a noticeable improvement in Albert quite shortly he will be given his congé.'

Dinner is announced. It is exactly nine o'clock.

Un grand merci. Gustave has saved them all from the guillotine. Armand says: 'Mimi has no idea that the Bastille has fallen yet, Vince.'

Castleton is looking at his wife. A nerve in his right cheek has begun to twitch. 'Won't this make it a bit late for him, darling?'

'Comment?'

Castleton says: 'It'll be at least ten o'clock before he can get to bed.'

'Ten o'clock is his bedtime,' Marguerite says. It appears George invariably has two hours in bed after lunch.

'Oh, I see.'

Achille comes in to take Ouistiti out.

'He will come back,' George assures his stepfather kindly. 'It is a petit précaution, don't you know?'

33

He still has got no higher than his stepfather's waistcoat for his eyeline. Naturally there is a lot of this waistcoat, but it is not actually disquieting in itself. He takes politely the large hand held out for him and goes into the dining room holding on to Castleton's ring.

In the splendid dining room he remains standing by his chair until the grown-ups are seated, when Gustave lifts him into his place beside his mother. He immediately ducks his head and crosses himself.

'Moumou,' calls out his mother. 'Are you out of your mind?'

He opens his eyes and looks at her.

'What are you about?' asks Marguerite. 'Armand, whom has he picked this habit up from?'

Armand says coolly: 'I guess he picked it up from one of the servants. Why, does it embarrass you?'

He tells George: 'Hear that, puss? Don't do it any more. It is distasteful to your maman.'

'It is ridiculous,' says Marguerite.

'It is ridiculous,' says Armand.

Ouistiti is brought back swearing, with an up-rooted flower clutched in his hand.

Achille says: 'That Ouistiti. I just done turned my head.'

'Hey, Salaud!' calls out Armand, kissing the cross little face. 'You'll get me in bad with Castletons', you case.'

'O look! O, mama, look what that bad Ouistiti has done! O, Ouisti, why you so bad all of the time?' George calls out, giggling: 'O, Uncle Benoir will kiss you severely for that!'

'George,' says Marguerite, turning her head to him.

He subsides instantly. It appears he is not permitted to speak at table until the dessert course.

Ouistiti hangs on to his uprooted plant until he sees nobody wants it any more, then he throws it on to the floor. Castleton sees his stepson bring up his napkin to stifle a laugh. He smiles across the table at him. 'Mim, do look at your son.'

He is eating decorously, using a special canteen of diminutive knives, forks and spoons. They are all of solid gold and were his father's as a child. He serves himself neatly from each dish as it is presented to him, though Castleton notices he takes as little as he can. It is obvious that he is expected to leave nothing on his plate. He feeds very prettily and surprisingly quickly and you can see it is all a terrible chore to be got through at all costs.

'I don't think he's finding much use for that meat, darling,' Castleton says.

She turns her head to her son and says: 'Serve yourself properly with meat or you will get no dessert.'

His friend Gustave is holding the splendid platter of *tournedos Rossini*, each crowned with truffle and creamy foie gras. George takes the smallest he can find. The thought of the foie gras is making him feel faint.

At Paris Joseph had told him that to make a really good liver the geese were strapped to a board in front of a hot fire and crammed with a special rich food like riz au lait all day. Joseph comes from Strasbourg. George knows it is true because Joseph has sworn it on his mother's head. He can feel his heart missing beats all over the place at the thought of the huge sick liver that has gone to make this dish which is the favourite of his Uncle Benoir, and into which, somehow, the head of Joseph's mother has got mixed up as well.

Marguerite turns her head sharply in his direction. At the same time Benoir says in unmistakeable tones: 'Let him leave the foie gras, Mimi, it could make him dream.'

A film of sweat is coating the child's pallor like wax. Castleton feels himself go red.

Marguerite gives her brother a dissatisfied look. Armand adds imperturbably: 'And only half the meat.'

The dinner continues, a long, merciless work of art. Armand smokes incessantly throughout the meal. He drinks nothing but champagne. Ouistiti is sitting on a cushion by his side. He is eating everything from Armand's plate with a napkin tied round his neck. Anything put for him on his special plate with his initials on it he completely ignores. He refreshes himself from time to time from Armand's glass and stares malevolently around him.

There are only two servants in attendance besides Gustave, Marguerite's maître d'hôtel. Armand dislikes a pack of servants falling over each other in the dining room. Any form of over-zealousness or noise, however well-meant, Benoir is completely inimical to.

All the Benoir servants are young, personable and perfectly trained. All are extremely light in colour. The Sioux have an antipathy to what they rather strangely call 'les noirs'.

Except for his mother's occasional injunction: 'Don't drink between each mouthful. Sit straight on your chair, moumou,' no

35

notice whatsoever is taken of George. The brother and sister talk and laugh together like lovers, roping Castleton in as if the child wasn't in the room at all.

Castleton feels an immense relief when the liberation comes at last with the most ardently longed-for and patiently awaited pudding course.

Throughout the meal George has been confined to Vichy, but with his sweet he is allowed a glass of champagne. He helps himself joyously to the splendid *Bavaroise aux fraises* his mother has prepared for him.

'Bravo!' says Castleton. It makes him laugh to see the little boy tackle the murderously rich sweet without winking an eye. 'He's got himself outside that all right.'

'O, it is superb. O, mama, you are darling to make it for me. O, I will kiss you for it when I may get down.' He points his spoon at Castleton and whispers politely: 'Don't he eat dessert, mama dear?' His tender upper lip is slightly beaded with champagne.

'Whom are you speaking of?'

'Your husband, mama.'

She leans across and slaps him once, fairly hard, on the arm. 'That is for you. And if you cry you may go straight upstairs to bed.'

'Oh, darling!' Castleton protests.

Armand says coolly: 'You've lost me a hundred dollars, my dear. That jew Viv will collect it from me when he comes.'

George applies himself in silence to his pudding. His eyes are on his plate. A vivid pink patch burns on his left arm.

'D'you want some more *Bavaroise*, moumou? Speak French,' says Marguerite.

'S'il vous plaît, maman.'

She helps him generously. He divides his portion meticulously in two. 'May I save half for Dédé, mama, if you please?'

If he wishes, though it isn't necessary. He can be sure Mammy will not allow Dédé to go short.

'No, ma'am, but she likes to eat something from my plate,' he explains earnestly. 'It is quite natural since she is my milk-sister, maman chérie.'

She tells him: 'Don't look at me through your hair like that. I have perfectly understood your pious wish.' If he has finished he may get down. 'Gustave will untie your napkin.'

He gets down with enthusiasm, the rigours of the long dinner

36

behind him. He goes straight to his mother's chair and puts both arms round her neck. 'Thank you, mille fois, for my most splendid dessert.'

'If you enjoyed it I am satisfied.'

She kisses his pale face most lovingly and then presents him with a piece of her peach. It seems that with the fruit he is permitted, even encouraged, to perambulate, doing the rounds of the table and visiting everyone—providing of course there are no guests.

'Here'—Armand throws him a cluster of grapes. He tells his brother-in-law quickly: 'Give him something.' Castleton rather awkwardly holds out a pear.

'Not that—something of yours.'

Castleton is eating an apple. 'Let him bite off it,' Armand says.

Marguerite says instantly: 'Vincent, not the skin.'

Castleton cuts some of the peel off and holds the apple out. His fingers feel all thumbs. The shy child comes forward, takes a bite and retreats.

'What d'you say, moumou?'

'Merci, petit-papa.' He still can't bring himself to look direct at Castleton. He stands half-looking at him through his hair. Castleton notices he keeps his left arm hidden behind his back.

'Mon dieu,' exclaims Marguerite. 'Look at moumou's hair.'

'Why?' asks her brother. He is peeling a grape for Ouistiti who has wrapped his napkin round his head. 'I believe this case is drunk.'

Marguerite says: 'What is going to happen to moumou's hair, Armand?'

'What should happen to it?' her brother replies. 'It will remain on his head, one hopes.'

'He looks like an Apache,' Marguerite says.

'Well, sweetheart, we couldn't do anything about it on the ship or the train. Puss couldn't lift his head from the pillow.'

Marguerite says: 'I refuse to let Albert cut it, Armand.'

'Then let Vince have his barber do it, or André can fix it for him when he comes to do yours. These things are not insurmountable, ma chère.'

She looks at her smiling brother and thinks: nothing is important to you but Maman's tomb at Mal Choisi. She says coldly: 'I do not consider Albert expert enough for George, Armand.'

'For the moment he is sufficient. When puss is eighteen he will

37

have two valets on his neck,' Armand says, 'for his sins.' He is feeding his monkey in a withdrawn sort of way.

Marguerite asks: 'Are you going to Mal Choisi this time, Armand?'

Yes, he is going. She is not there, of course. She is not anywhere, but he is going just the same. Afterwards he will console himself with Liane.

He says to George: 'Go tell Achille to give you the three leather cases from my small valise, will you, fella? You will find us in the p'tit salon for coffee.'

When George is gone, he says: 'He don't get around enough, Mimi, with other kids. Viv was bawling me out about it. It isn't easy because of his shyness, but Viv's right. Looks like the Sioux have missed that particular bus.' He has drawn his arm through Castleton's. They are going to the salon. Ouistiti is hanging round Armand's neck. He looks decidedly squiffy.

Armand says: 'Perhaps Vince'll be able to rustle up a few young Castletons for us, Mi. I'm sure they're more prolific than Benoirs.'

Castleton says: 'We could go to Antibes for the summer, darling. Old Cecil always rents a house there for his lot.'

His brother-in-law is looking at Marguerite. 'Yes,' says Benoir. 'Yes, something like that, hein, Mi?'

Castleton says: 'It must be terrible for him to be so shy. I've never met anyone quite as shy before.'

'No,' says Benoir. 'You are not likely to.' To Marguerite he says: 'I wonder where he gets it from, Mimi?' His eyes forbid her to answer this question he should never have asked. Oh, Benoir is terrible when he is in this mood. He is always like this before Mal Choisi.

Benoir says smoothly: 'I wish he'd give a piece of it to his cousin Bienville. My God, the sheer hide of that case, Vince. Someone ought to drop his pants properly for him just once, before it's too late.'

In the salon he seems more like his old gay self. Ouistiti is lying flat on his back staring at the ceiling through shining slits. Armand is waving a piece of sugar soaked in brandy and coffee in front of his face. 'That case. He's as pissed as a priest!' He says: 'Of course, puss is in a bad position for age, between Viv and Baudouin's little girl. What can one do? I guess he'll just have to make out with Albert and Dédé till something better turns up.

At least those two are flesh and blood, not something out of a charcuterie like that de Chassevent boy who only needs a lemon in his mouth!'

When George comes back he takes the cases from him. 'I want your opinion here, puss.' He tells his brother-in-law: 'I would not dream of making a present unless it had been passed by little Benoir. He has the second best taste in the family. The first is Mimi's for choosing you,' says Armand, whose speciality is making compliments in which he actually believes.

George goes and stands by his mother with his arm round her neck. Castleton notices he hasn't asked what is in the cases, or who they are for. Probably curiosity in children is not much encouraged by the Benoirs. The marks of Marguerite's fingers are fading from his left arm. He brings his face quite close to hers. 'Mama . . .'

'Have you something to tell me you are ashamed of, George?'

'No, ma'am.'

'Then don't whisper. Say what you have to say out loud.'

George says, flushing, 'Mammy done spoke to Albert about his disorderliness, mama. She says he will improve. She says Albert will try to please Madame with all his heart.'

With or without his heart he will do it. Or go. 'And speak French if you can't speak English,' Marguerite says. '"Done spoke." I don't wish to hear this Mississippi share cropper's talk any more. It is fantastic how you only pick up what is bad.'

'Yes'm.' He says in French: 'Maman, I said "bonjour" to Nicole and Pauline while I was upstairs. Sidonie was out. It is a pity. I would have liked to say "bonjour" to Sidonie,' says George.

It is not important. Tomorrow he shall say 'bonjour' to all his friends.

'O my Redeemer!' calls out the little boy, which makes his stepfather laugh.

'What doesn't he want to do, darling?'

His stepson's face has fallen a mile. He doesn't want to go out on to the big gallery and show himself to the servants. Apparently it's the done thing with the Sioux when you have been absent for any length of time. 'We will see how you acquit yourself this time.'

'O, I don't want it,' murmurs George. For the first time he seeks out his stepfather's eye and makes a small face.

Marguerite tells him: 'If you intend to pull grimaces you may leave the room. We will dispense with the pleasure of your

39

company at coffee.' He desists at once. Marguerite gives him a 'canard', a piece of sugar steeped in cognac and coffee from her spoon.

'Hey, puss,' Armand has opened two of the cases. 'What do you think of these?'

He has brought two bracelets from Paris, one for his sister, one for Liane. A twiggy bangle of bright gold with flashing thunder-drops of diamonds running off it is for Marguerite. 'Give this to mama with all my love.'

The sapphire and emerald bracelet, an art nouveau design of iris, is for his mistress. 'It will go exactly with Liane's new colouring,' Armand says. 'It will amuse you, Mimi, her new colouring. If you can recognise her,' Armand says.

'Is she here then?' asks Marguerite, raising her eyebrows at Castleton.

'Of course she is here. I have persuaded de Chassevent that some of his Delta property should be sold. They flew over last Thursday and are already installed at their town place. He is a talented cuckold, that de Chassevent. I am surprised he has not already called you up, Mimi.' He tells Castleton: 'My sister is his ideal of a woman. Her perfectionism appeals to his rigid army mind.'

'Benoir, you have no shame!' She is laughing at her favourite brother, who is mercifully quite himself again.

The splendid bracelets have drawn loud cries and exclamations of pleasure from the pale child. 'O, they are superb. O, mama, put yours on for me to see.'

Yes, she will put hers on to please him. 'Then you must go to bed. It is getting past your bedtime, ma souris.'

Thank God. His pallor has taken on a luminous quality that is getting Castleton down.

He is allowed to take two chocolates with him, one for himself and one for Dédé.

'Which d'you want?' Armand has cleverly turned the biggest ones towards him.

O, he is good. You are not supposed to touch anything you don't intend to take. And if you take too long choosing, it will get you a name for being a gourmand.

George puts his chocolates on a little gold plate while he is making his goodnights. 'Goodnight, my own sweet darling maman-chérie. Will you come up to me when I'm in bed?'

Yes, she will come up and bless him. 'Now disappear. Breathe through your nose, moumou,' says Marguerite.

'Yes'm. Goodnight, Uncle Benoir.'

'Goodnight, sweet dreams, and remember us in your prayers.'

'O yes, I will,' says George.

'Here's something to help you.' Armand throws the third case at him. It is very small.

'O look! O, mama, may I open it please?'

'Tomorrow. What is it, Armand?' says Marguerite.

'It's between me and puss. Let him open it.'

'O, mama, may I?'

Since it is Uncle Benoir's wish.

It is a rosary of pink and white pearls made specially for a child. 'O, it is beautiful. O, it is darling. O, mama, my Uncle Benoir is chic for me. O, I will keep it for dimanches only, it is so beautiful.'

'Success,' remarks Armand.

'He has at least five already,' says Marguerite.

'Half-a-dozen rosaries,' stipulates Armand, 'is the minimum required by a well-set-up Benoir.'

Marguerite says, smiling: 'You will turn him into a religious maniac, mon cher.'

'O, you are good for me, Uncle Benoir. O, I do thank you de tout mon coeur.'

Armand remarks: 'It's a providence puss still hasn't learnt German or we'd be getting Boche mixed in with all the rest of it.'

The little boy kisses his beads enthusiastically. It is obvious he would like to kiss his Uncle Benoir.

'That's all right, guy.' Armand fends him off. 'Say a prayer for me and breathe through your nose, there's a good fellow, for all our sakes.'

Marguerite says: 'Have you thanked Uncle Benoir for all the trouble he has taken with you?'

'No, ma'am, I'm sorry.' He says with great enthusiasm: 'Thank you for being a trouble to me.' Then he stoops quickly and kisses Armand's hand. The men collapse and even Marguerite is laughing out loud.

'Run, run to your bed quickly. You are quite stupid you are so tired.'

'Yes'm. Mama, do I have to say goodnight to Mr Castleton as well?'

She rather thinks so. 'And don't look at his shoes this time.'

He comes and stands in front of his stepfather. He is breathing conscientiously through his nose. His face is quite pink with the effort. He achieves the middle button of Castleton's shirt.

A little higher, Armand recommends, and he will qualify for the croix de guerre.

He raises his eyes and gets the full impact of his new stepfather's face.

O, it is like nothing he has ever seen before. The face is open in expression and fresh in colour without being red. The lips are fresh coloured too, and very strong and finely cut. George decides they have a quick-tempered look but are not at all strict. The chin is strong too, and cleft in what George considers a most interesting way.

Mr Castleton's hair is very thick and straight, and made up of different shades of brown and a bit of grey. George thinks this mixture curious but enchanting. The eyebrows, which are also mixed, are thick and short. But the eyes, they are the thing. Mr Castleton's eyes are literally all colours, black and grey and brown and green and blue all mixed up together in flecks and bars. George decides that as soon as he can get his courage up he will look at those eyes again. There are also a lot of deepish lines on Mr Castleton's face. Across his forehead and round his eyes. But they don't make him look old. That is about all George can bear to take in at the moment. He drops his eyes and Castleton hears him whisper: 'Goodnight, Mr Castleton.'

'Goodnight, old darling. Oh, I say, it's absolutely splendid, isn't it?' The child is holding out for Castleton's inspection his pretty new rosary of pink and white pearls.

The breathing is very elaborate.

'May I look at it?'

He gives it wordlessly and wordlessly takes it back. His heart is hopping about in his neck above his sailor top.

'Oh, I say, aren't you lucky?' Castleton says. He is trying to keep his voice down. It sounds ruddy awful. He bends down and gives the dreadfully pale cheek a kiss. 'Sleep tight, old pet.' He bolsters up the cheery injunction with a large wink.

There is a pause while the wink is digested, then the pale thing calls out to no one in particular: 'O, he is nice,' and bolts.

*   *   *

Directly George has gone, Armand tells his sister: 'Quickly, run up and bless your treasure or whatever you want to do, and let's get out.'

Six memorable days with little Benoir have put him in exactly the mood for tearing up the town.

'We'll show Vince some real dancing.' Orleans night spots leave the Paris joints standing, according to Armand. 'If we're lucky Vince will see some real Créole beauty there. Prototypes of the Sioux.'

'Ah, Armand, please,' says Marguerite.

'Please what?' says Armand. 'Are you trying to tell me little Benoir has imported those eyes from France?'

They can look in at Lowes' Crescent first, Armand says. They have at least three-quarters of an hour to kill.

'I adore the vaudeville shows here. It's a thing they understand.' Besides, there is absolutely no point in their being at the Bayou Tigre before midnight. The de Chassevents have one of their dinner parties on.

'Oh mon dieu, Benoir,' says Marguerite. 'It will land you somewhere one day, your aplomb.'

'I hope so.' Armand is putting the sapphire bracelet into his pocket. He tells his brother-in-law: 'You are looking disgustingly handsome tonight, Vince, in your British way. I don't intend to lose Liane to you. I shall get de Chassevent to asphyxiate you with his Algerian campaign. There is only one, but it is unforgettable.' He is putting on Ouistiti's chain.

Marguerite says: 'You are not intending to take that animal, I hope?'

'Most certainly. Ouisti goes everywhere with his papa. He is not your luckless child, my dear.' He tells his brother-in-law: 'Animals are something my sister has absolutely no feeling for.'

Marguerite prophesies: 'They will sling you out.'

'That is a bridge . . .' says Armand, 'how does it finish, Vince?' He says: 'For Christ's sake tell your wife to go upstairs or we shall be having the Dauphin served up all evening with our champagne.'

'Shall I come with you, darling?' Castleton asks.

It is not advisable, Marguerite says. He doesn't sleep very profoundly. 'He would sense your presence, Poilu.'

Benoir laughs loudly. Marguerite says coldly: 'It's true, all the same.'

43

'D'you believe her?'

'Not really,' Castleton says.

'Ça m'est égal,' says Marguerite, and goes upstairs.

Her brother shouts after her: 'You want to gobble him up all by yourself, that's all. Greedy pig! Aren't you ashamed?'

4

The Washroom

The two men go into the washroom, and Armand says immediately: 'Is it a promise, Vince?'

'What about?'

'About little Benoir.' He is waiting for his brother-in-law's answer, his inscrutable eyes fixed on the ground with a strangely diffident air.

'D'you mean about playmates?'

He means about everything. He makes an expressive gesture. 'He has absolutely nothing, Vince. He has thirty million and that's all that is left of his father for him. I don't intend to bore you with the whole mess,' Armand says, 'you may imagine what has happened there.'

Castleton says: 'Yes, well, I shouldn't worry. He'll be all right.' He is washing his hands.

Armand says: 'It was a tragedy for us all when Georges was killed, but for little Benoir it was total disaster. You can't imagine how much he misses his father. Not consciously, of course, he was only five when my cousin was killed, but the security.' Armand

45

says: 'Even that nut case Davis was better for him than nothing.'

Armand says surprisingly: 'He was quite good, in fact, that
Davis of Mississippi.' Armand says: 'Once puss feels you behind
him, Vince, everything else will come. He will do his best to please
you. He is not méchant, little Benoir.' He laughs. 'Any bad habits
you may set down to his cousin Benoir. I suppose he has some—I
don't know: I never enquire into these things. But I do know that
most of his misdeeds stem from his terrible nerves.' Armand says
sadly: 'He has inherited the celebrated Benoir nerves.' He gives a
sly smile and says: 'His mother has them too. You may have
noticed it, Vince?'

'Yes, I have noticed it,' Castleton says.

'So,' says Benoir, conclusively, 'do your best for me, will you?
Save him a few smacks.'

Castleton says he is all for it. 'I didn't care for that at dinner
much.'

Benoir says carelessly: 'Oh, that. He won't die of that, you
know.' He will not put up with the slightest criticism where his
sister is concerned. He says: 'Perhaps my sister isn't the most
patient mother in the world, but she would lay her life down for
her son.' He says it is extraordinary but his poor Marie, who is
nearly always souffrante these days, has actually better nerves for
puss than his own mother. It is a pity they couldn't exchange sons,
Armand says. 'Viv would have suited Mi down to the ground.'

He stands there thinking affectionately of his wife and even
lightly regretting some of his infidelities. 'Ma pauv' p'tite Marie,
Vince. She has une maladie de femmes. Her menopause has
started much too early.'

Castleton says: 'Oh, really?'—which sounds bloody silly.

Armand is letting Ouistiti drink water out of his hand. 'With
any luck he will want to piss in the middle of the floor show. That
should make de Chassevent's evening. My God, Vince, that poor
zombie—can you imagine going through life like that?' Armand
prevents Ouistiti touching a hot tap. 'Hey, you'll burn yourself!
That case is worse than a child.' He swings the tiny creature on to
his shoulder. 'Sit there, hear me?' He tilts his head to keep his
cigarette smoke from Ouistiti's eyes and tells his brother-in-law
quite gaily: 'One splendid point about little Benoir's nerves. They
are so taut you will be able to play any tune you like on them.'

'If he lets me.'

46

'He will let you. He has taken a bundle for you, Vince. Castletons are a taste we have in common, the Dauphin and I.'

'Oh, good.' Castleton is drying his hands.

Armand says, slyly: 'It could be difficult for you, of course. It could tax your British phlegm.'

'I shouldn't think so.' Castleton chucks his towel at his brother-in-law. 'Even if I knew what that was.' He starts to brush his hair. 'You are a bloody fool, Armand.'

Armand is swallowing a glass of ice-water. He seems to have cheered himself up. 'Mon dieu, que j'avais soif! Don't you want some, Vince?' Armand, like George, is perpetually thirsty, and Marguerite has ordered fresh iced water to be placed in every room during her brother's stay. He will touch nothing but water or champagne. He calls out enthusiastically: 'It's splendid to piss from a full bladder. You don't know what you're missing, Vince!' When he comes back he says: 'That cannibal Ouistiti has relieved himself too. Now there is nothing between us and de Chassevent's Algerian campaign. In the last resort I shall take off my shoes.' He catches hold of Ouistiti. 'Cochon, you are still wet.' He dries the weird, greenish fur with one of Marguerite's fine fringed towels. 'Vince, I have a feeling my poor Ouisti does not find favour in your eyes.'

Castleton says: 'I don't like monkeys much.'

The bloody thing is like a miniature man in almost every respect. He is giving himself like mad to Armand's caressing touch while baring his teeth at Castleton like a dog.

Armand laughs. 'He thinks you are competing for the honour of drying his tutu.' He kisses the warm round skull. 'He is not as pretty as the Dauphin, I admit, but what can one do? One is as one is. The Dauphin adores him, of course,' Armand says. 'The Dauphin adores everything that walks, flies, crawls, whistles or hoots. There is a long drawn out battle over animals between the Dauphin and the Clinic. The Dauphin is bound to lose, of course, because the Clinic has a powerful ally in Marguerite.' Armand says: 'It is a pity. Animals give him so much pleasure. I think they are good for his nerves.'

Castleton asks outright: 'How ill is George?'

Armand replies cagily: 'He is not well.'

There is another pause while Armand swallows another glass of water, then he says in a considered voice: 'I think it is a little better than it was. Not much, but it is better.' He is sucking a

47

splinter of ice like a sweet and washing his hands. 'My sister is quite formidable. She has even remembered my cologne.' He is pouring some over his wrists. 'She forgets nothing, that girl.'

Castleton says: 'What is the matter with George?'

'Oh, you know,' Armand begins evasively. He is holding his scented palms to his cheeks.

'No, I don't,' says Castleton. 'That's why I ask.'

He sees his brother-in-law looking at him over the pale mask of his small hands. The eyes are black, sombre and completely inscrutable. Benoir says in a cold voice: 'Puss has the same complaint as my brother Baudouin.' He comes right up to Castleton and says: 'He has a case of megaloblastic anaemia, my friend.'

Castleton waits. Armand takes his hands away from his face and says in the same inimical tone: 'It is not expected he will die from it. It is completely under control.' There is the vestige of a smile about his lips as he says: 'That poor kid suffers as much from the cure as from the complaint. Those assassins at the Clinic. What a life, eh, Vince?' Armand begins to laugh. 'What a dirty, filthy trick to play on a kid.'

'La vie est bête à pleurer,' says Armand. But all this will change. He takes Castleton's face between his hands and says with real enthusiasm: 'Everything will be better now we have you in the family, Vince. You are God's personal gift to the Sioux.'

'You silly prick,' says Castleton, beginning to laugh.

Armand assures him: 'No, I mean it. You are exactly the right man for my sister and for the boy. Everyone will benefit, and you will reimburse yourself for your nobility by getting the most wonderful wife in the world. She is a splendid fellow, my sister, and a formidable ménagère. There will be no Auteuil chaos for you, my friend,' Armand says laughing. 'I sometimes think our dining-room staff has been specially trained on the Paris Bourse. The cries, the confusions, the noise! We have a pair of Basques at the moment who are quite unbelievable. But every time the guillotine is about to fall Marie begs for their lives! Of course it suits the Dauphin down to the ground. He can chew peacefully on his chicken bone long after the course has been removed, and not a soul will bother him.' Armand says: 'That poor Dauphin, he has his worries, you know. The Clinic and that side of it. It can't be funny. I used to send him in to my Marie when he came back, to cry it out. His cousin Viv loves him to death, but if you're not out of your misery in two seconds flat you've had it for that case.'

Armand says: 'Sometimes I have seen him so brought down I'd like to blow the whole place up. Pouf! Le Clinic Benoir! Pouf! Pouf! Armand makes a blowing-up gesture. He says: 'Unfortunately I am not able to help him as much as I should.'

'I know.'

Mimi has told him, then. Eh quoi? It may be all the better. It may even make him take up his responsibilities the sooner for it. 'He knows, of course. Mi thinks he doesn't, but he feels it all right.' Armand says: 'I suppose I should force myself. I don't know. One is as one is.'

He laughs. 'My God, that terrible trip on the *Égalité*, Vince. I shall carry the marks of it to my grave.' He says: 'I wished your honeymoon at the devil a thousand times a day, my friend.'

Castleton tells him: 'It's your own bloody fault. I offered to fetch him for you. I could easily have come to Paris.'

Armand assures him: 'He would have died in his tracks from pure fright. You saw his reaction to you tonight.'

'Yes,' agrees Castleton. 'Christ.'

Armand says: 'The vomiting. It was a marathon. I'll never know how anyone could eat so little and throw up so much!' Armand says: 'I should have risked the altitude or flown him over in a mask. Better to throw a dead Dauphin at his mother's feet than to have put him through that ordeal.'

'Poor little devil,' Castleton says.

Yes. Poor puss. But it's all over now. Armand says: 'Happy days are here again for little Benoir.'

He begins to laugh uncontrollably. 'My poor Vince! It will cost you something. The Dauphin makes an implacable friend. It has happened before, with Davis.'

'Well, what about it?'

Armand calls out: 'He'll be your friend for life! You'll have the piss bored out of you!'

He is laughing so hard he is hanging on to the wash basins. 'The Dauphin has a truly terrifying sense of gratitude. You'll be annihilated by it, my poor Vince. Nothing can stand up against this terrible, slow gratitude of the Dauphin.'

'I don't mind,' says Castleton shortly. 'Don't bloody annoy me, Benoir.'

Armand is obliged to splash his face with cold water, he has laughed so much. He says: 'I hope at least you have an appetite for the naïf? Little Benoir is naïve beyond the limits of credulity.

49

Even the close proximity of that gone case his cousin Benoir has had absolutely no effect on it so far. Not a dent,' says Armand, still laughing helplessly, 'in the shining naïveté of little Benoir.'

Castleton says he's jolly pleased to hear it. If there's a thing he loathes it's a sophisticated kid.

Then little Benoir is the kid for him. Armand predicts they will get on like fire-engines.

'House on fire,' Castleton says. 'Christ, you really do talk cock.'

Armand says admiringly: 'I can see the situation holds no terrors for you. With your English sang-froid and your splendid nerves of reinforced concrete you will win through. Then too,' he says, 'we mustn't ignore the fact that little Benoir has certain qualities.' He asks his brother-in-law: 'Have you heard about these qualities, by any chance? They are quite famous.'

'Oh, those,' says Castleton, smiling. 'Yes, I've heard about those all right.'

'Ah, I can see my sister has not spared you any of les spécialités Dauphinois.' He reels the list off like a bill of fare. HIS OPEN NATURE. HIS LOVING DISPOSITION. HIS CELEBRATED INABILITY TO TELL A LIE.

'That's right,' Castleton says. He is looking squarely at his brother-in-law.

Armand says softly: 'Unfortunately it's all true.' He stands away to get a better effect. 'Aren't you afraid? Doesn't it make you tremble to realise you'll have this paragon round your neck for years and years?' His laughter is like a badly made parcel, escaping at all sides. He is completely happy again.

'You bloody silly prick,' says Castleton, laughing too.

'Come on, let's go,' says Benoir. 'I want to dance.'

He looks exactly like George. He tells his brother-in-law: 'You haven't made pipi yet, Vince. You must take a petit précaution, as your friend the Dauphin would say. I will wait for you and make encouraging noises like one makes for a horse.' He stands outside the door whistling softly. Ouistiti whistles too.

'For Christ's sake,' shouts Castleton, 'You're putting me off.'

'Are you a prude, Vince?' Armand asks him. 'Tiens!' When he comes out of the lavatory, Armand says: 'By the way, Vince, did you ever get that terrible Duty letter puss sent you on your honeymoon? I think you did, because he had a letter from you two days later from Jamaica.'

'Yes, I did get it,' says Castleton. 'It was terribly funny. All cher monsieurs and mes plus respectueuses.'

Armand says: 'He wrote it to my Marie's dictation. They spoiled about twenty sheets of paper between them.' Armand says: 'For some reason the Dauphin can't read or write English. Don't ask me why. It seems the Davis boys were trying to teach him when the marriage crashed. Puss seems unable to take in anything from Miss Merrick. I think he gets mesmerised by her teeth.'

Castleton says: 'It was a jolly nice letter. Mim rather went off the deep end about it, but I thought it was awfully sweet.'

Armand says: 'You know he still has your answer, Vince? He was too nervous to open it so he kept the whole thing. You know what fascinated him? You addressed the envelope to "Master" G-M. Benoir. The Dauphin has an insatiable appetite for the curious. I shall leave him my library when I die—to say no more it is extremely curious.' Armand laments: 'Mon dieu, Vince, I am thirty-six already! At thirty-six one is more than three-quarters dead!'

He scrutinises himself closely in the glass, but doesn't appear unduly depressed by what he sees. He remarks complacently: 'That Hippolyte really understands to cut one's hair. I suppose that cannibal Viv will wrest him from me. He has no pity for his ancient papa,' he adds mock-pessimistically. 'In any case, at thirty-six what does one need with stylish haircuts?' He puts his arm through Castleton's and says: 'Oh, fella, it is hideous beyond words to be thirty-six.'

'I'm forty-three,' Castleton point out.

'But you are British and therefore indestructible,' Armand bewails. 'The Sioux age so badly. After thirty our sins come back to roost.'

Castleton says: 'You're the best looking bloody lot I've ever seen.'

But Castleton is splendid looking too, in a Mt Rushmore kind of way. ('My God, the Dauphin's face when he first saw you!') Armand predicts: 'You will come crashing down to an honourable grave, full of good works and English rheumatism. For you the Castletons will trumpet into their handkerchiefs and their stiff upper lips will tremble.'

He tells his brother-in-law: 'It was the endearing way you blow your nose that made me introduce you to my sister.' He prophesies: 'The Dauphin will go mad about it.'

'Get out of it,' laughs Castleton, pushing him into the hall.

Armand is calling 'Moumoumou!' up the stairs. When Marguerite appears he calls out: 'Is he asleep in his basket, your moumou?'

Yes, he is asleep. Marguerite asks them: 'Where have you been, you two?'

They have been in the washroom, Benoir tells her. 'Pissing side by side as good brothers-in-law should.'

'My God, Benoir, you are horrible!' laughs Marguerite.

'Dis donc, Mimi,' Armand calls out. 'That husband of yours has taken a bundle for your flirt. He has completely fallen for the eyes from Martinique. I predict *une grande affaire*,' cries Armand who is shaking the fingers of his right hand as if he'd burnt them, and looking enormously French.

Marguerite tells her husband: 'Il est complètement fou, mon frère.' In the car she sits between her husband and her brother with their arms round her waist. Castleton gets Armand's small hand by mistake and they all laugh.

Mim looks absolutely radiant, Castleton thinks. She is over the moon with happiness at having her boy back.

5

The Bayou Tigre

He feels a frightful oaf partnering whichever luckless woman is not dancing with Benoir.

Mme de Chassevent is at least polite about it, but Mim makes it more than clear that she thinks his dancing pretty bloody, which of course it is.

She has asked him at least twice, quite seriously: 'Why do you dance so badly, mon ami?'

The Benoirs, of course, make nonsense of everyone in the room. They dance superbly. It is as vital to them as breathing, and as easy. Armand in particular seems seized with a kind of rage to dance. He is dancing with his sister like a lover. They are a perfect match. Every time they pass Castleton, Benoir calls out: 'Vive les Castletonnes!' Castleton is guiding Liane de Chassevent across the floor to their table. She has not said so, of course, but it is fairly obvious that she would rather wait for her share of Benoir than dance for dancing's sake with him.

Castleton can't say he goes for the de Chassevents much. He is suffocatingly conventional and typical French Top Brass.

Madame de obviously knows her onions. Castleton can quite see her attraction for his brother-in-law. She is bold, shrewd, well educated and amusing, and what Mim calls her 'seaman's' eyes are a bright predatory blue. Mim says she's completely like a man, but that's rot, of course. Mim never has much use for other women and Mme de is certainly neither masculine or hard. She is a witty and intrepid dresser with the courage to engineer her entire outfit for one astonishing effect.

She says politely: 'You are content with your new acquisition, Mr Castleton, the little son of Marguerite?'

The rough warm voice is very attractive.

'Oh very much so,' says Castleton.

'What a pity he is not in better health, pauvre petit bonhomme,' says Mme de Chassevent.

'Indeed yes. A great pity,' says Castleton, which thank God brings them to their table. De Chassevent rises like a phantom from the grave and pulls out his wife's chair. The Benoirs come dancing up, entwined and laughing. Ouistiti is riding on Armand's shoulder. He automatically bares his teeth at Castleton.

The polite phantom rises again and seats Marguerite.

'Merci, Yves,' Marguerite says. 'Benoir is completely mad tonight.'

Benoir has every reason to be gay. Benoir has been liberated by the British. He raises his glass to Castleton. 'To many happy trips on the Égalité, my friend.'

Castleton raises his glass.

'What is he saying?' asks Liane.

Marguerite shrugs. 'It is some nonsense between them.'

Armand is consuming shrimp gumbo with gusto. 'Dis donc, Mimi, it's good!' Like George he puts away vast quantities of bread. 'I adore Créole food.'

For how long?

Marguerite says: 'If one gives him anything more than twice he immediately gets bored with it.'

'But not with Vince the Liberator,' Armand says. 'I will never get bored with your splendid chap, Mimi, as long as he keeps the Dauphin off my neck.' He throws an affectionate crust at Castleton's face.

'Ah non! Armand!' calls Marguerite.

It is not permitted to throw bread at table. Mimi the Flic has spoken.

54

Armand says: 'But I am not your little tame moumou. What luck, eh, Vince? I would have had my arm well slapped for that. By the way, Mi, your husband doesn't approve your commando tactics for the Dauphin.' He holds his arms out to her. 'What are we waiting for? Let's dance.'

When they come back again, Armand says: 'How is the Algerian campaign coming along? Have you had it yet, Vince?' He assures de Chassevent: 'My brother-in-law will give you his undivided attention. He has been conditioned at the House of Lords.'

'Armand, please!' says Marguerite.

Armand, please! He lifts a warning finger. 'It is the voice of Mimi the Flic.'

He is sharing a peach with Liane which has been soaking in his champagne glass. He is playing with his bracelet on her arm. 'Who gave you that?' He stuffs the last piece of peach into her mouth and says with his mouth full: 'You should do this with Mimi, Vince, then you will never quarrel. There is a superstition about it around these parts, especially down at the Delta. You must ask the Dauphin about it, he is the biggest authority on domestic voudou.'

Marguerite says: 'I hope you won't ask him anything of the kind, Vincent. George was a mass of superstitions after Shiloh. I had the greatest difficulty to get him civilised again.'

De Chassevent observes that, while one should at all costs avoid the sweepingstatement, it has become apparent, in the light of recent events, that the practice of voudou is far more widespread in these latitudes than is commonly supposed. Even in New Orleans, a city of, one could probably say with confidence, not less than six million population, there have been instances lately which point to the fact that this cult indubitably exists.

Not only exists. It's on the up and up. Benoir says the Sioux practise voudou all the time. Especially Mi and puss. He tells his brother-in-law: 'He is the biggest wizard of them all, that little pale Benoir. He's out for your blood, Vince, and he'll drink it.' He teases his sister: 'Mimi, I suspect that child of yours of living exclusively on human hearts; supplemented, from time to time, by a modest bonbon or two.'

'You are a fool, Benoir!' Marguerite laughs. She tells the table: 'The blacks at Shiloh were as black as cannibals and abysmally superstitious. Perhaps they were cannibals,' Marguerite says. 'They were probably part of Davis's Great Retrogression Policy.'

She says: 'I don't pretend to know what went on down there. I only know my three months at Shiloh were the three longest months of my life.'

'Ah, Shiloh,' Armand says. 'Shiloh is a complete mystery. D'you know, Vince, no one has yet been able to discover what possessed Mimi to marry Davis of Mississippi? It's the only serious slip I've known my sister to make.'

Except her current marriage. Castleton says: 'That's a right muck-up, isn't it, darling?' They kiss.

Liane says boldly: 'I can quite see what Mimi saw in Davis.'

De Chassevent interjects stiffly: 'One understands the shooting in that region is quite exceptional.'

Armand laughs: 'It would have been even more exceptional if I hadn't rescued Davis in time. I believe my sister would have shot him and his three six-foot sons without the slightest compunction.'

'He has a terrific attraction, that man,' Liane avers. 'I find his personality magnetic.'

De Chassevent, speaking purely for himself, confesses he can find little to admire in an individual, who, having pulled off a species of Confidence Trick with the McLeod affair, now blatantly flaunts his refusal to withdraw from the Political Field.

There is a loud laugh from Benoir.

De Chassevent observes unsmilingly that it is doubtless Out-dated to hold such opinions, but Nevertheless.

Armand is demanding one valid reason why Davis should retire. 'He has never been more popular. The twin calamities of this McLeod thing, plus his marriage to my sister, have made a national hero of the man. The South is solid behind him as a direct result, and nothing would surprise me less than to hear Davis has been nominated.'

'D'you want to divorce me, darling?' Castleton asks Marguerite. 'If you re-marry Davis you'll be Mrs President.'

She would rather be Mrs Castleton. They kiss. She is adorable when she comes out with her new name.

'Hé, you two, kissing like pigeons over there!' Armand calls out. 'You can do that in bed!'

De Chassevent is scrupulously scrutinising the floor. 'At a venture one would say a mixed bunch . . . what is your opinion, Li?'

Castleton is asking Marguerite:'What about the magnetism, ducks? Aren't you going to miss it, if you stop with me?'

If Davis had any magnetism for her she has forgotten all about it. She says quite simply: 'Davis was raving mad. I had already washed my hands of him three weeks after the wedding.'

Armand says slyly: 'Puss hadn't.'

'Oh, don't bore us with your theories, Benoir.'

They are not theories. He has proof positive. He puts a snapshot on the table and announces: 'Straight from the secret cache of little Benoir!'

It goes the rounds amidst laughter. 'Don't let Mimi keep it, Vince. She will snatch it from the Dauphin.' Armand murmurs in Castleton's ear: 'She is the orginal Gestapo. For her there must be no secret places of the heart. All, all must be open to surveillance by the terrible eye of Mimi the Flic.'

'God, what a photo!' Marguerite laughs. 'It is too much. Where did you find it, Benoir?'

He says: 'I will never tell you. There must be positively no tidying up, my girl.' He tells his brother-in-law: 'She would bereave that poor Dauphin of his treasures, Vince.' He says: 'Incidentally, the Dauphin is very funny when he is bereft, he simply stands there with his mouth wide open emitting desolate shrieks.'

'I find him adorable in this picture,' cries Liane. She studies the photo for some time.

'She is looking at Davis, of course,' Armand says.

De Chassevent says in a colourless voice: 'One understands the fishing is very good up there.'

'Oh, you are stupid, Armand,' Liane cries. 'Il est un vrai amour, ton gosse, Mimi.' She hands the picture to Castleton. 'Look, he is chouchou in his enormous hat.'

Castleton smiles. The picture shows a group of tall Davis men with the Dauphin in the middle, almost obliterated by a palm-leaf hat. One hand is holding a palmetto fan, the other is clasped in the hand of his ex-stepfather, the reactionary and fanatical Davis of Mississippi. A cat-fish quite four feet long is stretched on the ground and upon this cat-fish the Dauphin has been induced to place a dainty foot. A rangy Davis stripling squatting on his hunkers like an Indian, supports the fish's hideous head. There is a welter of guns, fishing gear and palm-leaf hats on the grass, and

57

a couple of coon dogs are being held by two of the blackest negroes Castleton has ever seen.

The eyes of the Davis boys are screwed up against the blinding light, but the eagle eye of Davis of Mississippi is looking straight into the sun. The Dauphin is looking nowhere in particular. The expression on his face is mild and infinitely polite. Across this composition someone has scrawled: Hi, Googleye! Big hello from But, Jeff, Hank 'n' Paw!

The whole thing is terribly funny, but the thing that tickles Castleton pink is the expression on the face of Mim's chap. 'Your son's a bloody marvel,' Castleton says. 'They ought to stick this up in the Senate.'

'It is unique, that photo,' Armand says. 'Viv nearly injured himself laughing when he saw it. We raided the Dauphin's cache one night in Paris. He keeps his treasures in an empty nougat box. Vince, your letter was amongst them. Incidentally there was a charming coloured snap of Marie and puss sharing a muff. Marcel took it in the Bois one Sunday after mass. I have asked him for a copy of it.'

Marguerite says: 'A muff? In May?'

'Marie is human,' Armand says coolly. 'She has the advantage of not being a Benoir.' He tells his brother-in-law: 'Puss feels the cold cruelly. For him Paris might be Siberia.'

De Chassevent says one hears the weather in Paris has been unpredictable of late. This is bizarre in summer, he finds.

Armand takes back the photo and says in a provocative voice, 'Puss loved Shiloh.'

'What rubbish, Benoir!'

'Puss loved Shiloh, Vince. Mi doesn't want to hear it, but he loved Davis as well.' Armand tells Castleton: 'It was his big treat to go with Davis every morning to hear the whistling quail and watch the trucks from jail unloading. I needn't tell you the whole joint down there was run on convict labour.' Armand says: 'It's a pity Vince has only come in for the tail end of little Benoir's Shiloh phase. At his best period he used to say "persimmons" when annoyed. His cousin used to tease him specially to hear him say it.'

De Chassevent is heard to remark that the persimmon is an admirable fruit but that he has not tasted one since Liane and he last visited their Pontchartrain property.

The talk veers to property ('Don't touch it, Vince, it is the biggest stinking bore of all') and the newly completed sale of the de

Chassevents' place on the Delta. Armand advises: 'You should get rid of your Pontchartrain place too, Yves. They have no meaning any more, these places.'

It is a pity he doesn't take his own advice, Marguerite tells the others. 'You should get rid of St Cloud, Benoir. It is a complete white elephant.'

Armand says simply: 'Puss enjoys the birds. There is a splendid aviary there, Vince, which keeps him amused by the hour.' There is also a lake teeming with water fowl to which Benoir has this year made a notable addition. Flamingoes, roseate clouds of them, are to mark the occasion of Bienville's wedding.

'They are magnificent fellows.' Benoir is smiling, actually seeing for a moment the strange mallet-headed birds sitting like great roses on the shaven lawns, or moving slowly on vermilion stilts along shallows of the lake, dredging for food.

Benoir the incurable romantic!

Marguerite scoffs. 'If Bienville looks at them for two minutes to please you it will be a lot! Elaine will certainly not notice your famous flamingoes. In any case she will probably refuse point blank to go anywhere near St Cloud. Why should she?' Marguerite says: 'They would be fools to spend their honeymoon down in that swamp.'

In two years' time, she prophesies, her brother will have his lake entirely overrun by his new toys. 'And that's all you'll have left of your rose coloured dream, my friend.'

Many thanks! He had momentarily forgotten her genius for deflating dreams. Benoir says tranquilly: 'Never mind. Whoever else does not, puss will enjoy my despised flamingoes. He will be able to study them to his heart's content. If you come down, Vince, you will be able to catch the Dauphin in a state of nature which may well be unparalleled—at least one hopes so.'

Marguerite says: 'I have no intention of bringing moumou down to St Cloud, Benoir.' With the possible exception of La Taquineuse the air at all these delta places is too relaxing for him. And that is quite apart from a domestic situation which by now must have become untenable. The servants down there have been left to their own devices for so long they must have forgotten what work means. 'They are incurably lazy and think of nothing but sleeping and stuffing themselves.'

'Et quoi?' Benoir calls out. 'To be natural. That is the ultimate crime in Mimi's eyes.'

De Chassevent agrees with Marguerite absolutely. 'There must be a certain discipline . . .'

'Ah, foutez-moi la paix,' Armand tells him. 'What do you understand? Even my Ouistiti has more talent for life. He eats, drinks, sleeps and fucks everything in sight.'

Marguerite observes coolly: 'Benoir in pre-Mal Choisi mood.'

Liane says pleasantly: 'You should take Mimi's advice, Armand. St Cloud is not a property that can be run from Paris. You know, mon cher, your sister is always right. She has a very good head for business.'

'My sister has a disgusting philosophy. She is a Boche,' Armand says. 'She doesn't even want to leave the Dauphin his few innocent pleasures at St Cloud.'

'Oh, pack it in,' says Castleton, good-naturedly.

Liane has drawn her arm through Armand's. 'You aren't chic with your sister, Benoir.'

'Oh, leave him alone,' Marguerite says. 'It is useless to argue with him in his present mood.'

Liane asks curiously: 'Is it really true that your little Benoir is so fond of the country, Mimi? Tiens, je trouve ça extraordinaire!' says Mme de Chassevent to whom the country life is pure anathema.

Marguerite says carelessly: 'Moumou has an absolute thing about nature.' Benoir has it to a certain degree, but with that moutard of hers it is an infatuation. 'He has inherited it from our mother. Maman was only happy in the country among her animals and flowers. N'est-ce pas, Armand? Papa used to call her la petite paysanne. She dreaded any kind of social life. It can't have been easy for Papa sometimes, you know,' Marguerite adds coolly.

'I don't know,' Benoir assures her. His black eyes have taken on a punishing look. The white is showing underneath the iris. 'What was the difficulty, Mimi?'

'Oh, don't pretend you don't know,' Marguerite says. 'Maman was quite unfit to take her proper place in life.' She tells her husband: 'She was as shy as my poor moumou, Vincent.'

Benoir says softly: 'All the more reason why we must not get rid of any of our delta places. Your poor moumou must be permitted to enjoy them while he can. There is absolutely no guarantee that he will live to inherit them.'

That will teach Mimi to use Her name like that again! Mlle
Touche Partout!

Castleton sees his wife go very pale. 'Shut up, Benoir. Don't
take the slightest notice of him, darling.'

Armand stares at him inimically, then turns to Marguerite. He
is satisfied she has been well punished for her impertinence, petite
malhonnête. Mentioning Her name in public as if it were common
property. Well, if she does it again she will get another good one
over the knuckles . . . only next time it will be harder.

He is seeing the precise moment of Her death, with the stricken
servants crowding noisily into the room. He thinks cruelly about
his sister: And that's a thing she will have to make her mind up to
if it comes to it with puss. If she is going to set up an idol she will
find out the worshippers also have their rights.

He has gone frightfully pale. He catches Liane looking at him
and smiles.

'Ah, Armand,' remonstrates Liane. 'You aren't nice.'

Armand says: 'One is not nice with Apaches.' He takes up
Liane's hand and kisses it. 'You are nice tonight, my Li.' He puts
his mouth to her ear and whispers: 'Tonight you are . . .'

'Ah non, vous savez!' Liane is blushing richly. 'Ça c'est trop
fort!'

De Chassevent says in his dead voice: 'Liane, aren't those the
Schueders over there at that table by the wall?'

'Possibly.'

He tells Marguerite: 'They are an extremely agreeable American couple we met at the French Embassy in New York.'

'Mon dieu!' Armand has pinned the Schueders down. 'It is
not possible to look like that! What can they be made of, Vince?
They are not even separate.' Armand declares: 'They have been
hewn from a single block of Gruyère cheese.'

The brothers-in-law are laughing helplessly together in spite of
cool looks from Marguerite. De Chassevent is bending over his
wife's chair. 'One should perhaps go over and say a few words.
Vous permettez?' he asks Marguerite.

Armand calls after de Chassevent: 'Don't bring your Schueders
over here. I refuse to have the piss bored out of me by a Gruyère
cheese.' He kicks Castleton under the table. 'Look, Vince, look at
Mimi's face! O my Redeemer! as the Dauphin would say.'

Before the de Chassevents are properly out of earshot, Armand
asks Castleton: 'What do you think of Li?'

61

Castleton says, smiling: 'She's amazing.'

Benoir says, smiling: 'What does that mean?'

Castleton says: 'She couldn't be more Parisian if she tried.'

Marguerite says disdainfully: 'She isn't a Parisienne at all. Her grandfather was a peasant from Rouen who made his pile in the Franco-Prussian war selling French Army supplies to the Boche.' Liane is exactly like old Jacques Laurent: she has the same acquisitive peasant's eyes. Marguerite says: 'Give me some water, Benoir, it is insufferably hot in here.'

'Et quoi?' asks Armand, filling her glass. 'At least Liane's eyes are blue.' He tells his brother-in-law: 'You have to be a Benoir, Vince, to experience the relief of looking into a pair of eyes that aren't black.'

She says: 'You can keep her blue eyes, Benoir.'

He says: 'I do.'

Marguerite says: 'There is a distinct cast in the left one. I find it uncanny, a thing like that.'

'It is an endearing imperfection,' Armand says. 'Like Vince's dancing.' Armand says: 'She has no feeling for the little tendernesses of love.'

Marguerite says: 'I would a thousand times rather look into the black eyes of my son. They are good, honest, faithful eyes.'

Armand says 'She is wrong, of course. The eyes of little Benoir are utterly wild. They are the eyes of the Wizard of Martinique, the island of Voudou.'

'At least they are not calculating.'

Her brother points out coolly: 'He has thirty million, my dear, why should his eyes be calculating?' He says: 'Take her and dance, Vince. She must be punished till she learns to be tolerant.'

As they step on to the dance floor, Armand calls out at the top of his voice: 'Get her enceinte, Vince, it is the only way. Then we shall all be happy.' He adds: 'You should be able to produce something quite interesting between you two, and the Dauphin will have someone to play with.'

Everyone is staring at this small rowdy who is the famous A-M. Benoir, but he is quite unperturbed. He is busy having his shoes taken off by a waiter in readiness for de Chassevent's return.

'Oh, he is quite impossible, that Benoir!' Marguerite exclaims.

62

'My poor Poilu, what you have to suffer with that horrible brother of mine.'

'What rot,' Castleton says. 'I'm having a whale of a time.'

She promises softly: 'But I shall do it. Benoir is right. Quite soon I shall give you your petit cadeau aux yeux gris.'

6

Toast

At about two o'clock they take their leave. Mim's a bit tired after the excitement of seeing the boy, and the band is pretty loud. They decide to cut the floor show. Armand is dancing with his shoes off and Ouistiti round his neck. As far as he is concerned the night has just begun. He has been dancing with his mistress now for a long time in a pretty intimate way.

Marguerite predicts: 'We shall not see him till breakfast. Benoir is always like this before he goes to Mal Choisi. He is impossible.'

De Chassevent gives her his pale smile. 'We shall see something of you, I hope, Marguerite, during our stay in New Orleans?' He is bowing over her hand.

'We shall not be leaving for France for another eight days,' says de Chassevent. He is resting his cold eyes on her with something approximating pleasure.

Naturally not, Marguerite thinks, since it is exactly in eight days' time that Benoir intends returning to Paris. He will arrange it so that he has Liane for the whole of his stay here, as well as for the flight back. His aplomb is quite disgusting at times. She tells de Chassevent he must visit them whenever he wishes. 'You are not a stranger, Yves. Moumou will be delighted to see you. He has already talked about his parrain to his new papa.'

'Yes, rather,' says Castleton.

'Ah, vraiment?'—de Chassevent raises a correct eyebrow.

'Yes, rather,' says Castleton, trying to keep it up. They take a formal leave of one another.

'Awfully glad to have seen you.'

'Enchanté.'

Marguerite enquires coolly: 'Your Paul, is he well?'

He is well, and studying hard at his Lycée.

Marguerite says dryly: 'I wish I could say the same of my son.'

'Why, is he not well again, Marguerite?' There is something more than conventional solicitude in his tone.

'He is well. It is only his education that is at its last gasp. It's the usual fiasco with his governesses. I won't bore you with it,' says Marguerite.

She takes her leave by saying: 'À bientôt, Yves. Don't leave it too long before you visit us.'

She hasn't mentioned Liane, but de Chassevent says: 'It will give us both enormous pleasure, Marguerite.' He touches his dry lips to her hand and goes back to their table to await his wife's pleasure. If need be he will sit there until five o'clock.

'Poor devil,' says Castleton in the car. 'He doesn't stand an earthly with your brother.'

'Yves is a fool,' says Marguerite. 'He should beat her.'

Castleton laughs. 'So it's as simple as that, is it?'

She replies coolly: 'It doesn't seem to be complicated for my brother.' She says: 'My God, Benoir was abominable tonight. To talk like that about a harmless little creature like moumou. Of course, it was all to punish me for saying he has the same taste for the country as Maman. He is exactly like Maman in every respect, but Benoir will not accept it. It is grotesque this love my brother has for a dead woman. It is unnatural.' She says bitterly: 'He laughs about my son wanting too much love. My God, how I prefer that to not wanting to love at all!'

'He does, darling,' Castleton assures her. 'He adores you for a start.'

He may adore her but that will never prevent him hurting her through her son. 'Pauvre petit bonhomme.' She complains in a soft voice: 'Benoir will never kiss him, Poilu, and he will never permit George to kiss him. Did you see that with the new rosary tonight?'

'Yes,' Castleton says.

'Only his hand. It is insupportable.'

'Never mind, darling,' Castleton says. 'George's got you, and that's all he really bothers about.'

Marguerite says: 'Oh, if you had known my brother before my mother's death, Vincent, you wouldn't even take him for the same man. Benoir has become very hard,' Marguerite says. 'I think my brother cried so much when Maman died he has not got one tear left for anybody any more.' She says: 'He didn't even cry when Georges died.'

Castleton says: 'Don't let it get you down.'

They kiss for a long while.

When they get home, Sidonie takes Marguerite's wrap and she goes straight upstairs to look at her boy. There is none of the Castleton nonsense with Mim about not keeping the servants up. They wait up until they are no longer wanted, and that is that.

She is back in a very short while. 'He is asleep, Poilu. Do you want to look at him?'

'Yes, rather.' Castleton is pouring himself a drink.

'Bring it with you,' says Marguerite.

They go up in the lift to the Dauphin's apartment. The lobby is full of an overpowering scent from the flowers which have been taken out of the bedroom for the night. There is one great vase of white freesia left in the bedroom. It is nowhere near the child but Marguerite says angrily: 'Throw them out, Vincent! They would leave him to suffocate if one didn't look out. No one is reliable, not even Mammy. If this brings back his asthma it will be no-body's fault as usual!'

Oh, dear.

He is fast asleep on a massive French bed under a coverlet of rose-coloured surah. The bedstead is built entirely of bronze and copper with moustiquaires of rose-coloured gauze in the French Colonial style. Everything in the room is in Marguerite's impec-cable taste, simple, childlike and, above all, perfectly ordered. The air is very fresh and sweet and seems to be thermostatically con-trolled.

'You can touch him, Poilu,' Marguerite invites. 'Don't be afraid to lift him out of bed. If he wakes up, what does it matter?

66

He will soon go to sleep again. It will do moumou good to feel your arms round him.' Marguerite says:'You are his father now, you know.'

Castleton goes cautiously up to the bed. The heavy lashes are lying on the child's pale cheeks. His small mouth, slightly open, is the most pathetic thing that Castleton has ever seen.

'Oh Mim, poor little blighter,' Castleton blurts out. He can see how much he has hurt her and takes her hand in his.

'Why is he poor, Vincent?' She is smiling into his face.

Castleton says: 'He's so pale. Darling, I'm sorry, I can't get over it.'

She says that is a pity because it is a situation which is unlikely to change. 'My son has always been pale, Vincent, nothing can be done about it. I am sorry if he displeases you.'

'Oh, darling Mim, don't be an ass,' Castleton says.

But she returns quite coolly: 'The Benoirs are all pale. It has nothing to do with ill health. My brother Armand has never had a day's illness in his life and he is pale.'

'But not like George, darling,' Castleton says.

She assures him: 'It has no significance whatever. He is not an English child to have cheeks like choux rouges.'

He is afraid the grey-eyed cadeau is coming up again, but she merely says: 'Please, Vincent, I ask you not to bring this subject up again. It can serve no purpose and it annoys me.'

He says: 'Sorry, darling.' He simply can't get himself to say: I won't speak of it again.

Oh, darling Mim. She is as proud as Lucifer of her poor beautiful boy. He puts out a conciliatory hand. But she has turned her back on him and is settling her sleeping child in her commonsensical way, sitting him firmly up in bed while she repacks his pillows for him.

Apparently he sleeps almost sitting up. He is so asleep his head has fallen on Mim's shoulder. He is smiling.

'My God, what sort of débris has he collected in his bed again!'

She has plunged her hand behind his pillows and brought out the chaplet of pink and white pearls. 'I thought as much! We are in for a religious phase! Benoir has started something with that thing! You can throw it with his prayer book, Poilu.'

She has forgiven him. Darling, darling Mim. She puts the child back against his pillows with a little shake: 'Ferme ton bec, toi!'

The pale child smiles.

She scolds him vigorously: 'Petit diable! Veux-tu fermer tout de suite ton bec! J'ai mon oeil sur toi!'

The pale lips close at once. The child automatically takes his mother's hand, kisses it, and puts it under his cheek. He is still fast asleep.

Castleton is struck by the expression on his face. Very withdrawn, yet very happy in some mysterious way, as if he was laughing privately about something.

'Look, Mim, he's laughing at us.'

He's talking in a whisper, but she at once answers in her normal speaking voice: 'He is probably dreaming of Fernand's famous brioches. That would account for the beatific smile.' She assures him: 'My son may look like an angel, but his dreams are completely bourgeois. Thank God,' says Marguerite. 'I would have very little use for angels.'

She is wiping her sleeping boy's neck. 'It is fantastic. His whole chemise is wringing wet. They seem to have done exactly nothing about his night sweats at the Clinic.'

'What?' The private smile is haunting him.

'We can go now, Vincent.' She is turning out the light. 'Mammy will change his chemise.' Marguerite says: 'She is supposed to look in at him every two hours but it is doubtful if this ever really happens. She adores moumou, of course, but she would never permit that to interfere with her rest.'

'Are you coming, Poilu?' asks Marguerite.

Castleton says what about leaving the light?

'Pourquoi?'

'It's his first night here and everything. He might feel strange.'

What nonsense! His bonne is sleeping in the next room. If he wants anything he has only to call.

'Okay.' He's thinking of his young brother Robin, who had a nightlight till he was twelve.

As they are leaving a light goes on in Mammy's room. 'Not before time,' comments Marguerite.

Downstairs the haunting smile is haunting him again. He comes into her bedroom with a thought: 'Darling, you probably won't agree, but I thought tonight's dinner was a bit much for George.'

She answers him, smiling: 'We haven't yet had tonight's dinner, mon cher. It is not even breakfast time yet.'

Which means she doesn't agree, of course. He persists. 'It was, though, darling, I promise you.'

'He is accustomed to it, Vincent,' Marguerite says.

'It was pretty good hell watching him, though,' Castleton says. 'I kept thinking he was going to faint or something.'

'Oh, Vincent, please!'

Sidonie has left the room and Marguerite is getting into bed. 'Aren't you coming?'

'Yes, of course.' He goes off to finish undressing but comes back with another thought. 'Darling, why can't we have it earlier? Dinner, I mean, if you want him to have it with us? We could have a light meal or something.'

'Toast,' says Marguerite.

He doesn't get it.

Toast. Marguerite says: 'The English panacea.'

He doesn't care what it is. They could have supper together afterwards. 'It's a thought, darling,' Castleton says.

The thought is unacceptable. She merely says: 'It is nearly four o'clock.'

'I know,' says Castleton. 'It doesn't matter.'

He gets into bed and pulls her into his arms. 'Mim, don't let's do it to him any more.'

'What, mon cher?'

Castleton says: 'That bloody dinner.'

She says: 'Please, Vincent, don't persist in this. I have no intention of ordering my entire household to suit a child's convenience.' She says: 'Can you imagine Benoir sitting down to dinner at seven o'clock? It is unthinkable.' She says: 'I love you very much but this is a request I shall not even consider. I find it stupid,' says Marguerite. 'You have splendid eyes, Vincent,' says Marguerite, kissing them. 'When you are angry they go grey like the sea. Have I made you angry, mon cher?'

'A bit,' Castleton says abruptly. 'Mim . . .'

'Oui, mon amour?'

'Why isn't he allowed to talk at table?' Castleton wants to know.

She smiles at him.

'Why can't he, Mim? Or is it just another bloody Benoir tradition?'

No, it is not another bloody Benoir tradition, as he so charmingly puts it! It's simply a rule she has been forced to make in the interests of her son. She has no ambition to own a skeleton for a child. Marguerite says: 'With this no-talking rule one has at least some insurance against it. It was a choice between his free-dom and his plate. I chose his plate,' says Marguerite. She assures him: 'You'll get enough of my son's chatter, don't be afraid. Il est bavard comme un moineau celui-là!'

Christ.

'What is the matter, Vincent?'

'You. You're the full Barretts of Wimpole Street, darling.'

'What is that supposed to mean?'

'I don't like it,' Castleton says.

'I am sorry, Vincent.'

'No, you're not,' Castleton says. 'Mim . . .'

'What?' After that he doesn't deserve a better answer.

'I asked your brother outright tonight what the matter was with George.'

'Alors?'

'He told me,' Castleton says.

'Et quoi, alors? It is no secret,' Marguerite says.

'I wanted you to know,' says Castleton. 'I don't want to do anything behind your back.'

'It's not a secret, Vincent,' says Marguerite again.

'Mim,' says Castleton, kissing her. 'Mim . . .'

'What is the matter, Vincent?' She says she is perfectly happy about the situation with her son. She says: 'George has what my brother Baudouin has, and Maman died of, but I am not con-cerned.' She says: 'I have the word of three of the greatest specia-lists in this complaint that my son will be completely cured by the time he is fourteen. That is at latest.' Marguerite says in an in-exorable voice: 'Courvoisier has promised it for even earlier.'

It is terrible to hear the arrogance in her voice. She says almost gaily: 'The entire Clinic Benoir is only concerned with that one malady, you know. Armand founded it after Maman's death. There is a wing for children that has no equal called after her— the Marie Benoir. But Armand will never go there unless he is driven like the last time for moumou's tests.' Marguerite says: 'The association with our mother is too strong for him.' She says, smiling: 'My brother is a fool like that. Nothing is made better by not looking it in the face.'

He kisses her and says abruptly: 'It's a question of tempera-ment, my duck.'

But Mim comes out of her corner fighting. 'He thought he would punish me this evening simply because his mother is dead,

70

but my little stupid will live to inherit all those boring delta places like St Cloud and Taquineuse. By the time he is eighteen one hopes he will have had the sense to sell the whole lot and not make a fetish of them like Benoir makes of Mal Choisi. But he will inherit them,' says Marguerite. 'My son will live to inherit every piece of Benoir property that is his right.

She says in a clear, formidable voice that Castleton has never heard before: 'Courvoisier is the foremost specialist in megaloblastic anaemia in the world. There is no one over Courvoisier in his own field, and he has given me his word.'

She says: 'I shall keep George to his cure, Vincent, whatever it entails. At home there were endless dramas with Maman and Baudouin. The doctors prescribed raw liver. It was the cure of the day, but neither my mother nor my brother could tolerate it. Papa's chef did what he could to present it in an attractive way, but it was hopeless. Maman cried, Baudouin cried, the cook cried, and Armand cried for all of them. It was a shambles, Vincent, and I would never permit it for a single moment with George.' Marguerite says: 'My son will take whatever is prescribed for him. I am determined that he shall be cured. What he thinks about the cure is not in the least important.'

She looks at Castleton as if expecting an answer from him, but he just lies there feeling sorry for her. She is laughing about her brother Armand down at Taquineuse when they were all children together. 'Some perfect fool of a servant told my brother that if a healthy person got into bed with a sick person, his health would pass into the invalid's body and make him well. Can you imagine, Vincent, that fool of an Armand spent half his life hopping in and out of either our mother's or our little brother Baudouin's bed! Vincent, are you listening?' Marguerite asks.

'Yes,' says Castleton.

'Of course my father was furious about it, and if he ever caught my brother he would punish him really hard. My poor Armand' —says Marguerite tenderly—'he meant so well!'

She can see him still, with his splendid looks, and his enormous optimism, lying in maman's bed quite naked, trying to give her his superb animal health!

She has laughed so much her cheeks are quite wet. 'Give me your handkerchief, Poilu!'

Marguerite says: 'He used to post his valet outside to tell him when Papa was coming. There was a sort of code between them.

71

Armand was cleverer at avoiding panpan than that little stupid upstairs.'

Marguerite says: 'Can you imagine, Vincent, moumou is terribly afraid of being punished but he will never evade it. He is too proud.' She finds this really funny. 'Can you imagine that, Vincent? That little stupid up there!'

'Goodnight,' says Castleton, putting out the light. It is half-past four and the room is full of an utterly pessimistic light the colour of ash.

7

The Sioux

They hear Benoir at nine o'clock talking on the telephone. As usual the door of his room is wide open.

He is speaking in a special voice as if to a favourite child. He is talking to his wife before leaving for the Delta.

'Soigne-toi bien, ma petite Marie, mon petit chouchou adoré.'

'Ah, Armand, tu sais!' calls out Marguerite, who is seeing staff and giving out orders for the day. 'The plates for the entrée last night were hardly warm. I hope it will not happen again. You are making yourself ridiculous in there!' she tells her brother.

Armand retaliates by calling out: 'Fous-moi la paix in there, veux-tu?'

He sounds as fresh as a daisy. The Sioux are an amazing lot, Castleton decides. He is full of admiration for the toughness and vitality of this small roué who has spent the whole night making love and only came in, according to Mim, just before breakfast.

The girl herself, bless her, is very much up and about and setting her house to rights before seeing her brother off to the Delta.

'Why should I be tired, Vincent? I shall see Benoir off,

naturally. Are you nearly finished, Nicole?' Monsieur intends leaving by ten o'clock.

She can't possibly have got to sleep much before five, yet here she is, only four hours later, very much her cool and elegant self and turned out to perfection.

Darling, astonishing Mim.

Marguerite returns her husband's kiss with affection. 'Is Monsieur Georges back from Mass yet?' she asks her maid.

Nicole will see.

Mim's bit of nonsense has gone to the Cathedral to have his new rosary blessed. Castleton has already had an early glimpse of him got up to the nines and being driven off in state by Marcel, with the doggish Deckers slumped beside him. There had been polite exchanges from a distance, with the Dauphin very gracious and blushing furiously.

'We shall all be bored to tears with that rosary,' Marguerite predicts. 'Once moumou gets hold of a thing he will run it to death.'

Castleton says shortly: 'Never mind. It gives him a lot of pleasure.' He is finding the Benoir propensity for being bored a bit wearing.

By now Benoir can be heard telling his Marie that her bad husband will be coming back to her on Friday and she must look her prettiest for him because he loves her, and thinks of his small Marie every day.

'Oh, my God, Benoir! He doesn't believe one single word of what he is saying and that little fool drinks it in!' Marguerite declares: 'The more unfaithful he is to her the more considerate of her he becomes. She even believes Liane is her best friend!'

She calls out impatiently: 'Benoir! You will be late!'

Benoir is saying tenderly that when he comes home his Marie must put on for him the beautiful dress he has chosen for her to wear at Viv's wedding.

Marguerite says coolly: 'Can you imagine, Vincent, Benoir has to choose all her dresses for her. Marie has the taste of a child.'

'How different to Mrs Castleton.'

She laughs. 'You should have seen her at her wedding, Poilu. The festivities lasted three days! Marie was dressed up like a little effigy with a diamond on every finger, and the wedding dress made to her measurements by a big house in Paris and sent over without a fitting!'

Armand is telling his chouchou she will be the most envied woman at Viv's wedding. No one will have eyes for the bride. He tells her: 'She is already weeping with jealousy, your bad sister-in-law.'

'Ah, non, Benoir,' Marguerite calls out. 'It is developing into a farce!'

He calls back instantly: 'She sends you a Big Kiss.'

Oh God! Those Big Kisses from Auteuil! Marguerite says they can really affect one's nerves. She turns to Pauline sharply. 'But what has happened to Nicole?'

'I don't know, Madame.'

'She was sent out to enquire after Monsieur Georges. By this time she could have been to Paris and back.'

'Shall I go, darling?' Castleton asks. He has just finished shaving.

'Of course not, Vincent, are you out of your mind?' Marguerite says it is bizarre, the more servants one has round one the less they seem to achieve. She calls out in an impatient voice: 'Benoir, it is nearly ten o'clock!'

Armand can now be heard taking his leave and promising his Marie that Benoir will be very careful on the roads—

Marguerite groans: 'That fool, he is starting again.'

—and chouchou is not to worry because Benoir will absolutely not let that acute case Viv fly him home on Friday, but will come back, sauf et sain, to his chouchou like a good Benoir. 'I will leave you now, my little Marie. Be good to yourself, my sweetheart. Eat well, rest well, and remember your bad husband in your prayers.' He adjures tenderly: 'Take Rose to sleep with you so that you are not alone.'

Marguerite makes a face: 'She is afraid to sleep alone when Benoir is away so she sleeps with her maid. Rather that than with my son!' Marguerite says: 'I'm sure she took moumou to sleep with her while he was in Paris. I can always tell,' says Marguerite. 'That rosary under the pillow was a sure sign.'

She tells her brother: 'You will really be late, Benoir, if you don't finish in there. And what has happened with George? He cannot possibly still be at Mass.'

Benoir calls out: 'She has a fixation about punctuality, that one.' He tells his sister: 'The Dauphin has probably gone to the French Market with Marcel to eat a gaufrette and have a sip of Marcel's grog. They tell me it's the done thing in Paris after Mass.'

75

'Many thanks,' says Marguerite. 'One more bad habit to break him of.'

'But think what pleasure it gives you.' Armand makes breaking noises from the bedroom. 'Piff! Paff! All the Dauphin's Parisian Habits! Foutu!!' He says soothingly into the telephone: 'No, no, my darling, it is not Monsieur Castleton who is going to break poor puss.' Wicked stepfathers, Armand explains, are strictly for Perrault. 'In real life it is Mimi le Flic who does the breaking.'

He calls out: 'Vince! My wife is very easily alarmed. She says she has been praying you will prove chouchou for puss. Can you give her an assurance?'

'Yes,' Castleton shouts back. 'Tell her I will be chouchou. Give her my love.'

'You two are perfect imbeciles!' calls out Marguerite, who is in her dressing room writing a note for her housekeeper commencing "It should not be too much to expect" and signed M-M. M. Castleton.

'I've a good mind to come and knock your heads together!'

'That was my sister who is in her usual delightful mood,' Armand says into the phone. Marie is not to worry. Their good brother-in-law has just given his word that he will be chouchou for puss.

'Give her my love,' says Castleton.

'He sends you a Big Kiss, my darling.'

'Mon dieu,' groans Marguerite.

No. Unhappily, puss is not here for the moment. He has gone to Mass.

'To Mass, my darling,' repeats Benoir.

Marguerite exclaims: 'He has already told her once!' Marie is deaf in one ear. A neglected infection in childhood. 'She never saw a proper doctor till she married Benoir. Her father worshipped her, but he was a widower, and Marie was entrusted entirely to the nuns at Baton Rouge, and to those ridiculous Bienville aunts. They would never have consented to her being examined by a man.'

She is keeping her voice down so that her brother shouldn't hear. 'You have no conception of the way she was brought up.'

'What are you growling about in there?' Benoir wants to know. He is explaining the situation of George being at Mass into the telephone with the utmost patience. 'Yes, it is two o'clock in

Paris,' agrees Benoir. No, it is not two o'clock in New Orleans. In New Orleans, Benoir informs his wife, it is ten o'clock in the morning and this is why, unhappily, puss is momentarily not here to have a little word with her.

'He is at Mass, my darling,' says Benoir. 'Mimi, of course, suspects he is in a bistro somewhere with Marcel, but I am confident he is at Mass wearing his little knees out praying for all of us.'

Certainly he will send puss to the telephone the minute he comes home.

'You will not, Benoir.'

Naturally he will hold on until the Dauphin's return. 'He would never forgive himself if he missed the opportunity of saying bonjour to his petite Tantan, and of giving her a Big Kiss from himself and another Big Kiss from his maman.'

'Benoir!'

Nicole comes in to report that Monsieur Georges has just got back from Mass and that he will join Madame in one little moment. At the same time Armand calls out: 'Hey puss, here's someone wants a little word with you.'

A second later they hear the Dauphin chirping tenderly into the 'phone.

'Ah non!' Marguerite exclaims. 'We are not going to have this business with Marie all over again! Moumou!'

He calls out immediately in his high sweet drawl: 'It is my Tante Marie, maman.'

Benoir comes in, freshly bathed and scented. He is in terrific form. No one could look less debauched. He greets his sister: 'Big Kiss from Marie,' and tells his brother-in-law: 'The news from Paris is splendid. Marie thinks she has at last found a physician who understands her case. Vaugirard. Have you heard of him, Mimi? Marie tells me Liane put him on to her. It was chic of Li.'

Armand says: 'I shan't forget her for that.'

Marguerite says: 'That's probably why she did it.'

Armand looks at her. 'I confess I find you singularly unattractive this morning, my dear sister.' He addresses himself exclusively to his brother-in-law. 'This Vaugirard seems to know what he is talking about. Oh, if he can only do something for my poor Marie. She has suffered for so long. Can you imagine, Vince, when she had her first indisposition she was only nine.' His eyes are brilliant with angry tears. 'And that poor thing thinks it is the will of God!'

His sister asks him: 'Why should that surprise you? To me it is

77

typical of the Bienville attitude to life.' She tells her husband: 'You have no idea of the stifling narrowness of these rich Catholic communities round the Delta. They are disgusting,' declares Marguerite, 'and if it hadn't been for our father we would have had exactly the same upbringing as the Bienvilles. Fortunately Papa saw to it that we always had first-class teachers and lived in France for at least half the year. Papa used to call the Bienvilles "les mangeurs de crucifixes",' announces Marguerite who, Castleton suspects, is saying a certain amount of this on purpose.

Benoir says furiously: 'The Bienvilles are my mother's family and I forbid you to say anything against them. Be silent, Mimi.'

'Oh, mon dieu,' his sister tells him, 'it is always the same when you go to Mal Choisi. You are in a filthy mood.'

He says: 'If you cannot be sympathetic towards people who suffer, then please be silent, Mimi.'

She returns simply: 'I have no sympathy for people who invariably do the worst for themselves. It is indefensible to bring up a girl in the way that Marie has been brought up.'

'You have no sympathy, period,' says her brother. 'Happily, Liane has, and she has arranged for Marie to see Vaugirard. He has a very good manner for nervous patients, Li says.'

Marguerite makes a contemptuous noise.

'It is of the utmost importance,' Benoir insists. 'Not everyone is an Apache, like you. Which reminds me, Mimi . . .' says Benoir. But she is listening to her son cooing into the telephone. 'Benoir, since when has moumou been permitted to tutoyer Marie?'

He replies coolly: 'Marie has asked him to, I take it.'

Then she forbids it. Categorically. At nine years of age he is much too old to address grown-up persons in that way.

He looks at her. 'You are being ridiculous, my dear. Such a small liberty, whom does it hurt? I forbid you to forbid him.'

She says immediately: 'In any case, tell him to finish in there, Benoir, he will go on forever at this rate.'

Castleton says: 'He's got the Benoir passion for phoning, all right.'

She doesn't answer his smile. It's pretty plain she isn't best pleased with her brother's decision about George.

Armand calls out: 'Ring off in there, puss, hear me? Give Tante Marie a Big Kiss and come in here to us.'

The pale child comes running, all unknowing, and gets the full brunt of his mother's dissatisfaction with Benoir.

'Where have you been?'

He has been on the telephone. 'She sends you a Big Kiss, my Tante Marie,' calls out the little boy, throwing his arms round his mother's neck. 'O, she is better, mama, isn't it splendid? She has a new man, so we must hope for the best,' says the Dauphin, politely putting his stepfather in the picture. 'She has une maladie de femme, don't you know?' His smile to his stepfather is still very shy but distinctly friendly, even a shade comehitherish, which makes Castleton laugh.

'That is enough,' says Marguerite. 'And where have you been? You know perfectly well Uncle Benoir intends leaving at ten o'clock.'

'Yes, ma'am,' George answers mildly. 'It isn't only but just ten now and my Uncle Benoir is still here.'

She gives him a searching look but cannot fault his manner which is respectful in the extreme.

'Bravo puss,' Armand says. 'Mama had visions of your living it up with Marcel in the French quarter.'

O no, he has been only at the Cathedral. 'There were so many people to pray for, mama dear.'

He can spare her the list. Marguerite says: 'You would have done better to pray for yourself and ask to be made more obedient.'

'Yes'm, I did,' says George. He calls out ecstatically: 'O mama, I have had my new rosary blessed. At the Cathedral. Can you imagine? It is fantastically chic.' He declares: 'O, it will be even more precious to me now than ever. O, it will never leave me for a single moment, night or day.'

That is where he is mistaken. He will keep it with all his other rosaries, in his oratory where such things belong. She tells him this in case he had the intention of keeping it with his handkerchief like a concierge.

The Dauphin admits that this had more or less been the idea. He calls out comically: 'O my Redeemer, that is another delusion gone west,' and gives his stepfather what looks very much like the rudiments of a wink. Both men roar, but his mother beckons him to her side.

'D'you wish to see your Uncle Benoir off?'

O, yes, he wants it.

'Then behave. Have you said good-morning yet to petit-papa?'

'Yes'm. At least, sort of.' They have met earlier on when he was

79

going to Mass. George explains: 'We nodded to each other, mama.'

'Then go and greet him properly now, otherwise he will think you have forgotten your manners.'

The little boy steps forward, blushing richly, to kiss his step-father's hand, but Castleton stops him. 'Don't do that, ducky. Mim, tell him I don't like it.'

Marguerite shrugs. 'You hear what papa says?'

The Dauphin asks in a stage whisper: 'What shall I do to him, then?'

'Give us a kiss,' says Castleton, lifting him up.

George's idea of a kiss is very handsome indeed. He lavishes kisses, regardless of feature, all over his stepfather's face. 'Bon-jour, bonjour, bonjour, bonjour, mon cher Monsieur!' He is completely out of breath.

'Bonjour to you,' says Castleton. 'We're very bobbish this morning, aren't we?'

O, yes we are. George hopes politely that Mr Castleton is bobbish too? He has no idea what it means, but he finds it a most amusing word. He is really droll, this English husband of mama's. George has already noticed this from last night. He looks pensively at his stepfather. His eyes are black and soft as soot.

Armand says: 'Keep your legs crossed, Vince. I think it's hap-pening.'

Mim's bit of nonsense is dishing out the most incredible looks. Suddenly he steps forward and puts his hand into Castleton's. It is a purely voluntary gesture, and Castleton is surprised at the boldness of the touch. It is firm, warm, confident and there is nothing shy about it. Castleton keeps the small, bold hand in his. 'Look, Mim, we're coming on.'

She is deeply moved at seeing her shy son with his hand in the hand of her new husband. She merely says: 'Don't let him annoy you, Vincent.'

They all go out on to the front gallery where Benoir has ordered champagne to be brought before his start.

'I wish you wouldn't, Benoir,' Marguerite says. 'It could affect your driving.'

She has become very nervous since a moment ago when her brother had suddenly announced his intention of driving himself down to the Delta alone.

Armand remarks that it is female kill-joys like his sister who are at the bottom of the dismal English licensing laws. The beauty of a really good champagne is that it can virtually be drunk like water at any time of the night or day. He proceeds unhurriedly to drink most of the bottle himself. It is too early for Castleton, and Marguerite has made a curt gesture of refusal over her glass.

'Tant mieux,' Armand says calmly. 'Puss and I will finish it between us, then.' He hands a full glass to the Dauphin who is sitting serenely beside his stepfather still holding his hand.

Marguerite says in a severe voice: 'You may take one sip and no more. And let go of papa's hand at once. I hope you don't intend to make a habit of this familiarity or it will certainly end up by being a bore. Sit up straight, stop dreaming, and breathe through your nose.' Marguerite says: 'If this is the result of your prayer for obedience, I can't say I'm impressed.'

'Oh, Mim,' says Castleton. 'Christ, darling, do stop.'

She is terribly nervous about her brother. 'At least take Maurice with you. He can take over when you are tired.'

He lifts his glass at her and smiles.

'You will be going south for nearly a hundred miles. By mid-day the sun will be unendurable. Benoir!' says Marguerite.

He tells her serenely: 'I shall take only Achille with me.'

He is making her a present of Hippolyte for the four days he will be away. 'Let him show Albert how to cut the Dauphin's hair properly, and give him a general briefing as to what is expected of him in the Dauphin's service.'

The lily-featured Dauphin himself is sitting bolt upright as he has been told. His small nostrils are labouring at the task of breathing through his nose, and his tender flesh is marbled with the morning's freshness. Castleton wants to take off his coat but Mim won't let him make 'the sacrifice' as she calls it. A servant is despatched to fetch the short white reefer that goes with the white sailor suit and is lined with pearly satin.

'All right? asks Castleton, buttoning his stepson into it and giving the small cold hands a rub.

Marguerite asks sharply: 'Alors, qu'est-ce qu'on dit?'

'Merci, monsieur.'

'Mimi,' calls out her brother. 'Will you at least give that wretched Dauphin time to open his trap?' He beckons to George. 'Commission for you, puss. Ask papa if you may pick a few of his Cape jessamines for me, will you? I need three pretty ones to take with me. Not buds, not too full. You will know exactly what to look for.' Armand says: 'If you break a few branches you can blame Ouistiti, he will be down at the Delta before Mr Castleton has time to beat him.'

'O no, he would not, ever,' exclaims George earnestly.

'See, Vince, the kind of impression you've made?'

'Go ahead, ducky,' Castleton says. 'Pick what you like. It's all yours and mummy's, anyway.'

O, it is droll, that word he has just used for mama. George calls out warmly: 'Ain't Mr Castleton obliging for us?'

His stepfather laughs, but his mother says very coolly: 'I hope it will not take you too long before you can bring yourself to call your stepfather by his proper name.'

'O no, it will not,' George assures her. 'I am quite fixing, mama dear.'

She reminds him gravely: 'It was the same at Shiloh.'

'Yes'm, I'm sorry,' says George.

Directly he has gone, Marguerite says in a dissatisfied voice: 'It will be exactly the same as with Davis, Armand. If one doesn't oblige him to do a thing at once he will never do it.'

'Then he will never do it,' Armand says. 'Vince won't mind.'

On the contrary. Castleton would much rather the boy called him Vincent or something. 'It sticks out a mile he doesn't want to call me by the name he used for his father. Don't make him, darling,' Castleton says.

'Or if she wants it,' Benoir puts in, 'then let her give him time. She changes husbands every three weeks and then expects that wretched Dauphin to immediately adjust.'

She turns directly to her brother and accuses him: 'The plain truth is George has got out of hand, Benoir.'

He finishes for her with upflung hands: 'It is the influence of that terrible household at Auteuil!'

She says that she had noticed certain things at dinner last night.

He, on the other hand, has noticed not a thing. 'Except that you have a splendid chef, my dear.'

Marguerite says: 'I shall require it of him, Benoir.'

'Then he will do it,' Armand says, 'of his own free will. Because he loves you, Christ knows why.'

Castleton protests: 'No, Mim, he doesn't want to. Don't force the poor little blighter.'

She gives him a cool look to show him that his reference to her son as a blighter has not been well received, and neither has his protest on the blighter's behalf.

Castleton comes upon the sudden realisation that Mim can be an extremely awkward customer when she likes. This thing about names is sheer bloody-mindedness. Castleton hopes Mim doesn't go on like this too much because he knows he will only be able to take a certain amount of it.

He goes over to the gallery rail and watches the kid. That queer glide of his makes him look like a walking doll. It's a leftover from the measles, but Mim ticks him off about it: 'He will never lose it, Vincent, as long as he thinks there is somebody to condone it. In the beginning there was some disability, but now it is pure laziness.'

Oh, well.

The Dauphin is surrounded by his usual mob, all giving him advice. Marcel is standing by with the sécateurs ready to cut the blooms and pack them in a special container which is ready lined with cotton wool for the journey to the Delta. Ouistiti is causing much amusement by giving great vertical leaps like an enraged kangaroo. He is being held on a short leash and is absolutely furious at not being allowed to meddle with the container. In the thick of it and chatting affably with the Dauphin, Castleton spots with no surprise at all, the natty, jockey-like figure of his personal servant, Frederick Ernest Bone.

Ever since Castleton's marriage, F. E. Bone has made no secret of his ambition—which is to meet, gaze his fill at, and if possible actually speak to the pale shy child who is the sole son and heir of the late and great G-M. Benoir, the racing multi-millionaire, and who is now the Governor's stepson.

The Guv's stock has gone up no end in Bone's eyes since his union with the great French racing family whose revolutionary training methods and superlative stock have long held Bone's deep respect and admiration.

F. E. Bone, whose pale eye misses nothing, has just caught sight of the Guv on the gallery and sketched an upward salute intended to convey civility without servility, plus a very obvious determination not to waste a single moment of this Godgiven opportunity for a chat with little Benoir.

They seem tremendous pals already, and little Benoir calls out with enthusiasm: 'He is nice, your Bone.'

They may have to watch it there.

Bone has a truly staggering line in language, and as Mim's chap seems to pick up everything, Bone will have to be persuaded to mind his b's and f's, or there'll be trouble with Mum.

'Who is he talking to, Vincent?'

Marguerite has joined her husband at the rail. She slips her arm through his and asks her brother: 'Why have you sent mou-mou to pick flowers, Armand?'

'Because of a suggestion Vince came up with earlier on. We want your opinion of it,' Benoir says.

He sees the Dauphin's mob and says with satisfaction: 'That's good. He understands to make people feel at ease with him. It's an asset that will stand him in good stead later on. It's a special gift,' says Benoir.

'Et quoi?' shrugs Marguerite, who is holding her husband's hand against her lips. 'Moumou with his special gift!' She laughs into Castleton's face.

Her brother says smiling: 'I needn't tell you, Vince, it's a gift that Mrs Castleton has definitely not got. Neither has my son. Both Mimi and Viv treat the servants like dogs. The net result is that, to say the least of it, they are not popular with the sans-culottes.'

That is an honour Mrs Castleton will cheerfully forgo. She says to Castleton: 'I like my name.' She is looking directly into his eyes. He gives her a long kiss.

Armand says: 'By the way, Mi, has puss been out on the gallery to show himself yet?'

Yes, that business was transacted early this morning before he went to Mass. He acquitted himself quite well this time.

'Bravo, Little Benoir! How did you achieve this miracle, Mi?'

It was simple. 'I promised him a smack in front of Vincent if he failed.'

Benoir says dryly: 'I might have known it would be something like that, with you.'

Anyway, it worked. She asks, laughing: 'What have you two been conspiring over about my child?'

About her child Vince has had what seems to Benoir quite a good idea.

'I don't think Mim will buy it,' says Castleton, who has been looking at his smiling wife.

Nevertheless they will try and sell it to her.

Armand says: 'En bref, Vince thinks we ought to try an English specialist for puss.'

'Pourquoi ça?'

Castleton says: 'Actually he's an Australian. Chap called Crombie. I was talking to my brother the other day about our boy, and he told me that this bloke Crombie completely cured a little girl, daughter of a naval rating in Hong Kong. She had the same thing as George, but much worse. In fact she was in pretty bad shape. Now she's right as rain. Old Cecil tells me Crombie has the most marvellous way with kids.'

She asks him coolly: 'Since when have you discussed moumou with your brother?'

Lots of times. Why? Castleton says: 'I think this bloke Crombie may well be the answer to our problems, Mim.'

He is aware that he has said all the wrong things, and it is obvious that his brother-in-law thinks so too.

Old Cecil . . . bloke . . . right as rain . . . have done nothing to enlist Marguerite's sympathy for Crombie. And the mention of a naval rating's child who has actually shared the same disease with the Dauphin was a definite mistake.

But it is 'our' boy and 'our' problem that have really torn it with Mim.

She gives him a look that conveys exactly what she intends it to. Hands off my son.

It's not the first time he has seen the Snub Benoir administered, but it is the first time it has been given to him. She turns deliberately to her brother. 'And Courvoisier? Are you out of your mind?'

Benoir says that for himself he would be quite pleased to make a break and give puss a rest from Courvoisier. 'He has no manners, my dear.'

'What has that got to do with it?'

'A lot. That horse butcher hasn't even the common politeness to speak to puss when he goes for his treatment. I have seen little Benoir start to tremble when Courvoisier only comes into the room."

He is telling her nothing new. 'That is because he is afraid of the injections.'

'You are quite wrong,' her brother assures her. 'It is because puss feels he is being held in contempt the whole time. That brute hasn't even the decency to explain what is going to happen to him, so there is always some fresh horror sprung on him that he didn't expect.' Benoir says: 'It is an impertinence to behave like that to a sick child.'

Marguerite says: 'How he behaves to my son is immaterial to me as long as he cures him.'

Armand assures her: 'It is not immaterial to me, Mimi. A man who holds suffering in contempt forfeits my respect, and if I can get an equally clever man on to puss's case I shall give Courvoisier the boot.'

She says: 'I will not consider a change.'

He says: 'It is not necessary to decide anything now. We will speak about it again when I get back from the Delta.'

She has already decided. George will remain under Courvoisier. He turns on his heel and makes for the gallery steps. She calls after him: 'Benoir, Cartiers have sent me a parcel of pearls. I have already made a choice but I should like your opinion on it before you leave. Their man will be calling tomorrow.'

He calls out over his shoulder: 'Get Vince to do it. I am not interested in your pearls.'

She says to Castleton: 'Oh, you have started something with your stupid Australian! Benoir is always in a bad mood before he goes to the Delta. Now he will be unendurable.'

He says: 'I wish you'd try Crombie. We could fly him over here, there'd be no need to go to London.'

She will neither try nor fly Crombie. 'I love you both very much but I would never risk my son's health for one single second to please either of you. And least of all for that silly caprice of Benoir's. That is the biggest nonsense of all. What can it matter if a man like Courvoisier has a brusque manner? He is going to cure my son and that is all that matters.' Marguerite says: 'You give too much importance to sympathy, mon cher. It is an English weakness. Moumou gets so much love from all of us he doesn't need it from strangers.' In fact she doesn't think it at all a bad thing for her son to have to encounter a little hardness. He has no idea what life is about, that little sheltered thing. He thinks the whole world is stuffed with Mamans and Uncle Benoirs and Mr Castletons.' She laughs. 'Have you noticed he loves you already? That is because he feels you will be good to him. He has an unerring instinct for that sort of thing.' She says: 'Oh, when he put his hand in yours like that, it made me happy.' Marguerite says: 'It took him three months before he did it with Davis.'

She puts her arms round her husband's neck and says softly:

86

'Don't ask me to see your Australian again, my sweet Vincent. If there is one thing I absolutely detest it is to refuse you anything.'

'All right,' says Castleton, not smiling.

She says: 'Let's go and see what is happening with Armand's stupid flowers. I don't know why he insists on picking them here. They are supposed to be for Maman's tomb. They will be dead before he is half-way down to the Delta.'

As they are crossing the gallery she says: 'Benoir could make me do it, Vincent. He has complete jurisdiction over the boy until he is sixteen. It was George's father's wish. If Benoir makes up his mind to give the case to Crombie there can be no appeal. He is behind the Clinic Benoir and his word is absolute.' She says they must hope that by the time Benoir is back from Mal Choisi and has consoled himself with his mistress he will have regained his sense of values. 'He loves me very much and I know he would never willingly hurt me. All the same, if he brings the subject up again please don't support it. Benoir goes enormously by what you say and even a word from you could tip the scales.' She says quietly: 'If Courvoisier goes it will be the finish. I know it, Vincent.'

'All right,' he dries her eyes. 'I won't do anything more about it.'

He wants to wait a little, but she has recovered already.

'My God, Vincent, what is happening here? You seem to have the finale from a comic-opera in your courtyard.'

Marguerite calls to Castleton: 'Will you look at those two fools down there playing at funerals!'

Benoir is giving his full attention to the three perfect white blooms the Dauphin is offering for his inspection. 'Oh, look at moumou's holy mug! He is too funny!' cries Marguerite. She calls out to her brother: 'They will all be dead by the time you get down there, Benoir!'

Everyone melts away at her voice. 'You could have had armfuls of them at Mal Choisi. They grow like weeds down there.'

He returns coldly: 'I wanted to bring something from your new home, where presumably you are happy, Mimi.'

She replies, kissing him: 'Yes. You are right to take them from here. I am happy. Tell Maman I am happy, mon petit frérot-chéri.'

He tells her gravely: 'I am not pleased with you, at all.'

He turns to George and says courteously: 'They are perfect. Bravo, puss.'

'O, sir!' He is quite melted up in this rich praise. He whispers to his stepfather: 'They are for mémère's tomb at Mal Choisi. One from each of her children. Does Mr Castleton know how I mean?'

'George,' warns Marguerite.

'He didn't hear me, mama.' George explains quickly. 'We have not ever got to speak of mémère to Uncle Benoir. It is categorically forbidden.' George whispers in a satisfied voice: 'I got a flower for each of us, too, Mr Castleton. It was with my Uncle Benoir's full permission. You are her son-in-law so it is all right.'

George whispers: 'I got red ones so she will know which are from us. Bright colours don't offend the dead. Not if it is from flowers.' He is looking incredibly eerie.

'George, what are you whispering for?' demands his mother.

It was about the flowers for himself and Mr Castleton.

She cuts him short. 'Have you found something to send that pleases you?'

O yes. He has found two beautiful flowers. Two red hibiscus, George says they are.

She is delighted to hear it, and hopes they will now be allowed to finish with this preoccupation with the tomb. It is fantastic! One is completely surrounded by ghouls! 'I don't mean to hear another word about it. D'you hear me, George?' says Marguerite.

'Yes, ma'am.' George would only just like to add that Uncle Benoir has at this very moment put his flower and Mr Castleton's flower in the container. 'O, it is such an honour for us, Mr Castleton,' sighs George.

'George, will you stop!'

'Yes'm.' He simply can't resist the beatific murmur: 'He is her son-in-law, don't you know?'

'George, d'you want a smack?' asks Marguerite.

O, no, he doesn't want one.

'Then stop at once, or I will beat you like a carpet!' She is laughing in spite of her exasperation.

'My God, Poilu, he will send us out of our minds with his white flowers and his red flowers! And look at that other ghoul over there! That director of high-class funerals!' She remarks suddenly in a low voice: 'My God, look at Benoir's face. He is down there already.'

He has gone frightfully pale. She goes up to her brother and says tenderly: 'Don't stay too long at Mal Choisi, Armand. It isn't good for you, whatever you say.'

He smiles at her, but there is nothing for her in his smile. He is as pale as George. He cannot imagine why he is going to Mal Choisi. She is not there. If She is anywhere She is here, standing beside him holding his brother-in-law's hand.

He says with an effort: 'Mimi, it is possible that Viv will want to spend a few days of his honeymoon at St Cloud. I don't know what the domestic position is down there.'

It will be the usual domestic position of a household where there is no one in control. Marguerite says: 'They have all got so used to créolising themselves down there.'

'Se créoliser' is a splendid verb which Castleton thinks has probably been invented by Mim. It means to lead the lazy life of the traditional West Indian.

Armand says in an almost normal voice: 'Good. Then we may rest assured when Citizeness Benoir goes down they will get off their asses or the heads will begin to roll.'

His luggage is being stowed in the boot by servants, but the container with the flowers is lifted carefully on to the driving seat by Benoir himself.

Marguerite says: 'Promise at least you will eat while you are down there.'

She has no idea what he does when he is down there. She pictures him, a stranger, standing motionless in front of their mother's elaborate tomb, but that is all. Happily it only lasts four days at most, after that he is the old Benoir she knows again.

She thinks affectionately: That Benoir! He had his first *affaire* when he was fourteen and he isn't tired of it yet, thank God! Her moumou will be like that too, she thinks. Viv tells her he is already giving quite a good account of himself in bed. Apparently there are already little problems to take to Monseigneur! Little force-ripe, thinks Marguerite amusedly. When he is ready to laugh again, she must tell that to Benoir!

Now she says: 'I have ordered your meals for your entire stay exactly as for Lent. If you don't eat, it is the last time I shall take the trouble.'

He promises he will do nothing to make her more nervous than she already is. He adds dryly: 'If only for Vince's sake.'

Hippolyte comes up with Ouistiti, who takes a flying leap on to

Armand's neck. Hippolyte says, grinning: 'He ain't done a drop. He afraid monsieur goin' leave him behind.'

George calls out at once: 'You, Ouisti, y'all will got to hold it naow, Grand M'sieu he don't stop for nothing on the road. O, my Redeemer!' calls out George.

'George!'

He flushes scarlet.

'D'you wish to be sent upstairs?'

O, no, he does not wish it. 'O, I will not speak Miss'ippa, mama dear.' He is squeezing Castleton's hand.

'Then stop instantly!'

She says in a nervous voice to her brother: 'I'm simply terrified of your driving with that brute on your neck. Armand! At least let Achille hold him. An animal like that could cause a fatal accident. Benoir!'

Castleton knows she is thinking of the crash outside Chantilly which was caused by a skid on a wet road to avoid a stag. That bloody monkey is a liability, of course. He says: 'Don't worry, darling, Armand's a splendid driver.'

She answers briefly: 'So was Georges.'

Armand and she and Bienville had motored down directly the police had notified them, but it had all been over before they arrived. Some early workmen cycling to the local factory had found the car with the radio still playing and 'phoned the ambulance. Georges had been thrown through the windscreen. That Mario, that perfect idiot of an Italian chauffeur of Georges', had been no use at all. He had sat crying in the middle of the stained road with Georges' head in his lap. So they had motored all the way back to Paris again with Georges in her arms, and Viv had had that dreadful fit of crying. And on the next day, in the middle of her biggest misery, she had become twenty-one.

Marguerite thinks contemptuously: that chauffeur was never injured, of course, but since Benoir is still supporting him and his entire Italian family, the progressive paralysis—or whatever it was the shock of seeing Georges killed was supposed to have set up—is not likely to get any better.

Her little stupid is trying to comfort her. 'Ouistiti will not be méchant for my Uncle Benoir, mama darling, he will do only like my Uncle Benoir says because he is like a papa for him.' George explains: 'My Uncle Benoir is quite the same for Ouistiti as Mr Castleton is for me. Voilà.'

She thanks him for his assurance. The guileless Dauphin adds: 'Really, you can believe it. It is as simple as that.' He says politely: 'I am sweating. Can I take off my coat, mama, please?'

He can do anything. The question is whether he may.

'Yes'm, I'm sorry. May I, mama, please?'

He may loosen it. He is on no account to take it off. Castleton unbuttons the coat.

He is either too hot or too cold. He is practically never comfortable. That, Castleton is to learn, is just one of a pack of miseries that hound the Dauphin daily.

She says bitterly to her brother: 'You say you will do nothing to make me nervous and you are doing the very thing, driving with that beast round your neck.'

He gives a shadowy smile. He is thinking if it happened it might be the best solution. It is only about Marie. She would have to go back to the Bienvilles. The Benoir jeunes would certainly not be the answer. Viv would have the best intentions, but his filial piety wouldn't last the week, and, of course, Marie means less than nothing to Elaine.

Li might be an idea, though it is difficult to see in what way she could take over.

Still, it should be possible to get some idea of what her attitude towards Marie would be in the event of his death without arousing her suspicion. If the reaction is good, it will simply be a question of an appropriate bequest.

Li is a good sort. Just the same, he is convinced of her admirably realistic approach to money. It will have to be something really chic to compensate Li for her trouble, and also for his death, he likes to think. Though probably that would take less compensating. Benoir smiles. That poor Mimi with her nerves! He says gaily: 'What are you making such a fuss about, you silly goose? I have no intention of going fast. I will take it at a steady seventy-five.' He must make his personal will directly he gets back to Paris. That, in any event. Unmade, it could make a lot of trouble for that poor animal, Vince. He has quite enough on his plate as it is with Mimi and puss.

Marguerite says: 'Promise me you won't let Bienville drive you back on Friday. He is even more of a maniac on the road than you are.'

She gets another smile. 'Oh, you are hopeless!' Marguerite

91

calls out. 'It is quite useless to talk to you.' She is very near to tears.

He says: 'I shall leave you, then. Until Friday, ma petite soeur chérie.' He says, smiling: 'Try to behave yourselves with Vince, you two. Let him off easy, he happens to be a particular friend of mine.' He tells Castleton: 'Don't let them give you too much sass. They can be very sassy, those two.'

George calls out delightedly: 'O, we will both be good to Mr Castleton, Uncle Benoir. We will not give him sass or anything.' He predicts: 'He will probably turn out to be our most priceless possession.' He has flushed scarlet.

Armand says, good-naturedly: 'Well, let's get a few results this time. I want to hear only good reports when I get back on Friday. And see you don't wear your new papa out, hear me, puss? This one's got to last. You and mama tore through Mr Davis so fast it was all over in three months.' He is speaking to George but looking at his sister. 'I don't want another Shiloh,' Armand says.

'No, sir, we will be good,' George promises. He has turned very shy again, only his bold hand is questing Castleton's. He asks diffidently: 'Did you tell Mr Castleton, Uncle Benoir?'

Oh yes. Good news.

Armand says: 'We have decided to cut down on Floods at the Delta. Once a month I think it was we settled for, wasn't it, puss?'

'Yessir.'

Marguerite enquires if anyone has yet told Castleton about a certain other hobby of George's?

'No, mama, don't! Don't tell him, mama, please!'

The hobby is biting stepfathers. 'Moumou bit Davis with a machinelike regularity.'

Benoir says firmly: 'It was a mistake. Puss meant to kiss Davis but his teeth slipped.'

'I will not bite Mr Castleton,' promises George.

'I would not advise you to,' remarks his mother.

'Also puss has given me his word that he will positively not crawl under the furniture when visitors arrive.'

'No, sir, I will not,' says George.

'At Paris it was the done thing for Viv to have to haul him out from under the bed by his leg. But here that will completely change, of course.'

'I wonder,' says Marguerite.

92

'Yes'm, I will improve,' the child says, earnestly. His open face is candid as a lily.

'O, toi, alors!'

She stoops down suddenly and kisses him. 'Tu es mon pigeon blanc. Va—t'—en!' says Marguerite.

Mim's handsome fellow comes up and says haughtily: 'Bonjour, Monsieur.'

'Hullo, ducky,' Castleton says. He's on the gallery signing cheques as usual.

There seems to be nothing worth buying in New Orleans except ice. A weekly 1000 lbs of it! Ice cubes aren't recognised by the Sioux.

Everything else is flown over from France.

'I am not to annoy you,' announces the Dauphin, fixing his stepfather with a bitumen stare. 'I am not to make a nuisance of myself.'

'Well, you're not.' There are no cornichons à l'eau in New Orleans, no primeurs au premier choix. No savon de Marseilles, no eau de Javelle, whatever that is, no meat or poultry, though there seems to be any amount of milk and cream.

Butter is flown over direct from Normandy in astronomical quantities. Then there is something called lagniappe.

'What's lagniappe?' Castleton wants to know. This is something they have actually got in N.O.

'Well, it is molasses, everyone knows that,' returns Mim's chap, who is clutching a posh-looking box of chocolates to his chest.

'I didn't.'

Mim's chap regards him severely and says: 'Well, you do now.' He relents sufficiently to ask: 'Why do you work so hard? You could let your secretary do that.'

Castleton says mildly: 'Well, I must sign 'em. Mummy and you have got to eat.'

Mim's chap calls out disbelievingly: 'C'est vous qui paye pour nous alors? Tiens!'

His eyes are full of unshed tears. He's probably had a telling off

93

from Mim. Castleton can hear her practising the piano pretty briskly in the salon.

He puts his pen down and lights a cigarette. 'Want to come up?' He hoicks his stepson on to his knee. 'No extra charge for chairs.'

It's the kind of remark Mim's fellow relishes. The royal gloom lifts. He says in softened tones: 'You're good, ain't you?'

'Am I?'

'O, yes, I think you are good to pay for maman and me.' The Dauphin says royally: 'When I am sixteen I will repay you. You will have to wait till then because I don't have any money right now.'

'Don't you get pocket money?' Castleton asks.

O no, it isn't necessary. If he wants to buy anything, violets for maman, or a ride on the cochons hygiéniques in the Bois, there will always be Fräulein or Miss or Marcel or Deckers there to foot the bill.

'Oh, I see.'

He hasn't even got pockets to his sailor suits, but carries his little handkerchiefs in the front of his blouse.

The Dauphin says anxiously: 'I hope you will be able to wait.' The sight of his stepfather signing so many cheques so fast seems to be on his mind.

Castleton says he expects he'll be able to hang on. 'What've you got in that box? Something nice?'

It is pictures. George has brought his private collection for Mr Castleton to see.

'If it won't bore you.'

He confides: 'They are a secret. No one has seen them but me.'

It's the ex-nougat box, of course. The snap of the Davis boys is there, and the coloured one Marcel took of George with his little aunt in the Bois.

He catches glimpses of his own letter, the envelope still intact, in what must be a place of honour amongst the Dauphin's possessions, the Holy Lambs and Doves, the flowery Sacred Hearts.

A picture of a French plage is suddenly thrust at Castleton. The Dauphin announces: 'That is my papa under here.'

He is holding his thumb well over the face of a young man in bathing drawers who is leaping about in the surf with a fierce-looking baby astride his neck. 'That is Biarritz. That is me as a child. I was méchant, you can't imagine,' George adds proudly.

The young man is returned to his box without revealing his identity.

A scrap of silk is waved at Castleton and instantly whisked away.

Noir et blanc. My papa's racing colours.

Oh, very nice. With everything being whipped so fast it's a bit difficult to say the appropriate thing in the allotted time.

The young man is everywhere. At the plages. At winter sports. At the posh thermal resorts. In the saddle. At the wheel.

Aboard his American-built yacht with a peacock sea running past his blinding white shoes.

Doing it all at the races with his trainers, his jockeys, his buckets of champagne for the winner.

At the nightspots. At after-race parties with friends and friends and friends of friends.

Or alone with Mim and their fellow, in the sunshiny garden at Auteuil, a happy-family young man under the bullion fringed laburnums.

There's an uproariously snob job of him with the Dauphin aged about two, lording it over a basket-work équipage drawn by four spanking black and white goats. Castleton wants to look, but the Dauphin won't let him because of the young man who is making it all taboo by merely holding the reins.

The Dauphin says firmly: 'You have seen all the photos of my father now.' He is putting them all back at the bottom of the box where a few crumbs of nougat still linger. The Dauphin tidies up by scooping them into his mouth, remarking kindly: 'I would of offered them to you, only they are a little old.' Himself, he is quite enjoying them. He informs his stepfather: 'There are other photos here in case you like to see them.'

None of these others are taboo, so Castleton is allowed to take his time and is even graciously pressed into accepting a couple. An encounter in Central Park between the Dauphin and a peacock. The astonished fowl with emerald hair on end, its comet's brush stuck with glaring eyes, the Dauphin pearly calm, and everybody else showing dark as horseflesh against the snow.

An entrancing portrait study of Armand and Mim with the baby Baudouin in a swing of lilies-of-the-valley, and a snapshot of the fourteen-year-old Mim at her convent, in a black apron, exactly two years off her first marriage. What an enslaver!

His late father-in-law, on the other hand, Castleton finds rather the worse for the over-zealous attentions of the Dauphin. He has been rather oddly shaded in with sky-blue crayon wherever it has been impracticable to remove him bodily with the nail scissors.

'What on earth did you do that for, you juggins?' Even through the ectoplasm his likeness to Mim is staggering.

'He bores me,' explains the Dauphin simply, 'so whenever it was possible I cut him out.'

In several pictures it hasn't been possible, and the severed hand of Pépère Benoir can be seen clasping his children by the hand, or resting on their shoulders. But always in a sky-blue glove to mark the Dauphin's disfavour.

'O, he was stinking for my Uncle Benoir, that slouch! I hate him very much, Mr Castleton.'

He adds more moderately: 'Perhaps you would be good enough not to mention anything? If mama knew what I am doing with her father, I think she wouldn't be pleased.'

'She'd sort you out, would she?'

Castleton promises he won't say a word. 'I wouldn't dare to. You might colour me blue.'

O, no, he would not. Ever. 'You are my favourite step. So far.' George asks him shyly: 'Would Mr Castleton care to see my special picture?'

He would. Very much. An ordinary looking snapshot is pushed into his hand.

'It is my ultimate favourite,' says George. There is absolutely nothing to see. It's just a snapshot of a courtyard with a tree in the middle of such proportions that the whole photograph looks solid with its shade.

The Dauphin says meaningfully: 'C'est un pistachier, you know.'

Castleton waits for some further explanation, but nothing comes. The tree and its gigantic shadow is laid away without another word.

'Have these. I saved them for you.' His very rum stepson is looking at press cuttings now. He spells out slowly: '"Haitch Vincent Castleton to Wed." Dis donc, you have a second name? What is the haitch for?' demands the Dauphin.

'Henry, I'm afraid.'

'Tiens.' The Dauphin says simply: 'I am not really surprised.' He continues: '"Haitch Vincent Castleton to Wed Mrs Davis

Davis in Paris." That's your wife, Mrs Davis Davis. D'you want to hear more? After that it becomes rather difficult for me to read.' He hands the cuttings over, with the exception of one. '"Men of the Moment. 3",' explains the Dauphin. '"The Voice from Chantilly."' While putting it away, the Dauphin observes: 'Don't think I am impolite, but if I had to change my name every time my mother got married, I would go round the bend.'

A cutting headed 'Benoir. Four Hour Operation. Fifth Doctor Called' only elicits a shrug. 'That was pépère when he was kicking the bucket. You can throw that away.'

About the second headline, 'A-M. B. Flies to Father's Side'— 'I wouldn't of budged for that slouch,' comments the Dauphin stoutly.

He has fished some cartoons out of his box. 'O, by the way, if you like to laugh, these are amusing.'

They are a pretty toxic bunch, mostly from the French socialist papers, *Le Cri du Peuple* and the communist *Voix Humaine*. There is one from the *Cri* that really gets Castleton's rag. A ward in what is obviously meant to be the Clinic Benoir, with dwindling rows of parsnip-faced children being tapped by white coiffed nuns, while upstairs, in a luxurious suite, a small white kitten laps bowl upon bowl of blood with a terribly observed rapacity.

The eyes of the kitten are unmistakable without the hateful caption: Boire, boire, moumou. Il y en a encore!

The crust! The barefaced, bloody, damn impertinence! He must be puce in the face, because Mim's chap is saying a little uncertainly: 'That is supposed to be me, that cat! Ain't it too droll for anything?'

'Put 'em away, there's a good chap.' Bloody, bloody, *bloody* rag.

'Is Mr Castleton angry with me?'

'No, of course not.'

George says conciliatorily: 'Only you are a little red in your face.' He has put everything back in his box again.

'I thought they might make you laugh, but if they don't amuse you there is no point in showing them.' In any case he has to go now. Castleton notices the piano has stopped. 'I will show you them quite soon again. Not the cartoons,' George promises, 'only the photos.'

'Thank you.'

'Thank you for having me. I hope I didn't bore you too

much.' He has selected a picture of Governor Davis for a parting gift.

'You may keep that, as well. He is my ex.'

The burning eyes of his dramatic-looking predecessor glare forthrightly into Castleton's from gloomy caverns.

'He was a very handsome man,' observes the Dauphin admiringly. His hair falling straight as an Indian's to Davis's shoulders is clearly considered the cat's pyjamas by Mim's chap.

'It remembered me of a raving. It was complètement black.'

'It reminded you of a raven,' Castleton says. 'It was completely black.'

'O, yes, it was,' agrees the Dauphin warmly. Apart from being handsome, Castleton now learns his predecessor had been mild as well.

'Considering,' the Dauphin says, 'I guess he was pretty mild.'

'Considering what?'

'He was souffrant,' George says reproachfully. 'He had a heavy case of insomnia.'

'No, really?'

'O, yes, he was practically a martyr to it.' George says Captain Butler had told him his papa was pretty near riddled with it, and that he even couldn't sleep nights, his insomnia was so all-fired bad.

'Can y'all imagine, Mr Castleton?' George thinks it is bad enough you have insomnia without you can't sleep on the side.

'Oh, ducky, the piffle,' Castleton says, 'the rot.'

'It's true!' George says in an offended voice. 'Mr Castleton can ask who he like, ain't nobody going to tell him any different about Mr Davis.'

'What d'you think insomnia is?'

George says he don't know. Captain But ain't explained it to him, ever, but George figures it is some sort of a bad pain, perhaps?

Well, equally perhaps, it's nothing of the kind. 'Insomnia's just not being able to sleep, that's all. Got it, old love?' Castleton asks.

'Yes, sir.'

So he can pension that one off with the rest of his comic ideas. 'You've got quite a collection of 'em, haven't you, ducky?'

O, he is nice. But it is rather sad as well. George thinks if Mr Castleton has a fault it is this habit of exploding all your most cherished and long-established ideas and calmly expecting you to adopt some new and thoroughly unattractive theory in their place.

He announces in a subdued voice: 'I am going now. All the best.'

'Oh, must you go? I thought we were going to have tea together.'

O, he is really nice.

'I can come back, you know. I am only going to put my box away.'

George remarks airily: 'As a matter of fact, I have nothing else on. I am not allowed in mama's presence for the moment. Not till I am good again.'

Oh, Lor'.

'I will tell you about it when I see you. À tout à l'heure, then,' says the Dauphin. 'All the best.'

He's back just as Castleton is signing the last cheque. There are no laundries in New Orleans, either. All the princely household linen from Number 38 has to be flown to a convent near Paris, where it is seized immediately upon arrival by fallen women and got up regardless, under supervision of the sisters, with a passion obviously diverted from other pursuits.

And that's the last one, thank God. He lifts his stepson on to his knee again. 'Now then, what're you miz about, eh?'

O, it is nothing new. 'It is my usual, don't you know?'

'No, I don't know. What's your usual?'

Mim's chap says gloomily: 'I don't like to obey. You can draw your conclusions.' He is trembling slightly.

'D'you want your tippet?' It's said to make him laugh. His tippet is his fur-lined coat.

'No, thank you. O, you are droll!' His tippet has cheered him up. He is playing with Castleton's ring.

'O, I do hate it. O, I do hate it, Mr Castleton.'

'What d'you hate, my duck?'

O, everything. George says he hates just about everything in the whole world.

'I don't ever want to get up, or go to bed, or eat my dinner properly, or go walks, or learn my lessons, or have my tests made, or do anything ever at all.'

George says: 'O, I cain't stand to do what I'm bid. O, I just simply cain't stand it.'

'But, darling, everyone has to do things they don't like some-times,' Castleton says. 'I have to.'

But George says in a loud, bold voice: 'Well, I don't want to. Ever. It will just bore the piss.'

He says: 'I just want to be with mama and you and my Cousin Viv and Uncle and Tante Benoir and Ouisti and Marcel and Mr Davis.'

'Well, you are with us,' Castleton says.

George counters smartly: 'Well, I ain't with Mr Davis, am I?'

No; but he's with the rest of them. And he must eat and sleep and learn things because that's life.

'Well, I don't want it,' says the implacable Dauphin, 'and I don't ever want to go to that school in Switzerland either. They are all Boches there, Vivi says. They will all laugh at my chemises de nuit.'

'No, they won't, darling.' His nightshirts, swell eighteenth-century-looking jobs, are the traditional night-gear for kids with the Sioux and a sore point with the Dauphin.

And, anyway, it's not a German school. Castleton says: 'That part of Switzerland is French.'

He's heard about this Swiss place from Mim, and about the tussle that's going on to make her chap learn German, 'so that he doesn't arrive at his internat a complete and utter savage, Poilu.'

Her chap says now: 'Well, I ain't going there in any case. And if I am put there I will run home in my bare feet. So that is all about it.'

Bare feet are a must with Mim's chap for running away in. He's terribly upset. Castleton says he probably won't have to go there and that if they are going to live in Paris he will go to a Lycée.

But Mim's chap calls out: 'Well, I don't want to live at Paris for a start! I am perfectly sick of that bunch at the Clinic. That Courvoisier is stinking for me, you have no idea.' English words fail him, he calls out: 'C'est une ordure, celui-là!'

He's got it bad. Castleton says: 'How about some tea?'

George blows his nose.

Castleton says: 'It'll all come out in the wash.'

'O, you are darling for me!' George kisses his stepfather spiritedly on the thumb. 'That don't count! I know you don't want I should kiss your hand and I will never do it! Ever!'

Tea is brought on to the gallery, and Marguerite comes strolling out to join them.

'Hullo, our girl,' Castleton calls out. 'What fun.'

It's very rare for Mim to take anything in the afternoon. George flies to his mother, locking his arms round her waist, butting her with his head. 'Maman! Maman!'

'Alors, fais pas des bêtises, hein?' Marguerite kisses him: 'Papa will think you are a goat.'

'O, I am sorry, mama darling,' George promises, 'I will be different. I will behave.'

She hopes so. 'Run along now and have your goûter.' She kisses him again. Their row, or whatever, is over. Cheers.

'Come and sit down, darling,' Castleton says.

The little boy calls out ecstatically: 'O, can y'all imagine? Our girl is coming to take tea with us!' He is looking from one to the other. They are his favourite persons. He can hardly contain himself for love.

'Don't fidget, moumou,' Marguerite tells him.

He regales himself enthusiastically with an orange pressé, a madeleine or two, and a saucer of jam. He takes a careful sip of Mr Castleton's tea. O, that is good, as well. And after tea they are all going to take a little walk in the garden.

'I'll carry him down the steps, darling.'

'No, Vincent, please. Those few stairs he can manage by himself.'

'Well, hang on to the rail then, love.'

But Marguerite takes the small hand away. 'Let him take his place in life, Poilu.'

She's right, of course. Anyway, he's down the steps at last, and cavorting about between them, hanging on to their arms. His hands are like little forks, Castleton thinks: he'll probably put on flesh later. When he's settled down. Anyhow, it's jolly nice to be taking a stroll round the garden with your wife and family.

Mim is bowling the family along smartly like a hoop. 'Walk straight, moumou!'

'Yes, ma'am.'

He calls out ecstatically: 'O, I do adore it when it is just us three! When it is just you and me and the Guv,' says George.

'What did you say?'

The Guv.

George says: 'It means the Governor, mama. It is a British word.'

She knows exactly what it means. 'Walk straight!' says Marguerite. 'Walk straight at once or I will send you indoors!'

8

The Battle of Shiloh

They are playing Créole markets under the house. Marguerite can hear them shrieking and squabbling directly below where she is seated reading on the gallery. It is impossible to concentrate with that din down there. She closes de Courville's *Lettres à une femme particulière* and goes over to the gallery rail, the book still in her hand. She is smiling.

'Moumou.'

It is a day of glaring sun and high wind which is setting the leaves of the glittering bushes in the courtyard frantically clapping.

'What are you doing down there, moumou? Uncle Benoir will hear you screaming at the Delta.'

There are three of them down there, but she only addresses her son.

He comes out at once from under the house with Dédé hanging on to his hand. Albert emerges last and stays half-hidden by a trumpet-vine out of Marguerite's sight.

George calls up: 'We are playing Créole markets, mama darling.'

His smiling face is making her smile too. 'Don't drawl like that, moumou.' She thinks proudly: he is a beautiful child. He is exactly like the photographs she has seen of Benoir at his age, only thinner. If only the little stupid doesn't grow too fast. At this rate there will be nothing left of him.

A sudden vision of the terrible misery of her mother's last few days forces itself upon her. She calls out sharply: 'Hold yourself straight, moumou. How many times has one to tell you? And let go of that stupid child. What are you thinking of, letting her drag on you like that? She will make you quite lop-sided.'

'Yes'm,' he calls up. 'Will y'all come and buy from us, mama? We'll give you a good commission. O do, mama, do.'

She asks him teasingly: 'What have you got to sell? I suppose you have nothing but rubbish down there, as usual.'

O, no. They have rice and sugar and pois cassés and coffee beans and okra and sweet potato. Gustave has given them everything they want from the house and they have set it all out on little dishes.

'Gustave says if we break some of the dishes he won't care,' George says. 'It is good of Gustave, ain't it?'

Very, Marguerite points out dryly, especially as they are not Gustave's dishes. She says: 'You are saying "ain't" and "y'all" again, moumou. If you continue, you will speak only French to your cousin when he comes. Perhaps that will assist your memory.'

George calls out placatingly: 'I forgot. I am sorry, I am sorry, mama dear.' To draw her attention he says: 'We have a special marché des fleurs this time, mama. You will see, it is quite splendid.'

They have picked armfuls of the most beautiful flowers and made them all up into bouquets. 'There is a special boutonnière only for you. It is a yellow rose with heliotrope. It is very chic. Or you can have cape jessamines with pomegranate flowers. That is pretty rich, the red with the white. You can have whichever you choose. Neither will cost you dear.' He looks up at the smiling girl who is his mother and coaxes: 'O, do come and play with us, mama darling. O, do.'

The others take it up till there is quite a chorus of children's voices clamouring: 'Dites oui, madame! Dites oui, dites oui, maman-chérie!'

'For God's sake, moumou,' Marguerite calls down, half

annoyed, half amused. 'Don't drawl like that! You sound like Tante Marie.'

He begs: 'O, it will be such an honour for us if only Mlle Mimi will come and buy from us.' Mlle Mimi is his name for Marguerite when she plays markets with them and pretends to be a customer from a big house.

O, Mlle Mimi is more fun to play markets with than anyone else because she will always pretend to find fault with everything, and pick all the goods over, and nothing is ever fresh enough for her, and she will never pay the prices they ask for anything even if it is prix fixe. Also you can give sass and abuse her as much as you like and she will only laugh. Only you are not permitted to say 'fous-moi la paix' like the real market people do. The first time they had played this game he didn't know this, and mama had categorically forbidden him to say it again. George thinks this is bizarre because Uncle Benoir says it all of the time and with Viv it is every second word. It is probably to do with they are grown up and he is only a child.

He stands out in the bright wild weather with his hair blowing and the bushes rocking violently behind him, calling up at the gallery in a typical market-voice: 'Voilà des oeillettes, mam'zelle Mimi, voilé des belles, sont bien fraiches, mes oeillettes. Ah'm talkin' abaout fresh shrimp! Ah'm talkin' abaout fresh shrimp! Water*MELON!*'

It is fantastic how that child can copy anything he hears, especially from the working classes. If it is not carried too far it can be quite amusing, but of course that little stupid is too shy to do it in front of guests. She claps her hands and calls: 'Assez, assez. I have heard your repertoire. Come up and have your goûter now. Is Albert there, moumou?' Albert steps forward and Marguerite says coldly: 'What are you hiding yourself for, like that? Take Dédé back to your mother. She is not to play with p'tit m'sieu any more today. And get that rubbish cleared up down there before Monsieur comes home.'

The little boy calls disappointedly: 'O, we ain't only just begun to play. O, my Redeemer!'

'I have said it is enough.'

Tomorrow he may play again. If he is good she will play with him. But not if he says 'O, my Redeemer'. 'Come quickly now and get your goûter. And bring your basket with you, moumou, I want to choose my bouquet.'

He comes out into the thrumming day and starts to climb the gallery stairs. The bushes in the courtyard applaud his efforts wildly. It is appalling how long it is taking him to climb those few stairs. Another day he will fly up them like a bird. She can see Gustave hovering on the gallery but she won't give the order for him to carry the boy until she must.

'Eh bien, moumou, is that all you can achieve?'

Marguerite tells him: 'Give me your basket and hold on to the railing.'

'Yes'm, mama.'

'Don't speak while you are walking.' She has become alarmed at his extreme pallor and says sharply: 'Stand where you are. I shall tell Gustave to carry you up. You are not to move on any account, c'est compris? Don't answer,' says Marguerite.

When Gustave has lifted him on to the sofa beside her, she scolds him more gently: 'You have tired yourself out with this ridiculous Créole market. That cretin of a child is always hanging round your neck. Did you lift Dédé, moumou?'

'No, ma'am.'

'Vrai de vrai?'

He looks at her. There is nothing but truth in his eyes.

Then she cannot understand why he should be so exhausted. 'Is it this wind?'

He doesn't know. She cups his face between her hands and tells him: 'You are a little silly. I am in despair with you. What shall one do with you?' asks Marguerite.

He answers saucily in his sweet, languid drawl: 'Will y'all love me, Mlle Mimi?'

It doesn't seem to help much when one loves him, Marguerite says. Perhaps one should give him more panpan. 'Why are you so pale again, you bad moumou? You know how papa detests to see you without colour in your cheeks.'

He says: 'I will rub my face very hard before he comes home. Like that I will have a red face for Monsieur your husband.' He is laughing at her, petit polisson!

She tells him, smiling: 'You have still not managed to say papa, George.'

No. But he will say it, George promises, he will say it, if mama will only give him a little more time.

She will not give him long. The longer he has to deliberate the less he will do it and in the end there will be a second Shiloh.

She is picking over the bunches of flowers in the flat basket. 'Where is the bouquet you made for me? Which one is mine?'

He holds the yellow roses out timidly. She is angry with him. He can feel it.

'Is that all the choice?'

He holds out the gardenias. She doesn't like gardenias. She finds their scent stale, heavy, insupportable. 'Give me the roses. Are they fresh?'

'Yes'm.'

'How much?'

That will cost her two kisses.

Too much. She will give him one. He makes no protest. She is still angry with him.

She kisses the small pale mouth and thinks what a ridiculous life his illness forces him to lead. Anything less suitable for a boy couldn't be imagined. At his age Bienville was already taking his place in the world, while this poor sheltered thing is still amusing himself like a girl, making bouquets for maman and playing with the servants.

He hasn't done any harm to anyone in all his nine years, and this is his reward. Yet there are fools like Marie who drop on their knees every day to thank God for His magnificent gifts! For sick children like this, and for unfaithful husbands like Benoir. She thinks contemptuously: after Chantilly He can keep His favours.

She looks at the small, rich-smelling roses, so evocative of her son, and asks: 'Did you make this quite by yourself, moumou?'

'O yes, mama.'

Neither Albert or Dédé has helped him? 'I don't wish to wear what they have touched.'

O, no, he has made it quite by himself, only for her.

'Then it is truly mine.' She kisses his mouth again. 'I shall pay your full price for your roses.'

George calls out instantly: 'Another kiss, Mlle Mimi. They have gone up, Mlle Mimi, it's on account the weather, Mlle Mimi.'

'You are Jew.' He is delicious to kiss, her son. She is reminded of when he was a baby and Mammy used to bring him in every morning into their bed. They had almost eaten him up with kisses. Georges had called him 'le petit déjeuner'. 'Tu veux déjà ton petit déjeuner, Mimi? Fi donc, tu est gourmande!'

Oh, if Georges could see him now, his beautiful fat baby who

107

had relished Mammy's milk so much. She kisses the small blood-less ear. 'Go, tell Gustave he may bring your goûter. And tell him to take your basket away. Little bold thing,' says Marguerite, 'you have surpassed yourself with papa's flowers! If you have left three for the poor man to look at, it will be a lot.'

O no, he has left a deal more than he has took. 'I wouldn't rob him, mama darling.'

He cannot bring himself to say that name. She smiles at him. She says: 'Sit up and take your goûter, George.'

Gustave has brought it to him on a silver tray. A small warm roll in a fine napkin and a small crystal glass of beer.

'O, mama!' calls out George.

She replies: 'It is bière de la Meuse. It will strengthen you.'

O, he detests beer.

Nevertheless he will drink it. 'Uncle Baudouin had many worse things to take when he was your age.'

George calls out, pouting: 'It is for Boches, that bière de la Meuse.'

She leans across and slaps his left arm. She says: 'Now you have had your smack. I hope you are satisfied. Now you can show papa a red arm, as usual.' Marguerite says: 'It wouldn't be pos-sible for you to go one single day without panpan.'

He drinks his beer without another word.

'Are you crying, George?'

'No, ma'am.' He eats his roll quickly. It is very good and takes away the metallic taste of the beer.

'Is it quite finished?'

O yes, there is not a single drop left of this horrible bière de la Meuse.

She takes his arm and kisses it. 'Aren't you ashamed, moumou? To be punished like a baby at nine years of age?'

O yes, he is ashamed. He puts his arms round her neck and whispers: 'Mama.'

'Quoi?'

'I love you better than anyone in the whole world.'

She is glad to hear it. One would not think so sometimes from his behaviour. She says: 'I want you to be in bed by eight o'clock tonight, moumou. Papa and I are dining out. Gustave will bring you your dinner in bed. It will do you good to have an early night.'

She strokes his hair and says: 'Mammy may read to you for

half an hour afterwards, then you must put out your light.' She says: 'I have ordered a glace à la pistache just for my little glutton. Shall you like that, moumou?'

Yes, he will like it.

But . . . ? She is interested—there seem to be reservations?

He would like it better if they were all having dinner together. Just the three of them. George says he does like that so very much, to sit between them both.

He flushes slightly as he again skirts round naming the name.

Marguerite says: 'If that is supposed to be a protest against papa and me dining out, I don't intend to hear a single word about it.' She tells him gravely: 'You have been very spoiled in Paris, George, and the sooner you realise this, the better. I certainly have no intention of emulating Tante Marie and staying in night after night just to please you. Papa works very hard to look after us both, and I, for one, intend to see that he gets a little relaxation.' She says: 'I hope you don't intend to become possessive, George. It is not a course I would advise for you as I shall most certainly put a stop to it.' She says: 'I am extremely displeased with you. It is quite clear you have no thought but for your own wishes.'

He is terribly pale. The knocking of his heart is making the corner of his handkerchief tremble. He takes it from the bosom of his sailor blouse and wipes his wet cheeks with it.

She says: 'If you cry I will send you straight to bed. You will not go out on the gallery to wait for papa.'

He puts his handkerchief back into his blouse.

She asks him suddenly: 'George, when are you going to call your stepfather papa?'

He says he is fixing to say it very soon.

He has already had three days to say it in. 'I am not optimistic.'

O yes, he will say it, he will say it, if only mama will give him a little longer.

'No, moumou, I will not give you any more time. You will quite simply do as you are told for once, voilà tout.' She takes up her book again. 'Now occupy yourself with something until it is time for you to go and wait for papa.' She stretches herself upon a sofa with her book. 'I shall see if you can greet him properly this time.'

He comes and sits upon the magnificent carpet and leans his head against her feet. 'Mama, darling . . .'

'What is it?' She stirs his hair a little with her foot.

'May I give Dédé my third best rosary, please? I have got six now, with my pearl—the one that Uncle Benoir gave me.'

No, he may not.

George asks: 'Then may I give her one of my others?'

No, he may not. She lifts her eyes from her book and smiles at him. 'Have you already promised it to her, moumou?'

'Yes, ma'am.'

He gets no other answer but the smile. A flush washes over his face. She remarks: 'That will teach you not to promise anything without asking permission first.'

George exclaims: 'But I don't use any of them now except my pearl. Why mayn't I give Dédé one of my others, mama dear? She has only an ugly black one.'

That need not concern him. He may not give Madeleine one of his rosaries because she has said he may not. Marguerite says: 'Occupy yourself, moumou.'

George says: 'Dédé will think I have broken my word.'

Marguerite says: 'It is immaterial what that cretin thinks. Occupy yourself with something, George.'

'What shall I do, mama?'

'Take a book or practise your English writing. It is not so good that you can afford to rest on your laurels.'

George says: 'I don't know whom to write to. Tante Marie can't read English.'

She says: 'Write to your cousin, then.'

But George says: 'O, I have never written to Viv in all my life, mama. O, he would die laughing.'

She tells him: 'Then write. Quite simply, write.' Whether he writes a letter or not is not important. The important thing for him is to get practice. 'It is a disgrace that at nine years of age you still read and write like a baby.'

He seats himself at her desk and takes a sheet of paper. She glances at him from her book. His posture is irreproachable. He isn't even looking at his beloved medallions. He sits there, thinking deeply.

'Eh bien, moumou?'

She says she will expect a major philosophical work at least, from his great concentration.

He says: 'Will you allow me to write to Shiloh?'

'No,' Marguerite says. 'I had an idea that was coming.'

George says: 'But I like Mr Davis.'

She, on the contrary, doesn't in the least like Governor Davis. 'I have divorced him. Even you must know that when that happens people don't remain friends any longer.' The whole episode of Shiloh is closed and therefore George must consider his friendship with the Davises as also finished. She advises him in unmistakable tones: 'Don't be too long with your letter.'

He turns away from her without a word and starts to write. She smiles at the grave angle of his childish neck bent over her desk in utter concentration. She asks him fondly: 'Alors, moumou, have you at last found someone to write to?'

Yes, he has thought of someone.

Her guess is that it will be to his friend Ouistiti down at the Delta. 'I am sure he can read English at least as well as you can.'

O, mama is droll. 'O, will y'all imagine Ouistiti reading my letter!'

He laughs so much that she has to bring his attention back to what he is doing. 'Finish your letter, moumou.'

He takes up the pen and writes two words at the top of the page. Then he stops and looks at them with his head in his hands. The words are both quite short.

She asks: 'Is something troubling you?'

He answers vaguely that he doesn't know.

In that case he had better finish his letter without further delay. 'Do you hear me, George? Take up your pen and write. I shan't tell you a second time.'

He writes his letter to the end. When she sees him signing it, Marguerite says: 'Is it finished at last?'

'Yes'm, mama.'

She says quite pleasantly: 'Bring it to me. I will correct it for you. We shall see what progress, if any, you have made with your English writing.'

He brings the beautifully written letter to his mother. She takes it from him and reads it through. It runs:

Dear Sir,

I write to you on account you are not hear on account you are down town earning des gros sous pour Maman et moi. Vous etes bien gentil and Maman and also I love you. I send you a big kiss and embarass you very strongly.

Here there blows an epouventable wind. Have you got wind also?

Your affected and respectable son-in-law who loves you,
Georges-Marie A. Benoir.

She tears it through and through and hands him back the pieces. 'Throw this rubbish away.'

'Is it wrong, mama?' George says timidly. 'I didn't know how to put some of the phrases.'

It is wrong from start to finish. It is an absolute disgrace. A hotchpotch of French and English. The spelling would shame a child of two. Also who is this person he addresses as Dear Sir? Or is this George's idea of a business letter?

'No, mama.'

To whom had he written this letter? She is curious to know who was to have been the lucky recipient of this delightful note?

George says: 'It was for Mr Castleton.'

'For whom?'

'Your husband, mama.'

She beckons him to her side and says: 'This is the last time I will tell you, so I hope you are listening. If I hear you address papa just once more by any other name I shall punish you severely, and you know I don't make believe. I will not have you saying "Mr Castleton" or "your husband" one single time more. Is that understood?'

George says: 'O, I don't want to give my papa's name. O, please don't make me, mama dear.'

'Yes, I will make you.' She takes him by the arm and says: 'Listen, monsieur, you are no longer at Auteuil to have your own way in everything. You are with me. Those are two totally different things, as you will find to your cost before very much longer if you continue in this way. I will make you do this thing if it costs you every tear you have. I will not have a disobedient child. There will be no repetition of Shiloh, George. That I can promise you. You will call your stepfather by the name I have decided on or you will be accountable to me. Uncle Benoir should have obliged you to obey from your very first day here. You have been spoiled in Paris till you have become impossible. You have been disobedient and self-important ever since you came back. But it is going to stop. For every time you are disobedient or entêté I shall punish you—and I shall do it in front of papa. Perhaps that will shame you into obedience at last.'

112

It is the worst scolding he has ever had. There is no end to its griping severity. He sits absolutely still, huddled inside himself like a sick bird.

Outside the tall windows in the bright fighting weather the bushes are flashing like heliographs. He can hear the fountain splashing loudly. He is white to the lips.

She says in a tone of command: 'Now sit down at that desk and write that letter again. If it is not correct in every detail I shall punish you. It is as simple as that. Be quick.'

He goes at once, glad to be out of reach of his mother's anger. He sits down at her desk again and takes up the pen. He is looking out of the window where the fronds of the palms are streaming and screaming in the wind. A little sweet air blows on to his hot pale cheeks. He puts the pen down neatly, gets off his chair and goes towards his mother. He has written nothing at all.

She is reading again, and is astonished to find him in front of her, suddenly. 'Eh bien, monsieur, c'est déjà fini?'

No. He has not written it.

'Comment?'

He says: 'I don't want to.' He adds: 'I am not madly keen.'

He has picked that up from Vincent, of course.

He says: 'I will do everything else in the world you tell me to.'

He will do everything else and this as well. Of that he may rest assured. The sheer impudence of it! She is almost intrigued by the cool, the colossal, effrontery of that little meek son of hers.

She says without preamble: 'Obey at once, or I will punish you as you have never been punished in your life. Do you understand what I am saying to you, George?'

'Yes'm, mama.'

'I don't think you do.' She holds out her hand for him to take. 'Come with me. I want to show you something.'

He puts his small hand into hers quite confidently. It's evident that this spoiled brat still thinks that he will get his way!

A decision will have to be reached within a matter of minutes. She is becoming very bored with this whole situation. She leads him swiftly to her desk and opens a small drawer.

'D'you know what this is, George?'

'Yes'm.' He has never seen it before but he knows what it is. It

113

is a tiny whip like the one in the centre medallion. It lies coiled in the drawer like a baby snake. It has a very dark body and a small gay-coloured handle of beads for a head. It looks as if it were sleeping.

She takes it out of the drawer and it pricks up at once. It is very lively and alert-looking with a lash of a hairlike fineness. At the faintest vibration it sets up a peculiar sound like a silky twittering.

George says he doesn't like it very much.

She says he isn't meant to. It wasn't made for play. Whips like that were used on Taquineuse and other plantations to discipline slaves with. People who were bought and sold like dogs. Marguerite says: 'D'you want to be touched with a thing like that?'

O, no, he doesn't want it at all.

She says: 'Then will you obey?'

He looks at her.

'George,' Marguerite says. 'Obey or I shall whip you.'

He looks at her. His eyes are arrestingly beautiful, pupil and iris one profound black.

She says: 'Don't think because it is small it won't hurt you. It will hurt you very much.'

There is absolutely no answer except this amazing look. It is in this look that the resistance lies. She takes her pretty, disobedient child by the arm and literally throws him on to the sofa like a doll. The whip she throws into his lap. She says: 'I will give you a few moments to look at it properly. It may help to change your ideas.'

She is terribly angry with him, but she is still angrier with Benoir. He has spoiled her son till he is completely unmanageable and now it is the child who must pay. She steps through the French doors on to the gallery and stands looking over the rail. When that fool of a Benoir gets back from the Delta she will let him have her opinion of him in no uncertain terms.

The loud unruly fountain is spraying and spouting over everything in the fantastic wind. One side of the courtyard is quite wet already. If Vincent is driving with the hood down he will be drenched when he comes in! She calls out angrily: 'Turn that water off!'

It is inconceivable, in view of this wind, that nobody has

thought of doing this before! She watches the powerful, thrustful column of water being subdued, forced down, and finally dwindle limply back into its pipe.

She will go back into the salon. He will have capitulated by now. She has given him a terrible fright and he will never dare to call her bluff. Monsieur is not so eager to risk his skin. That little soft stubborn thing! She is still angry with him, but if he is truly sorry she will forgive him—though he must certainly not be allowed to get off scot free. She will pack him off to bed without his goodnight kiss. He detests that more than anything. And he will definitely forfeit his glace à la pistache. And tomorrow he will get an imposition. He will write his celebrated English letter to her dictation. She hasn't yet decided what else will be in it but it will certainly begin with 'My dearest papa!' It will break monsieur's heart to have to write it, but that must be his punishment.

Little mule! If he really got what he deserves he would get an impressive portion of panpan as well!

He is already waiting for her at the gallery doors. The rebellion is over. She thinks with affectionate scorn it was a typical 'moumou' demonstration. He will fight like a stag to keep an opinion, but at the first brush with authority he will collapse!

He is not by any means a cowardly child, thank God, but his illness has softened him so that he has no staying power left, only the characteristic obstinacy of the weak.

She is delighted at this hoped for capitulation. He richly deserves to be punished but she will be delighted not to have to do it just the same.

Little rubbish! She hopes he is shaking in his shoes at the thought of the scolding he will get from his maman. She is amused to see he is wearing the small meek air of appeasement he always puts on when he knows he has gone too far and is about to be presented with the bill. It is not surprising Vincent finds him so amusing. There is no part of this little good-for-nothing that isn't pleasing.

He is as neat as a bird.

When that strange, sequestered, almost countrified air his illness has conferred upon him goes, he will be as handsome as Benoir. It will probably leave him when he is about fourteen. Women will go mad about him.

Directly she steps through the gallery doors she sees that she has mistaken his attitude completely. He is not penitent at all. If he looks abashed it is because he has not had second thoughts about anything. The situation is completely unchanged.

It is imperative that monsieur should be punished immediately, without further argument or prevarication, otherwise he will take a notion that this kind of behaviour is going to be tolerated.

She will give him one cut of the whip and put a stop to this business once and for all. A really good one across the palm. It is exactly what he needs. It will probably mark him and Benoir will be furious. All the better. She is furious with Benoir.

She makes straight for the sofa, taking her son with her, and collects the whip. As she picks it up it sets up that disgusting twittering again. It will serve no purpose to think about it. If it has to be done, then the sooner the better. She says briefly: 'Hold out your hand.'

He holds his hand out to her, half smiling, a little uncertain of his mother's intention. He gets a cut across the palm, of a ferocity that leaves him in no further doubt. He calls out in an astonished voice: 'O, it hurts!'

She remarks: 'If you want any more, you have only to say so.'

He is crying broken-heartedly, his crippled hand pressed under his arm. 'O, it's bad, it's bad!'

With any luck it's over. She beckons him to her. He comes weeping and trying to put his arms round her neck. 'O, I love you, I love you.'

She takes his arms down at once. 'Are you going to obey?'

'O, I love you, I love you.' The shock has made him almost incoherent.

She is not concerned with his love at the moment. 'Are you going to do as you're told?'

He begs her: 'Don't make me give my papa's name, don't make me give my papa's name.'

It is inconceivable! The whole farce is starting up afresh!

He begs: 'O, let me call him Vincent, mama darling. He said I could. It is his given name. I swear I didn't ask him. He said quite by himself I could.'

'Be silent, George,' says Marguerite.

'O, let me, mama, please. Please, please let me. I swear I will never ask for anything else in my whole life again if you will only let me call your husband by his given name.'

'You will not bargain with me, George. That much is certain,' says Marguerite.

'It isn't sassy.' George assures her at Paris it is quite the done thing to call your parents by their given names. Zazie and Nana d'Erlanger always call their papa 'Raoul'. 'It is with his full permission,' George says. 'It isn't disrespectful, mama darling, I swear it isn't for sass.' George says: 'I would never be disrespectful for your husband, mama.' George says: 'I love your husband very much.'

'George, stop,' advises Marguerite.

'But why?' he calls out. 'Why can't I call him by his given name? Viv does it. Viv calls my uncle Benoir Benoir all of the time, and you don't say anything.' He is crying passionate tears. 'Even Viv calls him Herman to his face, he is let to do it because he is Viv. Viv can do anything, but I must do what I'm bid only because you say so, and if I don't you punish me.'

'Yes,' agrees Marguerite.

'You never give me a reason for anything.'

'No,' agrees Marguerite.

'O, God!' George calls out. 'O, God!'

'George, stop or I will kill you,' says Marguerite.

But he calls out astonishingly: 'O, you can kill me with that thing. I will be only too glad.' He is in an absolute paroxysm, a kind of fit of grief. He calls out in French: 'I know you will force me, but I will never do it in my heart! I will never give the name of my father to another—never, never in my life!'

It is unbelievable! It is like something from a novelette. He has only to fall on his knees now and press his rosary to his lips and he will have done everything!

He falls on his knees.

She says in a terrible voice: 'Get up or I will surely kill you.'

She hauls him to his feet, still crying: 'Jamais, jamais de ma vie,' and beats him till she can beat him no more.

He shrieks out in a high sweet voice like a terrified bird. 'Don't, don't whip me, mama! O, you will kill me with that thing! Pas plus, pas plus, maman-chérie!'

He has slipped down on to the floor, but she has still got hold of his hand. She beats it till she is satisfied. 'Will you dare to disobey like that again? Will you dare?'

A little clear water runs out of his mouth. She throws the whip at him and says contemptuously: 'Take yourself off to bed! When you have pulled yourself together I shall come up and we shall see what you have got to say to me.'

She turns on her heel without another look or word. He lies where he is for a long time, crying terribly. The room is full of a beautiful heartless light. It picks out the bright cruel colours of the tiny asp-tailed whip, and the rotten-ripe crimson of his hands as they all lie together abandoned on the carpet.

His mother's scent is everywhere. Light, dry, elegant and full of trouble for him. In the carpet, on the sofas, on the chairs, in the curtains and on himself where she has gripped him by the blouse to punish him. The tiny scourge is quite sweet with it, especially round the beadwork handle.

O, he would like to run as fast and as far as possible out of this scented, light-struck room which has witnessed his total defeat, and where the battle begun at Shiloh almost a year ago has been irretrievably lost to such a bold and experienced enemy.

Outside in the restless afternoon a huge heavy leaf, slashed by the wind from a cucumber tree, is shuffling about by itself in the empty courtyard. It is nosing blindly round the turned-off fountain where the water is slapping violently in the basin and slopping over on to the stones.

O, if Mr Castleton comes home now he will go mad with shame. His hands are blazing like furnaces but his face feels very cold. A heavy quaking overtakes his limbs as he makes the effort to stand up. As he gets on his feet he realises he has wet himself. He bursts into uncontrollable sobs.

The huge sad leaf has stopped moving about. It is lying flat under the fountain, only flapping a little from time to time and falling back on the stones. Only the mirror-leaved bushes are still rocking and clapping and doubling up under the whistling fronds of the palms.

9

The Fighter-Brooch

'Where's the family, Mim?' Castleton calls out. He is getting himself a drink. He has come in late from the office to dress for some dinner party or other with friends of Mim's. A Colonel and Mme de Chassevent.

'Do I know 'em, darling, by the way?'

Considering he spent last Sunday with them at the Bayou Tigre, she rather thinks he does.

Oh yes, that bundle of fun de Chassevent. 'Oh, jolly good, darling,' Castleton says. It's a bit of a bind having to go. Come to think, he can't be doing with Mim's friends much. That bachelor set that follows her about. The Bic de Huysims and the 'Baby' Pererezes. Or the French lot for that matter. Certainly not those two. Though probably the de Chassevents are more Armand's friends than Mim's à cause de Mme de.

It's an association of some years' standing; Marguerite reminds him coolly: 'They are George's god-parents.'

Castleton says the de Chassevents show jolly good taste.

'Where is he, darling?' He has brought their drinks into her room. 'I've got your porto frappé for you.'

She is already dressed and having her hair done. He kisses her shoulder so as not to disturb her maid.

'You look absolutely ravishing. Where's your chap?'

'I have sent George to bed,' says Marguerite.

Good for her. Best place for him in that wind. 'What about that bloody hurricane, then?' Castleton wants to know. Even downtown it had been murder. Round about four o'clock the whole building was swaying.

Castleton asks: 'How did your chap stand up to it?'

'It didn't affect George, Vincent.'

'Didn't it, though? I say. Well done, your chap.' There had been quite a few casualties at the bank. Mostly migraine. Two of the girls in Overseas had to be sent home, they were so under the weather.

'I thought of George,' says Castleton.

She makes no reply.

'Good idea of yours to keep him in bed. Do him a power of good.'

He is lighting a cigar. 'I must say it felt highly rum not to be leapt on the minute I put my nose round the door,' Castleton says. 'What's the matter, Mim?'

What should be the matter?

'You're so quiet, darling.'

Marguerite is studying her hair. She asks her maid: 'Is this supposed to be done, or what?'

'Madame is not satisfied?'

'I suppose it will have to do. I certainly have no intention of sitting here for another half an hour.'

'Very good, Madame.'

Castleton asks: 'What's the matter with it, darling? It looks a treat to me.'

Marguerite shrugs.

She tells her maid: 'I want to change my jewellery. Tell them to send up some brooches. I will make a choice. George has been punished, Vincent,' Marguerite says.

'Oh, I see. Oh dear. Oh well.' A vague British murmur escapes Castleton's lips. 'I'm sure he's sorry, darling.'

Marguerite says simply: 'Oh, yes, he is sorry.'

'Well, that's all right then, isn't it, darling?'

'I suppose so.' She asks her maid: 'Are you waiting for something?'

Sidonie goes.

Castleton says: 'Why don't you wear your rubies, Mim? They suit you wonderfully.' He had bought them for her in Colombo on their honeymoon and had had them set in London.

She answers him briefly: 'They are wrong for this dress. You haven't begun to get ready yet, Vincent.'

'Darling, you *are* depressed,' Castleton says. 'D'you want me to go up and have a word or something?'

What for? She has chosen a brooch from the selection Sidonie has brought. A diamond of such violent fire that it looks alive.

'D'you see how much better this looks, Vincent?'

She's right, of course. She is fastening the superb brooch in her dress. It's a named piece. 'The Coup de Foudre.' She says: 'D'you like it, Vincent? It was Georges' favourite thing.'

He doesn't, actually. It's a bit of a brute. He says: 'It's très Benoir. I think it wants to bite me.' She reaches up and gives him a warm kiss. 'That was from George. He was most anxious you shouldn't go without your goodnight kiss. He loves you very much, Poilu.'

Castleton says: 'He's a tremendous dear.'

She answers, smiling: 'Everyone loves moumou but no one dreams of checking him.'

'Oh, come off it, darling,' says Castleton.

'What did you say?'

Castleton says: 'I think you're going on a bit.'

'Is that what you think?'

'Well, he does rather take it off the chin at times.'

She says coldly: 'I have no idea what that is supposed to mean.'

'It means you're too strict with him, darling,' Castleton says. 'Honestly, darling, you're terribly hard on him. You do know that, Mim, don't you? Or don't you?' Castleton asks.

She knows that when her son needs correction he will get it.

'Oh, darling. Christ,' says Castleton.

But she insists: 'The whole business of this afternoon would never have happened if Benoir hadn't spoiled the child rotten while he was in Paris.' Marguerite says bitterly: 'That fool! He feels guilty because he can't love the child in the ordinary, normal way, so he tries to salve his conscience by letting him do exactly as he likes.'

'Darling, you're tired,' says Castleton.

Yes, she is tired. Tired to death of letting her child be ruined by meddling fools. But that is the last time she will let George go to Auteuil alone.

What a life for a boy! Marie treats him like a doll. They go on endless afternoon visits together. She even lets him choose her embroidery silks for her! Benoir relaxes every rule. His studies are neglected while he runs wild in the garden. He is petted by the servants till they make a perfect fool of him, and then Benoir calmly sends the whole mess back for her to clear up!

'It is Benoir who should have been punished this afternoon, not George.'

'Oh, darling, you didn't slap him?' Castleton says. 'I absolutely can't stand it when you do that.'

She replies: 'If you think I am hard with my son that is your own affair. Au fond, it has absolutely nothing to do with you.'

'Well, thanks,' says Castleton. He draws her to him, smiling: 'You don't know you're born yet with George, chum. You should have seen old Cecil's lot. Cripes! After they came home from Hong Kong. Cripes!' says Castleton.

Her face indicates quite clearly that she has no wish to see old Cecil's lot. Before or after Hong Kong. Castleton laughs: 'They bloody near wrecked two furnished houses before my brother managed to get the house in Wilton Place.'

Her shrug says simply: if your brother has no control, that is his look-out.

He kisses her: 'You're such a blasted little perfectionist you see every crumple, so your poor little roseleaf doesn't stand an earthly.' He holds her for a bit with the superb brooch struggling and fighting between them. He touches it with his finger. 'That's a splendid brute.'

'Does it please you, Vincent?'

Not frightfully. Never mind. She pleases him. Frightfully. He kisses her again: 'You lovely thing. You're probably right about George. I daresay I should spoil him hopelessly.'

He can't help adding: 'If your chap had nous he'd be a permanent invalid. I bet you're simply marvellous to him when he's ill?'

She asks him coldly: 'What am I supposed to make of that? Or is it just another English joke?'

She is terribly offended. He gives himself another drink. She remarks if they are not to be late at the de Chassevents he had better go and dress.

'God bless the de Chassevents,' says Castleton.

Marguerite says: 'You know, mon cher, as far as George is concerned you haven't the faintest idea of what you are talking about.'

Probably not. 'You haven't really told me much about him, have you?'

Then she will tell him now. Perhaps it will help to deflate that image of her as a martinet that he seems to have built up. The fact is that when George is eighteen he will have to face two major events. He will come into his main inheritance from his father, and at the same time he will become head of the family. Marguerite says: 'Can you imagine what a position like that entails? Benoir works like a dog,' says Marguerite, 'but Benoir has perfect health as well as a rigid self-discipline. How d'you imagine George with his bad health will ever be able to take his place unless he has early training to support him?'

'I don't know,' Castleton says. 'I think it might probably save time if he just quietly died.'

Marguerite says: 'I am afraid you will have to allow me to decide what is best for my son.'

'Oh, yes, I know I shall,' says Castleton. He takes her hand. 'I'll dash up and say goodnight to him, shall I, darling?'

'I have already said goodnight to him for you, Vincent,' Marguerite says.

'Well, that's a bit bleak,' Castleton says. 'Let's both go up and cherish him a bit. We can take our drinks along and he can have a swig of both.'

She returns: 'It is not a celebration, Vincent. George has everything he needs. He has nothing to do now but go to sleep.'

'I think I'll nip up,' says Castleton.

Marguerite says: 'I don't want him disturbed.'

'I won't disturb him,' Castleton says. 'I'll bring him a peppermint.'

Marguerite says: 'I have said I don't wish him disturbed.'

'He likes peppermints,' says Castleton, stubbing his cigar.

She says coldly: 'If you wish to go, of course I can't prevent you.'

'That's right,' says Castleton. He downs his drink and goes.

She follows him to the door and says: 'I shall wait for you in the petit salon, Vincent. If you haven't joined me in a quarter of an hour I shall start for the de Chassevents alone.'

His answer is a shout from the lift which could mean anything.

She goes into the salon and simply sits there without the energy even to open her piano. Her towering anger of this afternoon has left her curiously listless and depressed.

A dreadful thing had happened. She had gone up to look at the child and suddenly she had thought what Georges would say if he could see how she behaves to his son.

He had been completely besotted with the child. If she had only scolded moumou in front of him he had shouted at her: 'Mi! Veux-tu finir jouer la vieille Zantippe! Tu es completement folle, ou quoi? Ne m'emmerde pas trop, écoute!'

O, Georges. Mon homme. She is still so beside herself about his being dead! At the moment she is even more in despair about that brat of his who can't possibly remember his father but who had elected to make a martyr of himself over his father's name.

What a mess he has made for her of everything, with his resistance and his piety and now those hands! She had suddenly become so furious with the whole issue that she had then and there gone into his room and called out in a formidable voice: 'Stand up!'

When he was standing in front of her in his chemise she had told him in the same wicked voice: 'I shall do it again, d'you hear? Unless you instantly promise to obey, I swear I will do it again.'

He had come to her sobbing and calling her name: 'Mimi, don't do it! Mimi, I love you, I love you!'

She had caught him in her arms and they had cried together for a long time on the bed and he had been like a little lover to her, comforting her and begging her not to cry.

'I will be good! I will obey! Mimi, don't cry! I love you, Mimi!'

And she had kissed him till she could kiss no more: 'Tu es mon bon secours. Mon beau lys blanc. Mon premier et mon dernier soupir. Tu es mon petit sauveur à moi. Mon seul, mon précieux souvenir de ton père.'

After a while they had stopped crying and had lain without stirring in each other's arms, their lips smiling, their eyes locked, till suddenly she had kissed him, sat up, and, ringing the bell, had ordered a hot tisane of linden flowers for him. She had given him two cachets to take with it, and the hot drink had done him good and helped him to stop his trembling.

And she had made him eat a madeleine with his tea because he had had no dinner, and because it always gives her intense pleasure to see her child eat.

At table it is the thing she has always been mad about, and is the first thing she will do on sitting down, butter his roll for him and then give the bread directly into his nice little hands. Only this time she had had to dip his cake into his tea for him and feed him like a baby. And suddenly she had been in such despair about it all, and because there wasn't a scrap of flesh on him anywhere, and those butchers at the Clinic had massacred his poor little behind for him on top of all his other miseries. She had burst out in a perfectly furious voice: 'You! You will drive me into the grave with those bones! It is ridiculous to be as thin as that! It is idiotic!'

But he hadn't been in the least frightened at her outburst and had only smiled at her in his uncanny way.

Her pretty little devil! Her diablotin! She had scolded him roundly: 'Je veux que tu sois parfait! Parfait! Tu m'entends?' And she had started to kiss him in a way that this time she had really to force herself to stop. And as she got off the bed she had suddenly known she was enceinte.

Marguerite thinks: if I stop in this room much longer I shall start to cry again.

She will go and wait for Vincent in the car. What in God's name is he doing up there, that fool? Everything has been settled, but now he will see it all, and everything will start again thanks to his meddling! She feels fantastically tired.

*   *   *

In the lift he discovers he's bloody annoyed with Mim. This carry on with the kid is dead boring. The whole thing is, she's absolutely cuckoo about him, but in this lousy way.

He may be the apple of Mim's eye but she's determined not to let him get puffed up about it. His status as the Dauphin has never saved the royal ears from being well and truly boxed.

Mim is a *dévote* of *les bonnes gifles, les jolis claquements* and the almost *quotidien panpan.*

Panpan is quite Mim's favourite *punition*. She alludes to it lovingly as *moumou's smack*; and Castleton has hardly ever seen the poor matchstick arms without the vivid pink patch made by a brisk and recent application of his mother's hand.

The comic bit is he's utterly infatuated with Mum and only breathes to serve and so forth, so that there is no comeback whatsoever to be expected from him.

He is a pretty, polite and most affectionate child simply bursting with goodwill towards all. He is generous and unselfish to an alarming degree. Compared with Cecil's lot he is almost pathologically truthful. He is a very feeling child and will cry quite dreadfully over almost everything. At the same time he is a sociable little cuss and likes to laugh a lot.

In short he's a charmer, and there's no doubt at all that in a few years time he will emerge as a second Benoir, but none of this does him a ha'porth of good with Mim.

Au contraire, any one of these points seems sufficient to bring down a scolding of astronomical proportions on his defenceless nut.

These scoldings are the very devil and go on, apparently, from morning till night. They are invariably conducted in French, and Castleton can hear the luckless Dauphin getting ticked off first thing every morning in what he has come to call Mim's 'St Cyr' voice. The Dauphin suffers cruelly from servant trouble, and he and Albert and Mammy and Dédé all cop it alike.

'That camp up there! If I find the same *salade* tomorrow I shall sack the lot of them, whatever Benoir says! And moumou will certainly get his ears well warmed. Little tramp, he is supposed to establish order up there but, of course, at nine o'clock Monsieur is still at his devotions!'

A red-eyed harem goes submissively about its duties with Mim on its tracks like a tiger. It's often lunchtime before the first watery smile breaks through. After lunch there's a two-hour truce while the boy friend has his nap, but after that Mim hots it up for him again, and by the time Castleton gets home he's catching it worse than ever.

Christ, she does wade into the poor little sod! 'Address yourself to your meat! You have eaten none as yet!' If every scrap isn't eaten she will point to the sweet: 'That was to have been for you—eh bien, voilà!'

'Take yourself off! When you are good again you may present yourself!'

'Please, Vincent, don't take his part. There has been a conspiracy to ruin moumou since the day he was born.'

'You run to Mass at the slightest excuse, but any real effort bores you. Once you have done your penance you think you can shed all further responsibilities. We shall see what Monseigneur has to say when he hears how well you have benefited by your religious classes!'

'He will get a good smack, Vincent, that is all the explanation he will get!'

'Everything is a nine days' wonder with you! You promise and promise but until one beats you black and blue exactly nothing happens!'

He has a new medicine: 'Oh, you know there must always be a drama with George when a new medicine is introduced.'

'O, it's horrible, mama! It tastes like foie de morue!'

'That is exactly what it is. And when you have swallowed it you may go straight to bed. That will be the best medicine to cure your present mood.'

He has been fratting with Bone: 'Vincent, please tell your man he is not to speak to my son. He is not to speak to him on any pretext whatsoever. It may amuse you to hear moumou copy his slang. It doesn't amuse me in the slightest. Well, put it how you like, mon cher, but put it! It doesn't concern me if it offends your servant. As to *you*, if you dare to speak like that again I'll really give you something to cry for! You'll be astonished how you'll cry, my friend! I don't want to hear one word of anything but French from you for the rest of today! It is fantastic how you only pick up what is bad! Are you crying, by any chance?'

'No, mama.'

'That is for you. At least we know now what you are howling for. You have become a laughing stock with those tears. Everyone is bored to death with them!'

'Tell Mammy to dress you. It will be lunchtime before you start for your walk at this rate. If one left it to her you would be running about in your chemise all day. Be quick!'

'Yes'm, mama.'

'And you are not to play cache-cache or any game that involves running.'

'No, mama.'

'You are on no account to stand in the sun, or to attempt to lift that cretin of a Dédé.'

'No, mama.'

'And you are not to go one step out of Deckers' sight. Not one step, d'you hear me, George?'

'Yes, ma'am. I will stay with Jules.

'With whom?'

'Jules, mama. That is Deckers' name.'

'What has that got to do with you?'

'Nothing, mama.'

'Then you will call him Deckers.'

'Yes, mama.'

He gets a slap on the leg that sounds ·pretty hard: 'Walk properly! You are waltzing about like a cripple again! It's pure laziness, and if you intend to do nothing about it I shall find a way to assist you, mon vieux.'

Whew!

A remark made by the boy's nannie (not to him, of course) exactly voices Castleton's view: 'Sweet glitterin' Jesus, why she treat him such a mis'ry all of the time? Man, will y'all tell me what he *done* even?'

10

Floods at the Delta

He is not asleep when Castleton opens the door.

'C'est vous, maman-chérie?' He sounds as if he'd been crying for a week.

'No, it's me.' Castleton switches on the light. 'How's my favourite stepson?'

At the moment his favourite stepson is looking pretty out of love with life, and none the better for his recent encounter with Mum. It must have been a long session. Mim's scent is everywhere, dry, elegant and not reassuring.

'What's up, old love? Have you been doing something you didn't oughter?'

He can feel the heat streaming out as he stands over the bed. 'Have you been a madam and a miss?'

George nods his head and smiles. The stale sobs crowd his utterance so that he can't speak.

'Well, never mind. What about going to sleep? D'you think you can?'

George nods and draws his arms down quickly under the sheet.

He puts up his face. Castleton kisses the top of his head. His face is terribly chapped. The hair is like plumage, very thick and warm.

'What about my hug?'

George smiles. A tear slips quickly down his cheek and disapears into his hair.

'I came up specially. Aren't you going to give me one?'

Another tear runs silently down his face.

'Oh, ducky!'

He really is the most idiotic child. Mim's obviously slapped him, and he's ashamed to show his arms. Castleton says in a briskish voice: 'I shouldn't cry any more, old darling, you'll make your pillow shocking wet.' He dries his stepson's eyes with his handkerchief. 'Blow your nose.' Nothing happens. He will not take the handkerchief. He will not show his arms.

'George, don't be silly,' Castleton says.

Nothing happens again.

Castleton takes hold of the sheet. George calls out at once: 'No, don't!' A sob jumps out of his mouth.

'George,' Castleton says, 'don't be a bloody fool!' He tries to get the child's arms out from under the sheet. 'Come on! George!'

'O, don't you make me!'

He is fighting now with all his strength. Castleton feels a sharp nip on his thumb. 'George!' shouts Castleton. 'You really are the bloodiest child.'

A typical carry-on ensues. 'No, papa, don't! Don't make me!'

'George, stop this bloody nonsense and blow your nose.' He pulls the clothes back. 'Come on, it doesn't matter—never mind about your arms.'

He sees two small lumps of a glossy red-brown like raw liver.

'O, they are all foutus!'

He has clapped his hands between his knees. 'Don't look! Don't look!' His shaking is like something set up by machine.

'All right.' Castleton throws the sheet back over the bed. 'Blow your nose.'

'O, I am sorry, I am sorry I bit you,' sobs out George. He is spouting tears all over everything.

'Blow your nose,' says Castleton. 'That's all I ask.'

But he begins to call in a raucous voice like a cat's: 'O, I am fed up of everything! O, I am fed up! I am fed up!' He is

130

jerking his body about all over the bed. It looks like the start of a fit.

Castleton scoops him up in his arms: 'George, stop it at once!'

'O, yes, I will, I will stop!' He has clambered up on to Castleton's neck and is clinging there like a survivor to a rock. 'Ne me quittez pas! Ne me quittez pas!'

It's a deluge. Castleton has never seen such tears. Everything is blotted out. It's floods at the Delta.

'George, will you stop it! Will you stop it at once!'

The terrible floods boil up, roll over him and tear him away from his rock. He falls on the bed, calling: 'Ne me quittez pas!' He is bobbing about like a cork on the floods, trying to pull himself up on to Castleton's neck again.

'Come on! Come on, George!'

'O, yes, I will. I will.' Castleton can feel him hugging his neck, making the effort to stop. 'O, I will stop it,' gasps out George.

The floods come thundering up for the last time, roll him over and over and retreat. The deluge stops.

Everything is saturated. His face, his neck, the bed, Castleton's shirt. He lies half drowned, gasping and retching across Castleton's knees.

'Come on,' Castleton sits him up. He is recovering slowly, pressing his pale swollen lips to Castleton's hand, letting his mouth rest against it. His quilted eyelids remain shut. 'Papa . . .'

'What is it, old love?'

'Papa,' George is whispering against Castleton's hand.

'What, darling?'

'Papa, papa. O, papa.'

Castleton doesn't answer. He realises George isn't speaking to him. He holds him firmly till the whispering stops. The eyes open and look eerily at him.

'Hullo!' He reinforces the cheery greeting with a large wink. So far this combination has never failed to cheer his stepson up. There is a glimmer of a smile. 'I'm going to put you back to bed now. I've got to scarper,' Castleton says. That word should be good for a smile.

'Are you cold, darling?'

His trembling has come back again, though in a more civilised form. He nods wordlessly, but the smile is definitely there.

'I'll get your nanny for you. She'll make you comfy.'

He goes to Mammy's room and knocks. There is no reply. He

hears a murmur of women's voices behind the service-room door and looks in, catching a whiff of hot linen from the nightshirt Mammy is ironing. Mim's maid, Sidonie, very smart in her off-duty things, is sitting at the table smoking, with Dédé asleep in her lap. Both women's eyes are puffed with heavy crying.

Castleton says brusquely in French: 'M. Georges has urgent need of attention. Have the goodness to see him, Madeleine.'

He likes his stepson's nurse, but at the moment he is too bloody wild to like anyone much except Mim's chap.

Back in the bedroom he says: 'Nanny'll be with you in a tick, ducky. Will you be all right if I go?'

'Yes, sir.' O, Mr Castleton is droll when he calls Mammy that!

He submits quite docilely to being settled in bed. While Castleton is shaking up his pillows he asks hoarsely if petit-papa is dining with marraine and parrain tonight?

Yes. He is due at the de Chassevents now.

It will be very interesting there for petit-papa, George promises. There will be a splendid Spahi behind every chair. 'It's on account of parrain having served for France en Algérie, don't petit-papa know?'

'Yes,' says Castleton and kisses him abruptly. He has stopped saying 'Mr Castleton'. So that's what it was about. 'Give us a hug, then.'

George throws his arms round Castleton's neck. 'Goodnight, goodnight, my own sweet darling petit-papa-chéri!' His small spoiled hands are laid together in prayer: 'Please, petit-papa, please.' The thumbs are neatly crossed.

'Don't do that, there's a good chap.' Castleton puts his hands aside. 'If you want anything, tell me. What is it you want, old dear?'

He wants Castleton's handkerchief to keep under his pillow for tonight. Christ!

'Lor' bless you, no,' says Castleton cheerfully. 'It's sopping wet.' Christ, this obsession he has with objects and tokens of love. All the Benoirs go in for it, but with this one it's a rage. 'You don't want my mucky old hankie under your nice pillow. Good lor'!'

'No, sir.' He does, of course, but doesn't dare to say so. It's disgusting how easy it is to bully him.

'Goodnight, old pet. When I get back I'll come and sleep with you. How does that strike you?' Castleton asks. He is throwing it all away as much as possible. He sees his stepson staggering under his offer and says very firmly: 'Don't. Don't cry any more.'

He is very good. A few tears escape, but he is able to keep the main floods back. He is following his stepfather to the door with his eyes and holding himself in like one o'clock.

'Goodnight, pretty. Sleep tight. Bless you.'

He makes no answer. It's obvious he is afraid of breaking down. Instead, he kisses one of the lumps of liver and wafts it towards his stepfather with an almost courtly air. The look in his eyes is indescribably weird.

I I

The Quarrel in the Car

Castleton comes downstairs two at a time to be told that Madame is waiting for Monsieur in the auto.

She is sitting in the dark with her fierce brooch in abeyance, biding its time, waiting for the light. He can see her dissatisfaction with him by the cool turn of her head.

Maurice, Marguerite's personal driver, comes round to open the door for Castleton.

'Bon soir, Monsieur.'

'Vincent, you haven't changed,' exclaims Marguerite.

'Does he know where to go?' is Castleton's reply.

He flings the de Chassevents' address at Maurice and slams the partition shut. 'Congratulations!' says Castleton.

She doesn't turn her head. She remains withdrawn in her shadowy corner with the formidable brooch sleeping on her breast. The car slides out of the courtyard into the street. As each street lamp passes in quick succession the brooch jumps at the light, tears it to pieces and consumes it, throwing out bolts of fire, then waits in the dark for its next meal.

134

'Were you out of your mind?' asks Castleton. 'That's all I want to know.'

She keeps a fastidious silence. The purity of her features is almost austere.

'D'you hear me, Mim?'

Yes, she hears him. She imagines Maurice can hear him too.

'Fuck Maurice.'

She gives no indication of having heard. He can see her profile cool above the violent brooch which is now spouting like fireworks in the lights of an open square. As they get near the de Chassevents' Marguerite says: 'I hope you have no intention, Vincent, of imposing yourself on Liane and Yves either dressed as you are, or in your present frame of mind. Otherwise it will not be a very pleasant experience for our hosts.'

Castleton says he has no intention of going anywhere. 'I'm going back to George.'

'I do not wish it, Vincent.'

'Hard luck,' Castleton says. 'He cried for his father, in case it interests you.'

She turns her head to face him fully. 'I forbid you to visit my son.'

'He's got the shakes,' says Castleton. 'The bloody shakes. You've given him the D.T.s, old dear.'

She assures him: 'All this has nothing to do with you.'

'It has,' says Castleton. 'I promise you. You must have thrashed him with that whip.'

She says she has already explained the situation. 'I am not prepared to explain it to you again.'

Her scent has suddenly become very marked. He looks at her and laughs: 'I think you must be the most arrogant woman in the world.'

She answers coolly: 'George has been disobedient and I have punished him. That must content you, I am afraid.'

He says: 'I don't accept your explanation.'

She turns her head away and watches the street.

'I don't care what he's done,' says Castleton. 'I don't care if he's raped the cat. I don't accept your explanation, Marguerite.'

A slight but eloquent shrug is her reply.

He says: 'I promise you, Marguerite, something is going to be done about this bloody awful life he leads.'

She says: 'Tell Maurice to stop the car on this corner. You can pick up a cab. I find your company intolerable in this mood.'

By all means. He stops the car. He says: 'He leads the most disgusting life I have ever known. All of it. It's all absolutely and utterly humiliating and I will not have him subjected to it any more. I will not have it, Marguerite,' Castleton says. 'I hope you understand me. If you ever try to do a thing like that again I shall thrash you without the slightest compunction.'

She says in a low voice: 'I don't know if I shall be able to stand this for much longer. I shall ring Benoir directly I get back.'

He thinks it a good idea. 'The sooner your brother gets to know about this the better.'

Maurice comes round to open the door. 'Monsieur desires a taxi?'

'Yup.'

While he is waiting for it Marguerite says: 'What am I supposed to say to the de Chassevents?'

'Say what you like,' Castleton says. 'Tell 'em you've clobbered your son till his hands look like raw beefsteaks.'

He says: 'You are an abominable mother, Marguerite. Your beauty disgusts me.'

As he slams the door, the brooch sends out a great spurt like a flame thrower from the dark interior of the car.

I 2

F. E. Bone

F. E. Bone skates in with a couple of pillows from the Guv'nor's room.

Talk about R.C. Like goin' to bed in a church, altar and all!

Bone can see His Nibs lookin' at him from the bed. Pretty little chap. Late G-M. B.'s boy. Lost his daddy in a car crash. Four years next August. Shockin' affair. Only twenty-two. Biggest name in international racin' and a molti-millionaire. What a wicked waste.

Bone can still remember the phenomenal prices fetched by some of the horses when the powerful Chantilly stable was sold up. About thirty sold in all, includin' Cayman and Fer de Lance, the two Unbeatables.

Cayman was two years in succession Derby winner with the same frog jocky up. Raoul Mercier. Top class frog rider. Bone can remember the names of all the G-M. B. jockeys. Pol Benet, Coco Varnel, Reynard Renaud, Shaun Kelly, J. C. Toplady, Mike Lilley.

Mike Lilley made turf history by gettin' rolled on at Maisons-Laffitte. Mount fell on him and broke his neck. Broke her neck, too. Had to be shot. Four year old filly, "La Louisianne". Trained by Captain "Cissy" Leathers. Outclassed all opponents on the flat that season. Bang! Just when she'd started to show her quality. Bang!

Rumour has it that the Chantilly yard is shortly to be reopened by Mr Almond Benoir. For his son's weddin' or somethin'. Some wedding present! Have to pump His Nibs about it. Takes bleedin' dynamite to get anything out of the Guv.

'Good evening, Bone,' says His Nibs. Toujours la politesse as per.

'And good evenin' to you, sir,' says Bone. ''Ow's Mr George tonight?'

O, Mr George is very well.

'That's the style, sir,' says Bone. 'That's what we like to hear.'

Poor little sod copped a proper tanning from Madame tonight be all accounts. Bit of a B. when crossed, she could be, and Bone wouldn't be surprised. The Guv'nor was so friggin' wild there was a hell of a dust-up in the car. Bone had it from Maurice, the frog shuvver. All her own staff. Imported regardless. What a scream.

'Goin' to have company, eh? Guv'nor comin' to sleep with you?'

Yes. Papa is coming in the bed with him. 'O, I have made a salade with my sheets!'

Papa! The Guv! After you with the weed killer, sonny.

Still, you have to scream the way he comes out with things. Bone loves to hear the lingo.

'Give you a bit of a tidy?' asks Bone, only too glad of the chance of a closer butcher's at the sole son and heir of the great G-M. B.

Be worth thirty million sterling, that kid, time he's eighteen. And that's only for starters. From what Bone can find out, he's got as much again to come from her.

Tremendous wealthy family. Molti-millionaires, thinks Bone, who can't get enough of this word.

He straightens the bed-clothes expertly, turning the sheet down neatly on the Guv'nor's side.

Smashin' drop of bed though, when you come up close like this, you can see he's bin through it all right.

Poor little bugger's shakin' like a leaf. Backside still hurts him and Bone shouldn't be surprised.

'All right, sir?' asks Bone, taking it all in with his pale bigamist's eyes. 'Will there be anythink else, sir?'

'O, yes,' says His Nibs, a bit aërated. 'Be sweet and find my gloves for me, Bone.'

Never says please to the servants, His Nibs. Not allowed to. Considered borjwa.

'Your gloves, sir?' (Goin' to bed in our gloves now, are we?) 'Whereabouts would they be, sir?'

His Nibs don't know. His Nibs reckons Albert must of taken them after he'd given him his friction à cologne.

Albert's his nignog valet and a proper little twerp. The Guv can't stick the sight of him. Thinks he gets His Nibs into hot water with Mammon, as His Nibs calls her. Considerin' his family's off the peg, the Guv takes Father'ood rather serious.

'What about your dressin' room, sir?' Bone suggests deferentially. 'Would your gloves be in there, sir?'

O, yes. It is quite possible. That they are not in the bedroom is certain. His Nibs observes it is bizarre that one can never find what one is looking for, don't Bone think?

It is. It's a bazaar an' all. It's a bloody gents' outfittin', thinks Bone, taking a cool stroll among the fitments and wardrobes of George's dressing room. Everythin' lights up like a bleeding fairground when you slide open the doors.

Molti-millionaires.

'They will be in the Teerwa in the Armwa,' calls out His Nibs. Or words to that effect.

'I've found 'em, sir.' Dig the internal telephone for gettin' things done toot der sweet.

'If you can find some silk ones,' His Nibs pipes up. 'There should be some white silk ones there.

Likewise there are a few other sorts there, also, too, as well! Austin Reed's has nothin' on this lot, thinks Bone admiringly. He steps back into the bedroom with a minuscule pair in pure white silk.

'These do you, sir?'

His Nibs declares they are the identical ticket and tells Bone prettily: 'They was for my première communion, don't you know, but I ain't used them ever because I got souffrant.'

Got some fancy blood complaint, His Nibs. Very exclusive. Hederitary, of course.

His Nibs is sayin' as how he hopes to get communicated next time they go to Paris. Very 'ot on the religious jazz, His Nibs. Bone thinks it's due to him bein' such a shockin' little invalid and never quite knowin' when he's goin' to snuff it.

His Nibs is yawning now without his hand up. Puttin' our hands up seems to be another thing that is considered borjwa.

'If you will kindly put them on my Tarble der Nwee.' He makes no move to take the gloves from Bone.

So that is where we copped it.

Fancy her bashin' the kid like that, though. Never credit it to look at her. Regular stunner. Lovely action. Bet she knows her stuff, too, Bone thinks admiringly. That sort usually knows the game from A to Z. Real high-class French stuff. Bred for Bed. And very nice too, thinks Bone. Though personally he himself is givin' the Fair Sex a bit of a rest for the moment.

Well, we'll have to whistle for it tonight, won't we, if the Guv'nor's comin' in here to kip with His Nibs. Bit of a scream that, when you come to think.

'Well, I'll love you and leave you then, sir,' Bone says. 'You be all right, sir, till the Guv'nor comes?'

'O, yes,' says His Nibs, rollin' the old mincepies. 'O, I am looking forwards, don't you know.'

'I expect you are, sir,' grins Bone. 'Makes a bit of a change.'

'O, yes, it does not half,' ripostes His Nibs, very Breedin' Will Out. 'Thank you mille fois pour aiding me, Bone.'

'Not at all sir. Thank *you*, sir.

Back in the Guv'nor's room, Bone reports: 'Your little family's quite ready for you, sir.'

'Thanks,' says the Guv'nor, short and sweet, in the That-Will-Be-All style we run on in when we're soddin' wild and don't wish to Demean Ourselves in front of Staff. 'Is he asleep?'

'Asleep, sir? No, sir,' Bone says. 'We was just puttin' on the white gloves as I was comin' away.'

'White gloves?' barks the Guv, bashin' his head with the military hair brushes as if he hated himself.

'Oh, yes, sir,' Bone assures him. 'Proper little one-man welcome committee waitin' for you in there, sir.'

That's torn it. The Guv takes off like a blue arsed fly. 'Where's

140

my dressing gown? Where's my so-and-so blue pencil dressing gown?' bawls the Guv, very liberal with his b's and f's as per.

'Here we are, sir.' Bone helps him on with it. 'Will there be anythink more?'

'Get the hell out of it,' is the Guv'nor's kind reply, civility being his motto for tonight.

'Yes, sir. Thank you, sir. Goodnight, sir. And the best of British luck,' says Bone softly, shutting the door. What a scream! All the while he is putting the Guv's gear away, Bone keeps chuckling to himself. He can't wait to get out the Basildon Bond and write to the gentleman friend (at present doing for the Hon. Tarquin Couldrey-Brette) with whom Bone shares a nice little Key Flat in Goodge Street between jobs.

Mr Stanley Cakebread is kept well posted as to the exotic doings of molti-millionaires by his friend, Mr F. E. Bone, in a series of curiously frank and affectionate letters.

Contrary to common belief, Bone is not a bachelor. The trouble with Bone is that he has, rather absent-mindedly, got himself married to two ladies at once.

Still, for the moment, Bone isn't worrying. Neither Mrs Bone has uttered now for nearly two years, and for Bone's money, Catford and Bexhill, respective homes of the two ladies, are an absolutely ideal distance from New Orleans.

Bone lights a fag; takes a draw and begins: Stannie boy, guess what?!

13

La Perle

Someone has spread a coverlet of tailless ermine over the bed, and under this vast field of unbroken white, the white child is waiting for him.

He is in terrific form and seems tremendously pleased to see his stepfather. His small vivacious face is lit with welcoming smiles.

It is quite true about the gloves. Castleton eyes the small, decently covered hands gloomily: 'You really are a one, aren't you?'

George looks at him ingratiatingly.

'I mean, it's a bit dim,' Castleton says. 'It's a bit dotty. However,' Castleton says, 'there it is.'

Mr Castleton often talks that way.

'Never mind, ducky,' Castleton says. 'Never you mind.' He gets into the magnificent bed. The equatorial snowfield.

Oh, good *Lord*.

'Are y'all warm enough, papa darling?' enquires his pale host, who has perfect manners as well as megaloblastic anaemia.

'Oh Lord, yes,' says Castleton civilly. 'Thanks. It's absolutely splendid. How about you?' he asks his now apparently permanently shivering stepson. 'D'you want any more covers on?'

Friendship, he feels, can go no further. George says politely that he expects it will get warmer soon.

'Oh absolutely,' agrees Castleton, counting the hours that stretch before him till he can make his escape from this Devil's Island of a bed. 'D'you want a peppermint, old darling?' He has brought a couple with him in his breast pocket and shoves one into his stepson's mouth.

The swollen Buddha-look about the eyes and mouth has gone, but you can still see how dreadfully he has cried. George lies staring at his mother's English husband with unwinking eyes. O, he is nice, he has brought English peppermints from his room because he knows George likes them. He is sucking delicately at his sweet with that specifically French noise that the Sioux all make when they eat.

'Well, here we are, then,' says Castleton to no one in particular. He is lying on his back with his arms folded across his chest in a genial sort of way.

'Did y'all enjoy yourself, papa darling?' enquires the waxen child solicitously, shifting his sweet from cheek to cheek to give both sides a chance. 'Did y'all see the Spahis, papa?'

'Did I see the Spahis? Oh, rather. They were absolutely terrific,' Castleton says, mopping his neck. What the devil is he talking about?

'Did you taste the special kebab, papa?'

Special how much? Oh yes, the de Chassevents. Of course.

Oh yes, the special kebab was absolutely terrific. The whole thing, says Castleton, was absolutely terrific from the word go.

He emits a genial laugh and undoes the buttons of his pyjamas coat, taking a quick look at his wrist on the way up. Christ! It is only a quarter-past ten!

There is a thing like a pointed beard between Mr Castleton's breasts. George has never seen such a thing before. He promises himself he will look at it again as soon as will not appear impolite.

That special kebab is good, George says. It is a pity mama will not permit him to eat much of it because it is too heavy, but parrain will sometimes leave him taste some from his plate.

'O, he is good for me, my parrain,' George says earnestly. 'He has very good qualities, don't you know.'

'Like bread?' asks Castleton.

'No, not like bread! Only mama and Uncle Benoir and you are like bread. And Tante Marie and my cousin Viv,' amends George. He is feeling the hair on Castleton's chest. 'O, it is soft!'

'Wot, only five loaves?' says Castleton, pinching his cheek.

'O, petit-papa is bad,' cries George. 'He is laughing at me.'

'Don't you feel tired yet?'

O no, he don't feel a mite sleepy. 'O, don't y'all wish it wouldn't never end?' cries George, who is stroking the hair on Castleton's chest as if it were an animal.

'What wouldn't never?'

'O, tonight! I mean tonight!' cries George. 'O, don't y'all wish it would go on and on?' He is spending himself like anything.

His stepfather assures him that at the moment tonight shows every sign of going on.

And on. And on . . .

'I think we ought to pack it in, ducky,' says Castleton. 'After you've finished your sweet,' Castleton says. 'I think you ought to have a bash at going to sleep, old love.'

'Yes, sir.' The pale spendthrift reluctantly damps down his newly rekindled enthusiasm for life.

'No hurry.' But Castleton knows he will not now delay the diminishing of his sweet by a single second. His terrible sense of honour won't let him.

He spends his remaining moments playing with his stepfather's ring and talking of La Taquineuse, the plantation on the Delta where he was born and which is his favourite of all the Benoir estates. He keeps on saying: 'C'est bien mon pays, vous savez? C'est mon beau pays,' and talking about a little negro girl called Minouche who has stigmata and who lives not far from Taquineuse on the levee. 'Mammy took me to see her. The stigmate is white. Can you imagine, Mr Castleton, how curious, the white on the black skin?' He is about to go more fully into this fascinating topic when he comes to the end of his sweet.

'I done swallowed it,' George announces. 'Will I have to go to sleep now, papa?'

Castleton says he'd be obliged if George would have a go. 'Let's pull this shift thing down from under your arms.'

The peacock-coloured bruises Mim has never stopped going on about are still on his thigh. 'Are they sore, ducky?'

'No, sir,' George says hospitably: 'You can look at them if you like.'

It's obviously an honour. Castleton feels he is neck to neck with Davis now. Even a little ahead. George says he can't stand the Clinic much. 'They are all religieuses in there, papa. They are all in white like those two my Uncle Beau has.'

'Yes.' Castleton recalls Mim's younger brother at their wedding, sitting in his special chair between two white-winged Carmelites. Cold, impatient with his illness, indifferent to the world, his sombre smile only for Mim and for his little girl whom he absolutely idolises.

The Dauphin is saying: 'You have to call them Madame because they are the brides of Jesus. O, this poor Jesus!' exclaims the Dauphin, who is not a Sioux for nothing.

Castleton had found young Baudouin pretty unsympathetic in spite of his uncanny likeness to Mim. He had tried talking to him at the reception but Baudouin had barely turned his head. His eyes had been all for his lively little daughter, watching with tender amusement as she had darted shrieking among the guests, chased by her Mammy and her English governess.

Mim's chap is saying: 'I don't hope I have to have a chair like Uncle Beau when I am grown up.'

Why ever should he?

Mim's chap says simply: 'Well, I got la perle.'

La what?

Perle. George says: 'It is the same like Uncle Beau has got.'

The Pearl.

It's the most frightful name for it Castleton has ever heard. Where the hell did he pick it up? It's worse than megaloblastic anaemia. He says: 'Do me a favour and don't say that again. I don't like it.' Castleton says: 'See?'

It must have sounded as if he meant it because Mim's chap says apologetically: 'It's only about my cousin Viv, papa. He couldn't stand to see me in a chair.'

'Hard luck and all that,' Castleton says.

George says: 'Mr Viv says whenever I go to the Clinic for my tests he will not visit me one single day so it will teach me to be souffrant. O, he detests that, when I am sick, my cousin Viv.' George says suddenly: 'O he will be mad at me. He simply can't stand for me to get punished.'

Castleton says: 'Bienville can mind his own business.' He says to George: 'Could you sit up? I want to turn your pillows.'

George says it is quite a mercy that Viv and he are favourite cousins.

It is. For Bienville. Castleton says: 'Sit up, there's a good chap.'

George says: 'He will not want to own me any more.'

'Nobody owns you,' his stepfather tells him. 'They had a civil war, remember? Abe Lincoln and everything? You want to buck some of your ideas up, old love.'

George says nothing. Mr Castleton looks rather strict. But he is putting the pillows very nice and asking when you are going to get some roses into your cheeks? O, he is droll! It is a question he will ask for every time he sees you, nearly.

'Goodnight, pretty,' Castleton says in an absent-minded way. He has just caught sight of his watch again. It is twenty past eleven and that is all!

It's no good. He lies sweating and little Benoir just lies, and the Nessos bed does its stuff. He turns on the light and surveys little Benoir.

He says apologetically: 'I can't sleep.'

'D'you want a drink?'

He gets an enigmatic smile.

'George!' shouts Castleton, whose temper has been got at by the bed.

Little Benoir says 'thank you'—which is a fat lot.

'George, for God's sake, d'you want anything to drink? Shall I make you some tea?'

Little Benoir, when permitted, is quite partial to a cuppa now and again. He is very knowledgeable about putting the milk in first.

He sees the faint, by now familiar, colour wash over his stepson's face. Christ, this bloody Benoir bushido. Castleton says rudely: 'Are you thirsty or not?'

Yes, he is thirsty. George reckons he could pretty near drink the Miss'i'ppa dry.

Then why the devil can't he say so? Castleton says in a fed up voice: 'What? You're not still shy with me, are you? What?'

'No, sir.' George says he knows that he can ask for most anything he likes. O, he is what-ing again.

Then why the devil doesn't he? 'If you know all these things? Crumbs!' says Castleton rudely, slapping his stepson's behind. 'What an ass!'

George holds himself discreetly while Mr Castleton is doing

146

this. That is one British custom he has never been able to get up much enthusiasm for.

'I suppose you want some of your ruddy eau sucré?' Castleton says affably.

Mr Castleton's scoldings have a habit of blowing over almost as soon as they blow up.

'Papa . . .'

Castleton says he won't be long. The eau is already laid on, so all he has to do is rustle up the sucre and de la glace. 'Beaucoup de la glace, eh?'

His French usually goes over so well with little Benoir he is surprised to see his stepson's face. He has gone very red.

'What's the matter?' Castleton teases him. 'Don't you like sugar water any more?'

O yes, it is still his favourite, but George don't think he'd better drink any more tonight.

'Why not? Are you afraid it'll make you sick?'

'No, papa.' He seems inclined to leave the matter there. Castleton is not. He wants to know why, if George is thirsty, he can't have a drink. 'Why not, old dear?' He isn't actually looking at his stepson, but standing with his head down as if listening to an intercom. 'Why not?' asks Castleton again.

George looks at him placatingly. There is that thing in Mr Castleton's cheek. He says: 'I got no permit.'

'No what?'

He says: 'No permission to drink.'

'How's that?'

'Mama has disallowed it,' George says. 'After I had my tisane mama said she didn't care for me to have anything further to drink tonight.'

'Oh, I see,' says Castleton in a casual sort of voice. 'So what are you going to do about it?' He is still at the intercom. The nerve in his face is ticking like a watch.

George says he doesn't know.

'So you're going to do damn all?'

'I beg your pardon?'

'Damn all!' says Castleton in a loud voice. He has come away from the intercom and is sitting on the bed. He looks at his stepson for quite a while. 'I'll get you an orange,' Castleton says.

George takes his hand.

'Don't be silly,' Castleton says.

147

'Let go, old darling,' Castleton says. He goes straight downstairs, gives himself a quick drink and a smoke on the gallery. Then he takes a cold shower and changes into a pair of trunks. In ten minutes he is back in the bedroom.

Little Benoir has been having a go at his new rosary. It is lying on the bed under the respectable-looking hands. 'I done pray petit-papa should come back tout de suite et le voilà qui arrive!' announces little Benoir, who apparently thinks in a mixture of French and Ole Kintuck.

'Oh, well done,' Castleton says. It sounds frightful, but it can't be helped. He has collected a couple of oranges from the Dauphin's service room, a plate with his monogram on it, and a knife, fork and spoon of solid gold in a case also monogrammed G-M. B. From the Dauphin's bathroom he has taken a towel of fine linen, fringed, embroidered, and—of course—initialled G-M. B. He has also collected a battered carton of sugar from a hitherto unsuspected cache in his dressing-room where he is not in the least surprised to find Bone keeps a teapot amongst his shirts and a packet of digestive biscuits with his handkerchiefs. He has abstracted a couple of these in case of emergencies. They may come in useful for sopping up operations in case little Benoir really makes a stand about not drinking any juice. By the looks of him it is more than likely, Castleton decides.

Christ, those eyes.

He is watching his stepfather prepare the oranges with great interest. He says with a suave smile: 'Petit-papa understand to fix everything so nice.'

That probably means he will not drink the bloody juice. Castleton says: 'I'm afraid it's not quite up to Gustave's standards but it'll quench your thirst.' He spreads the monogrammed towel over the monogrammed sheet. 'There you are, old love. Mop it up.'

The pale child looks at him. Those eyes can drive you up the wall. I will not bully him, Castleton tells himself, however fatuous the carry-on. I will not bully him.

He says briskly but kindly: 'No one is making you drink anything, George.'

'No sir,' George says. 'There is a lot of juice.'

'Of course there is,' Castleton says cheerfully. That was the whole point of oranges, otherwise George might as well eat bananas to quench his thirst. He says: 'I've put oodles of sugar on them for you.'

Oodles and caboodles. The words conjure up a ghostly smile.

'George, get on, do,' says Castleton.

The child takes the fork from him, but Castleton says: 'Take the spoon as well, ducky. For the juice.'

George takes the spoon as well as the fork. His hands are all over the shop.

'Here—let me do it.' Castleton takes the spoon and fills it. 'George, get a move on!' explodes Castleton suddenly. 'For Christ's sake, my dear chap, get it down your neck.'

Why am I speaking to him in this disgusting way? He is obviously terrified of disobeying Mim and I am speaking to him like a horse-coper.

He says there is no question of George's disobeying anybody. 'You've not been forbidden to eat, have you?'

'No, sir.'

'All right, then.' If you ate a thing you ate it and that was that. The juice and what-have-you was part of the orange and perfectly in order for him to swallow with the rest.

He says uncertainly: 'Yes, papa.'

'Got it?' asks Castleton cheerfully.

'Yes, sir, papa.'

'Open your gob, then,' Castleton says. George opens his mouth and Castleton puts a piece of orange in. The section is much too large. 'Start chewing, ducky,' Castleton tells him, 'then you can get some down.'

The child seems quite unable to grapple with the fruit. Castleton can see the delicate lining of his lower lip. His terrible nerves are making him shake.

'Spit it out.' Castleton holds a peremptory hand under his stepson's chin. The limp warm section is ejected into his hand. George murmurs in a deflated voice: 'I'm very sorry.'

His stepfather makes no reply. He is engaged in making several sections of the orange very small.

'Now try.'

This time it is successful. The child is able to manage the small bits of orange very well. He feeds docilely and eagerly from his stepfather's hand as if intent on slaking his thirst.

'All right?' Castleton asks him. 'Is it sweet enough for you?'

O, it is very good. A drowned smile is reviving in the pale thing's eye. 'Don't y'all want some, papa darling?'

'No, it's for you,' Castleton tells him. 'Get as much of it down as you can.' It's like feeding a rare mammal. The capacity is terribly small. 'D'you want a rest?'

They wait a few seconds, then Castleton begins feeding him again. George is eating very placidly now, the smile shining brilliantly in the pure unclouded black of his eyes. The smile is for his dearest Mr Castleton. His dearest, dearest stepfather and friend. Mr Castleton's fingers smell very nice of cigars and oranges and that carnation toilet water he always uses.

'Had enough?'

'Yes, papa. O, it was chic, that orange,' says George. Chic is a great Benoir word. George says he is not a speck thirsty any more.

'Oh, jolly good.' Castleton takes the plate away. He says: 'I'm not terribly happy about those gloves of yours.' His tone is deceptively vague. 'They're making your hands swell. I think we'll have 'em off, ducky,' Castleton says, 'what?'

They're making a vein stand out on his right arm. A dirty-looking thing like a gorged leech.

'Let's get 'em off,' says Castleton.

Of course he doesn't want to. He is begging quite dreadfully with his eyes.

Castleton says quietly: 'Don't carry on any more, darling. Not with me. It's dead boring.' Castleton says: 'We're supposed to be friends.'

The sick thing lets him take both his hands at once. He doesn't speak a word. The shakes have got him by the scruff of the neck till he nearly falls out of the bed.

'George,' says Castleton.

He opens his eyes. Castleton tells him: 'Look, darling, it's no good if you're going to carry on like this. We'd better leave 'em on.'

He puts the hands down on the bed again.

'No, you can take them off,' says George. His face, neck and chest are dyed with a vivid pink flush; the eyes are tightly shut against coming humiliations.

'No, let's leave 'em,' Castleton says, 'if you feel like that about it. I don't want to make you ill. It's not worth it.' Castleton says: 'I'm not cross, it just makes nonsense of our being friends.' Castleton says: 'Could you look at me, ducky?'

George looks at him.

'Well, what d'you want us to do?' asks Castleton.

George says he would like petit-papa to take his gloves off.

'Are you sure?'

Yes, he is sure.

And he won't make a song and dance about it and get himself into a State and generally drive his stepfather up the wall?

No, he will leave petit-papa do everything because he is his friend. 'You are my dearest friend,' says George. He hands his left hand to his dearest friend and says in hospitable tones: 'Take it, take it. You can take it, mon trésor.' The fatherliness of his tone is indescribable. He sees his stepfather over the first business of taking his hand, then dissociates himself from the whole thing by turning away his head. The painted flush remains.

The left glove comes off quite easily. There is a single welt across the palm. It is a bastard, but there is only one.

'That's one off,' says Castleton, who does not know he's looking at the 'good one' that was intended to make all the other ones unnecessary.

There is no answer. His stepson is engaged in gazing at the wall. His bright shame is giving him a healthy glow. A polite smile is playing round his lips.

Castleton says: 'That's a good job, isn't it?'

'Yes, sir,' George says politely. Nothing would make him look at his left hand.

Castleton examines the right glove. It's a proper fuck-up, with the stains all over it. Back, front, all over the bloody shop. He is aware he is grinding his teeth. 'I'm afraid it's stuck, ducky.'

'Ah, yes?' the child says in a de Chassevent voice. For him there is no hand, no glove, no problem.

'George,' says Castleton softly. 'Don't bloody annoy me.'

The child enquires politely, as if it was somebody else's hand: 'Is it bad, papa?'

'Yes, it's stuck. It's stuck. It's bloody stuck.' Castleton kisses him roughly. 'Could we get a move on, George?'

'Is papa waiting for me?'

He is, slightly. He wants to soak that glove off and they seem to be getting nowhere rather fast. And he would take it as a personal favour if George could see his way to taking his bloody eyes off the wall! 'George!' thunders Castleton.

It does the trick. There are tears, of course, but at least it has shocked him off his astral plane. He is actually acknowledging his left hand sufficiently to use it to wipe his eyes. Hooray.

'Come on now, lovey. Let's have you out of bed. Can you stand up?'

'Yes sir. I am fixing.' He can't, of course, and the shakes are assuming D.T.s proportions as Castleton gets him out of bed. He is clinging to his friend with chattering teeth and gasping: 'Ah merde, it is cold. It is cold, papa darling. It's cold.' He is pining for his Devil's Island of a bed.

'Won't be long.' Castleton carries him into the heated bathroom where he stands rocking and weaving about in front of the basin and longing for his bed. Castleton draws a basin full of hot water and carefully lowers the hand in.

'Is it all right for you, pretty?' He is supporting the pale thing between his legs and vigorously rubbing his back to take his mind off the business.

'O yes, it is exactly right.' It's obvious that even if it isn't he doesn't intend to talk about it. He stands in front of the basin chatting of this and that in his beautiful pure French and standing on his stepfather's feet which seems to give him pleasure. His own tiny feet are cold as ice. He keeps on saying: 'Can we go now, papa? Can we go back to bed?'

Castleton keeps saying: 'In a tick.' And the bloody glove won't budge. They are hearing about Sasha, the de Chassevents' Russian cat. 'He is chouchou, papa. When parrain calls him he makes miaou, miaou,' calls out the pale creature who is wambling about and looking excessively French. 'Can we go now, papa-chéri?'

'In a tick.'

George adores cats. Does petit-papa adore cats too? 'O, it will not come off,' cries George, 'so that is all about it!'

'Oh yes it will.' Castleton says he likes dogs best.

'O, Mr Davis was a one for dogs. Can you imagine, papa, he had seven. They were chouchou. A nigra only got to come near Mr Davis they would tear him in pieces.' George says cain't petit-papa pull it off?

Castleton smiles at him.

'I wouldn't cry or anything.'

Castleton smiles at him. George says nothing more. Instead he says: 'It was nice at Shiloh. Mr Davis was polite for me. He used to call me Son.'

'And did you like that?'

George says at first it made him shudder, but he got used to it.

152

He says in any case they couldn't speak together. 'I couldn't speak English when I was young.' George says he learnt every single word of English that he knows from the Davis boys. 'Can you imagine that, papa?'

Castleton says he can imagine it. Very well indeed.

George says there were three Davis boys. They were his brothers-in-law. He says: 'There was Captain Butler, Mr Jeff and Hank. He wasn't but fourteen, so I was excused from calling him Mister. They were polite,' says George. 'Captain Butler told me if he had any say he would inject all Southern goods going North with cholera. It is the only way, Captain Butler said. He ain't cared for Yanks too much,' says George. 'Papa, can you imagine, those Davis boys used to call they papa "Paw"? Wasn't it too droll for words? Viv'n' me nearly died laughing about it.' He says: 'Mr Davis wanted I should call him "Paw" too, but mama forbade it, so I just called him nothing mostly.' George says: 'I didn't want to call him papa.' George confides: 'I don't like it much.'

'No, I know.'

O, he can read you like an open book. George says it is better not to think about it.

He offers obligingly: 'Shall I say a little prayer to La Sainte Vierge about my glove? She will like to help. She is our saint for us, you know,' says George, politely introducing her.

He can if he likes, Castleton says, but he doesn't think it will be necessary. 'It's started to move.'

George doesn't say his prayer aloud, he has no wish to embarrass his stepfather who, though he will always kindly bless you when you sneeze, is not, George thinks, really croyant at all.

There is a short silence. 'It will come now,' George assures him. 'She will do her best for us. Benoirs is all named for her, don't you know?'

Mama is called Marie-Madeleine Marguerite. Uncle Benoir is called Armand-Marie Xavier. George is called Georges-Marie Armand.

'Did y'all know I was called Armand as well, papa? Is it a surprise for you?' George wants to know.

It is. A big surprise. Castleton says: 'I think it's coming off.'

'O, yes, she will certainly do it for us,' George confides. 'Mr Viv ain't named for her, papa. Uncle Benoir wouldn't permit it on account it was mémère's name.' George says: 'My cousin

Benoir he don't ever call me anything but Marie. It is his special name for me. Is it bizarre?'

'It is a bit.' The glove is ballooning slowly out. 'It's off, ducky,' Castleton says.

George says in a polite voice: 'I will arrange to thank Her when I am in bed.' He has turned his head away. He says his Uncle Baudouin is called Marie too—Baudouin-Marie Placide. George says: 'It's wrong, because he is souffrant, but I don't like him much.'

Castleton says pleasantly: 'I think you have a point.'

He has let the water out of the basin. The scarlet hand lies crouched at the bottom, steaming faintly. 'Have you got anything to put on this, love?'

Apropos of names George says it is bizarre he don't ever recollect hearing Mr Davis's given name. 'Mama just called him Davis.'

'That's his name,' Castleton says. 'Davis Davis.'

George calls out with a great show of astonishment: 'O, did you know him, papa?'

'Everyone knows him,' Castleton says. 'He's Davis of Mississippi.'

'O, will you imagine? Davis of Miss'ippa!' He keeps on exclaiming: 'He is my ex. He was my father-in-law.' He seems completely taken with the image of Davis as a public figure. It doesn't mean a blind thing to him, of course. It's just a ruse to gain time.

'Come off it, ducky.' Castleton turns the proud rouged-looking face to his. 'Can I have something to put on your hand?'

'Put?' enquires his stepson politely. It might be de Chassevent speaking.

'Put,' agrees Castleton, 'can I have something to? Come on, George.'

De Chassevent replies he believes there is something.

'Could we have it?' Castleton asks. 'If it's not boring you too much, that is.'

De Chassevent believes it is behind the vitrine.

'Which is it?' Castleton says. 'Will you show me?'

'Oh George,' says Castleton in despair.

'C'est celui-là. Le grand au mileu. Le grand en cristal.' He has forgotten his English. He remains anchored to the washbasin at the bottom of which a freshly boiled lobster is lying. He is holding

154

on to the lobster because he has no option. It is attached by the wrist to his sticklike elegant arm.

Castleton says: 'Is this it, ducky? Will you let Pa put some on?'

George cannot answer. He has forgotten the English for everything, so that is that.

Castleton says: 'N'aie pas peur, mon petit, ça ne te fera que du bien.'

It is quite nice when he speaks French, but George can't answer him. He will do everything because he has given his word he will go through with it, he cannot be expected to talk as well. He hears his stepfather telling him to put his other hand into the basin.

'Ta main gauche, mon chéri, veux-tu?'

He puts it in at once. He is being very good. He stands pin-still but when he feels the cool heavy lotion swathing his hands he calls out in a loud arrogant voice: 'Ah merde! Ah, ça alors vous savez!' He has caught sight of the lobster, cheerfully scarlet with the bright white cream lying thickly in the ruts. He stands there staring at it in a stony, contemptuous sort of way. 'O, but you are charming, I must say. O, I will have to hear it from Viv about you. O, but you are just what the doctor ordered, I don't think!' exclaims George, who evidently still frats with Bone. He calls out furiously: 'O, Viv will shampoo me for this!' He means, of course: 'il me lavera la tête.'

'George, shut up, darling,' says Castleton. He is swathing the hands in a towel, but George calls out bitterly: 'O, I wisht I was dead, I wisht I was dead, I wisht I was dead.' He is stamping with both feet.

'George,' says Castleton rather loudly. 'Shut up at once.'

He shuts up at once and stands silent, watching his stepfather putting things away, flushed to the forehead with his rage and his shame. Presently he remarks in a strange accusing voice: 'They are better now. Everything is better because of you.' He is feeling it so intensely he sounds almost vindictive. 'I shan't forget you for this.'

Castleton gives him a kiss. 'Will you go back to bed now, my duck?'

'No, I will wait for you.'

'You're sweating, you'll catch a chill.'

'I have said I will wait for you,' returns the creature, tossing

155

his head. He hangs about, waiting for Castleton, his hands held in a kind of muff which Castleton has improvised for him from a towel. His nightshirt has slipped from one shoulder exposing one breast and the gold chain and medal round his neck. He looks like a small street walker with his haughty face still painted vividly and an almost hard look in his brilliant eyes. He patters after Castleton everywhere, soliciting in his high sweet drawl: 'Will y'all come back to bed with me, dear sir? Will y'all come?' It's obvious he expects to be abandoned now his hands have been done.

'All right, I'm coming.' Castleton wants a wash.

While he is washing, his stepson crowds up close, guarding him with a jealous eye and making congratulatory and intensely personal remarks. He refreshes himself by taking in every detail of his stepfather's person, shifting his position from time to time in order to get a better view. 'You are nice.' George adds: 'There is not one part of you that is bad. It doesn't signify that you are old.'

'Well, hooray.'

George says calmly: 'O yes, I love you to distraction, only I have not got to say it all of the time.' It is quite possible, mama says, to love a person without declaring it twenty times a day, but George says for himself he finds this restriction a little dispiriting.

'I wouldn't let it worry you.' Castleton says that despite the handicap George is managing to put up a pretty decent show.

'O, sir, do you think so?' George asks him happily. 'I mean, could petit-papa guess I was distracted and everything?'

Particularly distracted. That part of it comes over specially well. Before a fresh proposal of marriage can come up, Castleton says: 'Shall we get back to bed?'

'O yes, O yes, O, will y'all walk me back?' shrieks out the creature, jumping on to Castleton's feet. Castleton smiles down at the small excited face from which the flush is at last fading. 'Don't you want to go to the lavatory first?'

There is a small chill pause. Castleton invites: 'Have a pee while you're about it, darling. Just for kicks.'

There is a dignified silence before George answers primly: 'No, thank you, papa.' It is the merest infant of a Snub Benoir, but it is unmistakable.

'I can't think where you keep it all.'

156

O, it is shocking how outspoken he can be at times. Sometimes it is better to disregard him altogether. He is surprised at getting a sudden and very energetic kiss.

'Have I offended you, George?'

'No, sir.' The voice is faint but very dignified. There is a lot of intricate breathing going on.

O, you can't ever tell when he is laughing at you, that is the worst.

But Mr Castleton is saying politely: 'No, it was very rude of me. Will you forgive me, please?'

O, he is nice. He is asking your pardon like you were grown up. It is a thing they will not ever do at Benoirs. George forgives his stepfather with all his heart.

'It was a little faux pas, voilà tout,' declares the lily pale Dauphin, who has just this very second replaced the small rouged strumpet from Basin Street, and whose kindness can now be seen shining on his guileless brow.

His stepfather comments drily: 'You've got a too forgiving nature, ducky,' and advocates that for the future a firmer line be taken with stepfathers who cannot or will not observe the finer niceties.

'Come on,' says Castleton abruptly. 'Hop on up.' He walks him back as far as the bedroom where the creature deserts him instantly for his bed.

High, sustained shrieks proclaim that the pale exile is back on Devil's Island again. 'O, my Redeemer! O, my own sweet fascinating bed. O, it is warm. It is warm. Ah, comme il est bon mon beau lit. Il est chaud comme tout. Come quick, quick, papa darling. You will be snug like a rug if only you will come quick.' Snug is his latest acquisition from Bone.

'George, can we have less carry-on?' asks Castleton, who thinks he has just heard Marguerite come in. He strides to the door which connects with the salon and locks it.

'Papa.'

'That's all right.' It's absolument défendu to lock any door, of course. The whole of the Dauphin's apartment must be kept permanently open to inspection, jour et jolly old nuit.

'Hullo,' says Castleton, getting into bed and chucking his stepson under the chin. 'What are you getting yourself into a state about?' He has just heard a faraway ringing which means that Mim is being put through to her brother at the Delta. Of course her boy friend has heard it too. His pallor is scarcely to be distinguished from the sheets.

He keeps on asking anxiously: 'Will mama come? Will she come up here?'

'No, of course she won't, ducky.' He has clasped his arms behind his head and is looking, he hopes, enormously reliable.

'O, my Redeemer,' sighs the boy friend in disconsolate tones.

He's disappointed! He's actually dead disappointed Mim isn't coming to bed with them!

'O, it would be so lovely if mama would come too!' He asks his stepfather politely: 'Will it be only you in bed with me, papa dear?'

'I'm afraid so, ducky.' Castleton says: 'Try not to take it to heart.' It's too bloody funny.

'Cheer up, my duck,' Castleton says. 'What would you like to do?' He must have something to make up for his disappointment over Mim!

It really is too bloody funny. At this rate he needn't have bothered about any of it!

'Ouwoodland Friends, papa?' chirps up the boy friend at once. 'Shall I fetch your specs?'

Our Woodland Friends is a dim little reader full of blurry photographs of shadowy places which Castleton has dug up from some ancient trove and which finds great favour with the nature-loving Dauphin who is taking unofficial reading lessons from his English stepfather pending the reappearance of Miss Merrick. Fifteen minutes before dinner, unless there are guests, ('there is no question of it tonight, Poilu') sees them out. Progress is slowish though the Dauphin is an avid pupil—if only, Castleton suspects, for the novelty of seeing his stepfather wearing heavy rimmed glasses. Spectacles are as unknown among the Sioux as are hearing aids and trusses.

'It's getting a bit late for *Woodland Friends*, darling. We'll have 'em again this evening, shall we?' It is now, the Lord be praised, a quarter to one.

'O, it is nearly morning,' exclaims the Dauphin, already in mourning for what apparently is his idea of a splendid social evening.

'Never mind, lovey. You tell Pa something for a change. Something nice,' says Castleton.

158

George says immediately: 'About Shiloh? Shall I tell about Shiloh?'

'Please do,' says Castleton civilly.

The quaint old fever-hole is trotted out once more. They are having SHILOH IN THE SPRING this time. According to the Dauphin the entire local animal creation converged upon Shiloh in the spring—'pour faire des petites, vous savez?'

There were bob cats and 'gators and mourning doves, and something which the Dauphin refers to as 'spreading adders'. 'You don't only find them at Miss'i'ppa, papa.'

Which might be just as well, by the sound of them. Castleton asks slyly: 'Were they chouchou?'

O, no, they were not chouchou at all. 'They are serpents, papa.' The Dauphin says that every spring his brothers-in-law, the Davis boys, were severely discommoded by a huge writhing mass of water-moccasins monopolising their swim-hole. 'It wasn't anything you could do about it. They were in love, those serpents.' The Dauphin adds simply: 'C'était comme ça à Shiloh.'

Hooray for Shiloh. Steaming, teeming Shiloh.

They are wandering now through the tall woods of lower Mississippi, the 'Grand Bois' of the Dauphin, picking the flowers with the hideous-sounding American names like stink weed and mad weed and pig weed and fat weed. They have fetched up under a vast green tulip tree by the side of the oily beer-coloured waters, whose surface only reflects as the hard bright blue of the sky strikes it. There is a bluff with a rock on it, and out of this rock wild honey is flowing. This rock is claiming a few nostalgic sniffles from the Dauphin. 'C'etait bien bizarre, vous savez.'

'It must have been,' Castleton says. 'Don't cry.'

George says the honey from the rock was much prized by 'coons, which would go to any lengths to get it. The raccoons are also drawing a few tears on their own account.

'Turn it off, darling.'

While Castleton is wiping his eyes, George asks suddenly in a matter-of-fact voice: 'Will my nails drop off?'

'No, of course they won't.' So that is what it feels like.

'It is only about Viv,' explains the Dauphin. 'Viv wouldn't like it.'

'Will you shut up about your bloody cousin?'

He is Pure Gold and all that, but inconceivably maddening.

George asks his stepfather placatingly: 'Is petit-papa been married before?'

Not that he knows of. Why?

It is only he understands to fix everything so good. George had made certain his stepfather had been in the family way before. 'I mean before y'all married mama and me.'

'Oh, so I'm married to you too, am I?'

'O, you know how I mean. You just being bad for me. I mean I thought y'all was a widow like Mr Davis.'

'Was Mr Davis a widow?'

'Yes, sir. At least, he was a gentleman widow,' George says. 'Can papa guess what I'm fixing to do?'

Castleton has no idea. Except that he hopes that George is eventually fixing to go to sleep.

O, certainly George is fixing to do that as well. But this here other thing is something special. 'Cain't petit-papa guess?'

No, petit-papa is rather a dud at guessing. 'You tell me.'

George says solemnly: 'I am going to thank La Sainte Vierge every day on my bare knees for sending you to me. I will not use my prie-dieu, I will kneel on the floor like my Tante Marie does when she thanks Her for sending her my Uncle Benoir.' George says: 'Elle est tellement croyante, ma Tante Marie. To drop on her knees is like breathing for her, but I will do it because you are my most priceless possession.'

George says that during Lent he intends to kneel on pois cassés or, failing that, on lentils. He remarks: 'It will probably not do my knees too much good but it will be worth it.'

Castleton says: 'Thank you,' which sounds pretty feeble.

'Il n'y a pas de quoi.' George asks politely if his stepfather is fixing to smoke?

'Not in your bedroom.'

But the hospitable Dauphin assures him warmly: 'You can do it, papa darling. Mr Viv always smokes when we are in bed together.'

'When's that?' asks Castleton.

George tells him happily: 'O, whenever he has a little moment, don't you know? He will not ever stop long away from me, my Viv. We are favourite cousins.'

'So I have gathered.'

'O yes, I adore him beyond reason,' calls out the all-or-nothing Dauphin. 'O, he is good for me, my cousin. Even if I am catawampus beyond the limits of endurance, Viv will not ever get me into trouble.'

'I should damn well think not, indeed.'

'O, Vivi has the right, you know,' the child assures him earnestly. 'Vivi is over me in age and I have not to dispute his will in anything.' O, it is farouche how strict he looks whenever you mention Vivi. George says ingratiatingly: 'I know my cousin is delighted for you to own me, papa. Viv couldn't stand for me to get anyone bad or strict. O, you have quite revived his opinion of the British. He wasn't madly keen on them before.' George has to admit: 'Viv is not like me in that respect. He hasn't the experience,' says the much much married Dauphin.

'The rot,' says Castleton. 'The jolly old twaddle.'

O, it is nice. He is laughing again. 'No, it is true I love the British,' the pale Anglophile calls out. 'My Uncle Benoir adores them too. He will go only to London for his suits and autos.' George adds truthfully: 'I think he doesn't adore the cooking. That is another who will smoke in bed, papa. My Uncle Benoir.' George says he will not, naturally, do it 'en grand lit' because of Tant Marie's indisposition, 'but when he is with Mme Li they will both smoke together. They are amis de coeur,' explains the Dauphin. He says suddenly and firmly: 'I will never sleep alone when I can choose. Not for one single moment. I have sworn it. Just now,' says George.

'Who are you going to sleep with, ducky?'

O, whoever he was married to at the moment. 'That in any case, papa.' Then with his cousin Viv—'If he wants to bring Mlle Elaine it will be in order.' Then he would like a little monkey and a little dog like the white japonaise of his Tante Marie. 'She is chouchou, papa. Her name is "Miss"—but I love her a hundred million times better than that Miss Merrick, whom I detest quite terribly.' Then with his amie de coeur. 'I cannot yet say who it will be. And if there are any children in the house who are afraid, they can come too.' He seems a little vague as to whether these children would be his or not. 'Anyways, there would be room for everyone in my bed.'

'Who are the children who are afraid?' asks Castleton.

George says evasively: 'Well, there are always children who are afraid, ain't there?'

'I don't think so,' says Castleton.

George says nothing. He is engaged in pulling his stepfather's

161

eye long with his left hand, using only the index and little fingers. The other fingers are cleverly employed in keeping the 'good one' covered.

'Tiens, now you look like a Chinese man.'

Castleton puts the hand away. 'Are you afraid to sleep alone, ducky?'

'I beg your pardon, papa?' He has heard the first time, of course.

'Are you afraid to be alone at night?'

George says vaguely: 'There is La Sainte Vierge and there is Mammy. Mammy is never far away.'

'Precisely,' agrees Castleton.

George says: 'I am afraid to die in the night.'

Castleton says in a bland voice: 'Why, ducky?'

O, when he speaks like that it means he will make you tell him. George says: 'O, if I were to die now I would go straight to Hell.'

'Oh no you wouldn't,' says Castleton.

'O, yes,'—a tear spills out of the child's eye and he says quickly: 'O, it is such a mess. O, papa darling.'

'No, it isn't,' Castleton says. 'And turn that tap off!' Castleton shouts. 'For Christ's sake, my dear chap, you're giving yourself the habdabs.'

Castleton says he is of the opinion that his stepson hasn't got tear ducts at all. They're a Device, like windscreen wipers. He suggests George loans it out to Marcel to spray the cars with. 'Then we'd be shut of it.'

He wipes his stepson's face and says: 'No more tears. I love you dearly and all that, but positively no more tears.' He shoves the handkerchief under the pillows. 'Not to be used again to-night.'

He rakes his stepson over to his side of the bed. 'What was it about? D'you want to tell me?'

The pale child says in a diffident voice: 'It isn't only ever about the one thing, you know.'

'What's that?' asks Castleton, who knows.

'Obedience,' says George. 'I just can't learn it.' He stops because Mr Castleton is whistling.

'Get on, old dear,' says Castleton, who is cheering himself up with Annie Laurie.

But George says: 'No, it is all a mess, and I am sick and tired. It is no use to talk about it.'

162

'Oh yes, we must,' says Castleton. He has started Annie Laurie again, this time through his teeth.

'No, it is N.B.G.,' says George. He is in such despair he is quite perky with it. He gives a short dismissing laugh which is supposed to close the subject.

Castleton says, fairly disagreeably: 'You're just being silly, chum.'

He is not, of course, talking to his pale pal the Dauphin, but to a small sophisticate who has suddenly turned up in the Dauphin's bed wearing the Dauphin's nightie. Castleton hasn't actually met this small sophisticate before but he recognises him instantly.

He is a self-possessed little beggar and very much the son of his late father, the late G-M. Benoir. He's nothing like the Dauphin and Castleton doesn't like him, but he admires him very much. This waxen-lidded bigot whose filial piety has already cost him a fortune in tears is the authentic, genuine, accept-no-other Little Benoir.

Castleton is looking at Little Benoir who is looking back at him in a dry-eyed, disillusioned sort of way. He makes no attempt to touch him. There is nothing cosy about Little Benoir who is much older than the Dauphin both in years and experience.

Castleton notes with satisfaction the dry, dry eye of Little Benoir. No Floods at the Delta here. He misses his dewy-eyed pal the Dauphin, of course, but this unamiable little tough will be much easier to tackle.

He decides on a little light bullying, and says: 'What're you getting yourself into a state about, Old Duck?'

Little Benoir answers huffily: 'I am not getting myself at all. I think it is no good to talk about it, voilà tout.'

Castleton says in that case it is pointless for him to remain, and he intends going back to his own bed. 'Goodnight, Old Duck.'

But Little Benoir calls out furiously: 'Will you stop with that name?' He likes the English sweet-names, but not this terrible 'Old Duck' which he detests like anything. He says: 'I will tell you what you want, but stop with that name!' He is in such a temper about it, his eyes look like black fried eggs.

Three cheers for Little Benoir. Directly Castleton is back in bed, he says haughtily: 'You are not to look at me.'

He satisfies himself he is not being looked at, then he says: 'It was about my papa's name. I don't want anyone should have it.

Not even you. It was the same at Shiloh.' He says: 'Well, I will have to give it now, so that is all about it.'

'I have given my word, that is the worst,' says George.

Castleton strokes his hair.

'O, I am perfectly sick of everything, you have no idea!' George says suddenly: 'It had a beadwork handle.'

'Give it a rest, darling.'

But Little Benoir calls out with spirit: 'It is all right for you, but if I have to get it with that thing again I will go mad.'

'You won't,' says Castleton. 'I promise.'

But Little Benoir says simply: 'O yes. Mama has promised it if I disobey. She will not ever break her word so I will get it.' He says: 'It was very sharp. It wasn't possible to stand it.'

'George, do shut up,' says Castleton. 'It's finished.'

But he is so wound up he can't stop talking about it. 'It was perfumed, I think. It had a beadwork handle . . .'

He has begun to tell himself off in an angry voice: 'I don't ever want to obey, that is my trouble. Even if Jesus ordered me I wouldn't want to do it. It is my pride. I can't ever bear to have it taken down. O, it half kills me.'

'Christ, my dear fellow! Do give it a rest,' says Castleton.

But Little Benoir is bursting out afresh with now he will have to go to Viv's wedding in gloves and Viv will be fed up of him. 'O, it is perfectly stinking. Uncle Benoir will be fed up of me as well. He told me at Paris I was not to make another Shiloh with you and now I have made it.

'George, will you listen to me?' asks Castleton.

Yes, he will listen but it will not be any good. 'I have given my word and that is all about it.'

'George, when you've finished,' Castleton says nastily.

Little Benoir calls out unamiably: 'Well, I can't be more listening than I am. O, you are funny.'

Castleton says it makes no earthly difference what George calls him. It's only a name.

Little Benoir remarks gloomily: 'It was my papa's.'

It still is. Castleton says nothing can take George's father away from him.

Little Benoir says nothing except: 'O, you are funny.'

'You're not giving anything away that's his, darling.'

Little Benoir says nothing to this either except that he is cold. 'Ah, merde! C'est froid, vous savez? Ah, merde alors!' He shrugs himself swearing under the covers. He seems to be able to stand anything but cold.

'Are you going to be sensible about this, George, or not?'

'O, I suppose I got no option. You are really funny, you know.'

He has shrugged himself down to the bottom of the bed and is kissing the calf of Castleton's leg and tickling the soles of his feet at the same time. Little Benoir goes in for this sort of thing quite a bit. He calls out in an offhand way: 'You are good. I shall pay you back for this.' He calls out: 'I am coming up now.'

Castleton asks: 'Are you happier now, darling?'

'Yes! I have said yes!' There is quite a lot of Little Benoir left. He calls: 'Look out. I am coming up now.'

He doesn't come. 'Look out,' calls Little Benoir.

'George, come on out, ducky.'

There is a suspicious silence.

'George.'

He emerges reluctantly. There have been tears, of course. The Dauphin says dejectedly: 'I did not mean to cry.'

Castleton is delighted to have his pale pal back, despite the fact that tears are dropping effortlessly out of the Dauphin's eyes as usual.

The Dauphin says typically: 'It isn't really crying. It is Tears of Joy.'

'Tears of which?' shouts Castleton, delighted at the chance to be furious.

Of Joy. The Dauphin says you shed them when your Heart is Full.

'What rot,' Castleton says rudely. 'They went out with the Civil War. Nobody sheds 'em, you silly little noodle.'

But he does. Tears of Joy are simply gushing down the face of his olde worlde stepson, presumably pumped up from an Overflowing Heart. After a bit he lets himself be mopped up.

'Now what was that in aid of?' asks Castleton, getting the handkerchief out of bond.

'I beg your pardon, papa?'

'The Overflow,' says Castleton, yawning amiably. 'The Bursting Heart?'

O, it was because he is so good for George and because he is George's Friend.

Ah, Tears of Gratitude. Castleton gets the idea. 'Have you finished now, lovey, or would you like me to call a plumber in?'

O no, he has finished.

'D'you want another sweet?' He has found the second pepper-mint in his breast pocket. It's a bit bent but none the worse. 'Here, suck it slowly and try and get to sleep.'

'Yes, sir, I am fixing.'

Christ, he is having a go at his rosary now. With his left hand. 'Cut it short, ducky,' says Castleton civilly. As a heretic he naturally doesn't want to overstep the mark.

He is surprisingly quick. The beads are kissed and pushed under the pillow along with the handkerchief which Castleton hopes sincerely will not have to be fetched out any more tonight.

'O, papa, you are so lovely and warm.' The pale creature is shivering politely somewhere round the small of Castleton's back.

'Are you still cold, darling?'

O no. O, George is lovely and warm now, if papa will kindly let him lay up close.

'Like this?' Castleton nurses him vigorously. It is not possible to hold him any closer short of swallowing him. George calls out in an ecstasy: 'O yes. Like that! O, it is quite dreadfully cosy now. O, it is just about the end of cosiness, don't you think?'

It is as far as Castleton is concerned.

'Papa?'

'What?'

'Papa, you know what would make it even more cosier than it is now?'

'I'd hate to hear it. What would?'

'To have the bed curtains drawn.' George sighs. 'O, it is such a pity mama will never leave me have my bed curtains drawn. It would be not healthful in a warm climate, mama says.' George says it is bizarre, has petit-papa noticed, nothing is ever healthful if it is nice?

Yes, he had noticed something of the sort. 'Never mind, pretty,' his stepfather consoles him. 'It's damned cosy as it is, you must admit.' The sweat is running down his back as the pitiless Nessos gets into its stride.

The Dauphin says: 'I don't guess we must speak any more.' It's not clear whether he is asking his stepfather or telling himself.

'No, I don't think so, darling,' Castleton agrees.

The terrible sun in the bed has risen to its full meridian and is spreading its torrid rays. The pale sleeper lies basking on his heat-struck slope, the mysterious smile already forming on his lips. For exactly ten minutes he will be completely comfortable then he will begin to sweat. Now he is happy and warm and relaxed.

He lies with one leg flung over the legs of his dearest friend who loves him and who has taken his troubles away. And while he sleeps, the cheeky bright lobster scrambles out of the bedclothes and lies down by the side of the pale 'good one' in a kind of sad millennium.

14

The Cousins

The young husband-to-be, the eighteen-year-old Bienville Xavier Égalité Benoir, comes bounding into the room.

'Hey, you Marie! Where you at?'

'Vivi!' George calls out. 'I'm in the bath!'

'Ah'm in de baht,' Bienville mimics him, scooping up bath water with both hands and inundating George.

'O, don't,' shrieks out his cousin. 'O, you are boring me!'

So. Just for that, you sassy concern. Bienville catches his cousin by the legs and tips him up.

'Now am I boring you, you sassy concern?'

Oh yes, he's boring. He's boring. 'Oh, turn me loose—you silly bleeder,' shrieks out George.

'Hey!' Bienville smacks out righteously at his cousin's leg. 'Hey! You trash! Who'd you get that from?'

'O, don't you dare!' George calls out, escaping from the bath.

'Who'd you get that from?' Bienville still wants to know, plunging into the bedroom after him.

George says pertly: 'You don't own me. I don't got to tell you everything.'

'Hear me, Marie?'

George says he got it from Bone.

'Bone?'

'Mr Castleton's man. He's British,' explains George.

'I'll say he's British,' Bienville says. 'Tante ever hear you use that expression, boy, she's going to have a Bone to pick with Bone.'

They shriek about this for a while, rolling about on the bed. Albert says gloomily: 'P'tit m'sieu all wet still.' He dabs about him lackadaisically with a towel.

'That nigra ought to get liquidated,' says Bienville. They shriek about that too. 'You want to watch yourself, though, Thingo,' young Benoir says authoritatively. 'I don't want to hear you use that kind of tramp talk again.'

George answers placidly: 'Mr Castleton swears.'

That's because he's British. The British always swear a lot. 'It's the cooking,' Bienville says.

O, Vivi is droll! George nearly falls out of the bed.

Bienville says sharply: 'How's he making out?'

'Who?'

'Tonton Vince.' The phoney baloney British Punk.

O, it is funny how he does not ever want you to like anyone outside of Benoirs.

'O, Mr Castleton is obliging for me,' George says. 'O, Vivi, I do love him.'

Bienville says goodnaturedly: 'You'd love an alligator if Tante married one.'

O, Vivi is a nut case! George shrieks out: 'O, will y'all imagine an alligator for a father-in-law? O, we would got to keep him in a tank.'

'Father-in-law! Christ, Marie! You the nut case,' Bienville says, not displeased at making such a hit.

'But you like him, don't you, Vivi?' persists George. 'You do like Mr Castleton?'

'I like him like I like a case of hookworm,' Bienville says. 'The British should all get liquidated anyways.'

Albert puts forward his opinion that Mr George ought to be getting dressed—'if p'tit m'sieu got to wait on Mr Benoir 'bout 'leven, hit's gettin' to be pretty near a quarter of now.'

'O, my Redeemer!' calls out George, tumbling out of bed.

'What's Benoir want to see you about?' asks Bienville, fixing his cigarette into the exaggeratedly long kind of holder he and Armand both affect. He watches his cousin being dressed with a proprietary air. That Thingo. He'll get by. He is intensely proud of George's looks. 'Hey, Force Ripe, you bustin' out. Rapid thing!'

'Don't, Viv.' George flushes a faint pink under his cousin's hard stare.

Oh, it is farouche the way Benoirs will look at you, as if there is not a single part of you they do not own. Mama will do it a lot, and so will Viv, but Uncle Benoir he will not ever look at you even if you are dressed.

Vivi is smoking and eating grapes and reading the *Picayune* all at the same time, the way he does, without ever letting up on what he's concentrating on. He is looking at George through narrow eyes.

'Son,' begins Bienville in the hideous nasal drone he uses when he is taking off George's ex-stepfather, Governor Davis: 'Son, y'all had noos from Pellagra Junction, Son?'

Pellagra Junction is Bienville's name for Governor Davis's place.

'Oh, don't you start, Vivi,' George calls out. 'It ain't anything like Mr Davis case you got hopes.'

'Then what are you getting mad about?'

'Well, you are silly,' says George. Oh, Vivi is hateful when he makes those long eyes at you. He will find out what you like and demigrate it till you don't know where you're at. O, if only he don't start on Mr Castleton as well.

'Son, y'all fixin' to tell me y'all hain't had one single mite o' noos from yo' po' ole pappy back in Copperhead County?'

'I am not even listening,' says George, who is at the dressing table having his hair brushed to indigo satin.

Albert complains: 'Mr Viv keep on buggin', I ain't gonna be able to fix p'tit m'sieu's hair good.'

A grape pip hits him squarely on the cheek. Present for a sassy nigra. Bienville says to George: 'What are you getting into those crazy duds for? You're going to frighten Herman to death.' Herman is Boche for Armand. Anything Boche gets Benoir crazy as hell and anything that gets Benoir crazy is sweet potatoes to Bienville.

'O, I cain't help what I got to wear,' George says testily. He is being dressed in white from head to foot, only the ribbon on his sailor blouse is black.

Christ! He's got white gloves on even like he was going to communion.

'You look like the Klux.' Bienville is eating pralines now as well as grapes. 'Son, I sho' is relieved yo' done joined the Klan at last.'

'O, you are stinking,' calls out George. 'Mr Davis was very good for me.'

So's worm physic. Bienville says contemptuously: 'That shot up type!'

'He was not, he was not, he was not shot up!' shrieks George, kicking his cousin on the shin.

'Hey!' Bienville drops the Senator Davis act pretty smartly and slaps his cousin on the hand. 'Hey! You gone crazy or what?'

'O, now you hurt me,' calls out George.

'Where?' Bienville wants to know. 'Show me.' He catches his cousin by the wrist. 'O, don't,' cries George, fighting to get free. 'You'll get me late.'

But Bienville has already guessed.

George calls out quickly: 'It don't affect you, Vivi!'

'So that's what papa wants to see you about.'

'I said it don't affect you,' calls out George.

'You case!' says Bienville in a furious voice. 'You case! You've had a session again!'

'Don't scold me, don't scold me,' begs George.

His cousin shrugs him off. 'You stop away from me! Hear me? Just stop away from me, that's all!' Bienville says in a disgusted voice: 'You're getting to be a regular cut-up. I don't want to love you any more.'

'O yes, Vivi, yes!' cries George, bursting into tears.

'Chrissakes, Marie! You don't ever learn! You just don't ever learn! Christ, I said Give In. Give In, I said. Every goddam time I said it. Ain't I told you one hundred times, ain't I said to give in no matter what?'

'Yes, Vivi.'

'Then do it! Chrissakes! How come you ain't learnt obedience yet? I promise you, Marie, Tante will make you do it at the end.' Bienville says: 'She may love you best in all the world, but, feller, she will see you dead rather than have you disobey.' So he can

171

make his mind up to it, Bienville says, because that is how it is going to be. And George can quit that bawling. 'Don't cut no ice with me.' He says in a hard voice: 'Hear me, Marie?'

'Yes, Vivi.'

'Then start to behave! How you think I gonna feel, showing Benoirs up all over Castletons? I mean it, Marie. Just one more session I won't own you any more.'

'O, yes, O, own me,' sobs out George.

Is it a promise then? Bienville says sternly: 'I want a promise from you, Marie.'

O, yes, it is a promise. 'O, Viv, O, say I am your favourite cousin,' cries George. He is clasping his cousin round the waist and stamping with both feet.

'Hey! Will you stop that!' says Bienville, slapping him down. 'Veux-tu tout de suite finir gigoter comme ça!' Bienville thoroughly enjoys the authority his superior age gives him over George and is specially pleased with his lifelike impersonations of Tante.

In the middle of it Armand's valet, Achille, puts his head round the door. 'Monsieur is ready to receive Monsieur Georges.'

'O, my Redeemer, I am not half ready,' cries George.

Oh, it is beyond everything to see Thingo standing there dressed fit to kill and bawling like a stuck shoat. Bienville begins to laugh uncontrollably. 'Papa sure going to admire that watermelon act of yours. How're you going to explain those great tomato eyes?'

'O, if he asks me I will got to tell him.' The prospect makes him howl afresh.

Christ, it is unbelievable. He will not tell the simplest lie to save his hide! Bienville calls out: 'Hey, Washington! That's your new name—Watermelon Washington!'

'O, bloody shut up!' George is in despair. He would like to ask Achille to wait for him but doesn't dare for fear of further exciting Bienville's scorn.

'O, do come with me, Vivi,' begs George, childishly blowing his nose. 'O, I don't want to wait on Uncle Benoir.'

'What are you scared at?' Bienville wants to know. 'Papa wouldn't hurt a fly, you know that.'

Oh yes, he knows it.

'So?'

'O, I don't want to go and see him, Vivi.'

Too bad because he'll have to. 'Get moving, Marie. You know Herman don't tolerate being kept waiting.'

'O,' whispers George sickly. He has turned frightfully pale.

'Chrissakes, Marie!'

He looks like he is going to throw up.

'Shall I call Mammy?'

George shakes his head.

'Well what?' asks Bienville in, for him, a fairly patient voice. 'Want me to tell papa you're sick?'

George shakes his head.

'Chrissakes, Marie.' You'd think papa was an ogre the way he's acting. 'Want me to come with you? Is that what you want?'

'Yes, Viv.'

'Well, get cleaned up then. Chrissakes, you look like Quasimodo or something.' He waits impatiently while George blows his nose. 'Come on, let's go.' He grabs the pale child by the hand. They get as far as the door.

'Vivi?'

'What?' He can feel the small nervous hand pressing and kneading his palm.

'Don't say.'

'Say about what?'

'Don't put a word in for me with Uncle Benoir.'

'Don't? Why ever not? That's what I'm coming with you for, ain't it?'

'No, I don't want it,' says Thingo in that piss-awful prideful voice he can use, like you had offered to rape him.

Christ, it's unbelievable! He is a nut case all right.

Bienville is really angry now. He says in a loud hard voice: 'Look, I am offering to put a word in for you with papa so you will not be forever getting cut up and shot up and spending the rest of your goddam life in the doghouse. Fair deal? With any luck papa will succeed in sweet talking Tante around to his way of thinking. He can swing anything with her,' Bienville says very clearly, 'because he is her favourite brother. Compris?'

'Yes. I don't want it, though,' George says. 'I am not keen.'

'And I am not keen to come with you,' says Bienville, flinging his cousin's hand away. 'All right! Get stripped down. See if I care.'

George stands quite silent, he is not crying or anything.

'You want to watch that pride of yours, Marie. That's going to

173

bore the piss out of everybody pretty soon.' O, he is mad because of being turned down. It is the thing Viv will not ever tolerate.

'Will you come with me, Vivi?' murmurs George.

'No. Scram,' says Bienville. 'Don't you pester me.'

'Just to the door?'

'Deal me out,' Bienville says. He is over at the telephone putting a call through to Paris. He stares at his cousin with unfriendly eyes.

'Just to the door, Vivi?'

'I said don't pester me.' He has turned the radio on full and is practising dance steps while waiting to be put through.

'Just down the stairs?'

''Bye,' Bienville calls, flipping a cool salute. 'Hey! Cut up! Whyn't you fix your next session for my wedding? Then you can show those eyes of yours around the half of Paris as well. Idea?' asks Bienville, who specialises in this kind of remark.

'O, you are hateful,' says George in a stifled voice. He has gone very red.

But Bienville has turned his back on George. They have put him through to Paris and he is entering a world that is strictly not for kids. Bienville embarks on a telephone conversation that will probably last two hours. He speaks to Elaine in French, making love in a rapid, impudent, slangy way that is making her laugh. At a certain point in the proceedings he is aware that George has left the room, but Bienville pursues his telephone marathon relentlessly, making outrageous love, taking revenge for his slight and exciting Elaine's jealousy for his cousin at the same time.

15

The Inherited Smile

His ordeal comes knocking softly at the door. Armand goes into action at once.

'Entrez!'

He is lying stark naked on the bed like a small king, his tiny ape spreadeagled across his chest. His valet throws a towel across his loins and goes to open the door. Armand clicks his fingers at Hippolyte. 'Disappear. Come back in ten minutes.'

That is the limit he has set for his ordeal. Achille brings George in and withdraws with Hippolyte into the dressing room. Armand has fixed his eyes on the door. His ordeal is coming in. He is dressed in white from head to foot. Only his eyes and hair are black and the ribbons on his sailor blouse. The likeness is complete.

'Bon jour, mon Oncle.'

'Come here.' Armand puts out a small, imperious hand. A bracelet set with rubies is loose over his fine wrist. He feels the child's soft lips kiss his hand and a faint tingling starts in his arm. Armand says in his pleasant voice: 'I hear from mama you have been misbehaving again.'

175

'Uncle Benoir . . .'

'Yes or no?'

'Yes, sir.'

'I have only one answer to that sort of thing. Bend your head.'

He takes up a glove and flicks George lightly across the face with it, a flick for each cheek.

A hot flush rushes over George's face and neck. It didn't hurt at all: it is this thing of having to bend your neck. It is this special punishment they keep for you at Benoirs to bring you down when you have been disobedient, or entêté, or have an Answer for Everything.

Armand says calmly: 'I will not have you disobedient towards mama, George. You are to obey her in everything. Compris?'

'Yes, sir. I will try.'

'Don't try. Do it. Voilà tout.' He points to George's gloves. 'You going to cause a scandal like that in Mr Castleton's house again?'

O, no, he will not ever.

'Is that a promise?'

'Yessir, Uncle Benoir.'

'Then that account's settled.'

Armand says kindly: 'Tell those two types to come in again, will you, puss? They're probably out on the gallery smoking. Be midnight before I was dressed if I left it to them.'

'Yessir,' says George. O, Uncle Benoir is good. His panpan don't hurt at all and he will not ever permit the servants to see you bend your neck. He stands looking with love at his beautiful little uncle who is lying like a king with his small favourite clamped to his chest.

'Get going, puss.'

The eyes of his ordeal are a pure unclouded black in which a smile is shining brilliantly. This smile is unendurable. It's the inherited smile.

When Achille comes back Armand tells him: 'Have Gustave send up a bottle of champagne. And see it's cold this time. If I want to drink piss tell him I can make my own.' Everybody laughs. Armand calls out after his valet: 'Two glasses, hear me? We got distinguished company.' He turns to George. 'Want to take Ouisti, puss? You can hold him whiles Hippolyte gives me my friction.'

176

He prises loose the tiny hands that are clinging like grim death to the chain round Armand's neck.

'O, he is darling,' breathes George. He is holding Ouistiti tenderly with both small gloved hands. Armand knows without looking what sort of expression there is on his face. He says to Hippolyte abruptly: 'Start with my back.'

Hippolyte starts massaging the perfectly proportioned back with a richly scented cologne. For George this cologne has an incomparable perfume which is the special mark of his Uncle Benoir.

'P'tit m'sieu heap better'n Mr Viv at holding Ouistiti.' Achille is putting the links in a fine cambric shirt.

Hippolyte grins. 'Mr Viv hol' him, she done kick up by now.'

Armand says: 'Mr Viv just plain trifling. Ain't but one thing that cannibal understands.'

Achille and Hippolyte are laughing and his ordeal is laughing too. That case Viv has certainly brought him up-to-date!

Gustave comes in with the champagne. ''Bout time!' Armand rolls over on to his back while the bottle is being uncorked. 'It's good 'n' cold, Monsieur.' Gustave is pouring the rushing white torrent into the glasses.

'Better had be!' Armand says good-naturedly. 'Hey, it's good!' He holds the second glass out. 'Here, puss.'

George shifts Ouistiti carefully on to his left arm and puts out his right hand to take the glass. The champagne is spread out in a shallow blond pool, the lively bubbles jumping at the crystal rim.

O, Uncle Benoir is indulgent beyond belief. To take champagne with Uncle Benoir is just about the highest honour you can have. His right hand is trembling heavily and very weak. Ouistiti is riding on George's left arm, suffering himself to be held. His small cross eyes are fixed intently on Armand.

'Want to give him back?' So that is his worst hand. 'Come here to papa, you case.'

Ouistiti skitters up Armand's arm and flies into the shelter of his neck. As George comes near to take his glass he shoots out a spidery arm and pinches George viciously on the arm.

'Hey! You gone crazy?' Armand calls, cuffing the leaf-like ears. Ouistiti lets out a shriek of rage.

'O, don't you hurt him!' George calls out.

Ouistiti sits twittering with wide-open jaws. His teeth are like a tiny cannibal's.

'Hey, salaud!' Armand threatens him with a finger. 'Hey,

177

don't you ever dare do that again. You start that pinching routine with me,' says Armand, 'you going to be in heavy trouble, my friend.'

He hands the raging Ouistiti to Hippolyte. 'Take him away. He can cool off in the garden. I don't need that kind of behaviour in here.'

'Ouisti,' grins Hippolyte, 'why you so bad with p'tit m'sieu all of the time?'

He is fixing the slender chain to the low slung belt. Armand calls after him: 'See he don't ruin the flower beds, hear me? Mr Castleton'll have my hide.'

'That salaud Ouistiti,' he says to George. 'He hurt you, baby?'

'No, Uncle Benoir.' His heavy lashes are fanning slowly on his colourless cheeks. There is quite a mark on his arm.

'Drink your drink, pussy,' Armand says kindly. 'It'll buck you up.' If possible he doesn't want to have to touch the arm. 'You got a fright, I guess.'

'Yes, sir.' A tear slips quickly down his cheek.

'Floods at the Delta?' enquires Armand.

'No, Uncle Benoir.'

He is glad to hear it. 'You want to get out of that crying for everything,' his uncle tells him. 'It's getting beyond a joke at your age.'

'Yes, sir,' the child says meekly. 'I am fixing to try.'

'Well, do what you can for me, will you?'

Armand says pleasantly: 'Drink your champagne.' He touches George's glass with his. 'Chin-chin!'

O, Uncle Benoir is droll! George takes a careful sip. His wrist is pretty weak. He is afraid it will turn over and spill his glass. O, the champagne is good. George knows that Uncle Benoir will make no comment if he brings his head down to the glass to drink. O, it is good. Heavily iced, with the prickling bubbles throwing the musky flavour of the grapes into his face.

'Like it?'

'O, yes.'

Armand brisks it up for him with a little gold whisk. That hand is pretty near useless. It's acute the way he is practically drinking off the bed!

Hippolyte comes in with an unrepentant Ouistiti gambolling along on his chain.

178

'That case Ouistiti,' Hippolyte calls out. 'Know what he done? Catched him a butterfly! Monsieur ought to seen! Done torn both wings off and crunched it all up!'

'Ouisti,' says Achille, 'you just a gone case.' He is skilfully removing every vestige of hair from under Armand's arms.

Ouistiti lands whistling into the middle of Armand's lap and bolts under the loincloth.

'Hey, salaud, I need that!' Armand yanks him out by the tail. 'Case you think I lost interest or something,' Armand says.

Achille and Hippolyte are rolling about. George calls out in his high sweet drawl: 'Oh, don't you steal that from my Uncle Benoir, you Ouisti, it is his most proudest possession.'

Hey that's immediately gay! Little Benoir is certainly learning fast! That gone case Viv has put him in the picture all right. And that's the other thing that will have to be sorted out before the British attitude stiffens. Way it is now, Vince gets that North Atlantic look every time he seen those two together. It will be a relief when that trash Viv finally gets himself married. He says sharply: 'Look what you're at with that razor, will you? I felt it just now.'

'Yessir, Monsieur,' Achille says. 'I just couldn't hold laughing at p'tit m'sieu.'

Well, the joke's over. He tells them both: 'I want to be out this room by twelve-thirty, and I don't mean maybe. Compris?'

'Yessir, Monsieur.'

The two young octaroons get on with the business of getting the small dandy dressed for lunch. George watches the proceedings with a rapt attention. O, it is a pretty sight to watch Achille and Hippolyte getting him up so nice. Achille and Hippolyte are Mammy's nephews and George is very fond of them indeed. O, he is quite like a prince, his Uncle Benoir! Mama once told him that when they were children at Taquineuse Uncle Benoir climbed to the top of a high, high tree to get a cat down. The tree tore all his clothes and the cat scratched him and on top of it he got panpan from pépère when he got down and wasn't allowed any dessert for a whole week. George has an idea he would not much have cared for this pépère who was so very severe with his princely Uncle Benoir.

Achille says in a low voice: 'P'tit m'sieu gettin' to look more like Madame votre mère ever' day, don' Monsieur find?'

'Special she smile,' says Hippolyte. 'Man!'

179

'Got that special look,' Achille says, 'like he dreamin'.'

Armand asks smoothly: 'You two fixing to get me late?' The pupils of his eyes are black as lagniappe with the whites showing dangerously underneath. He asks George: 'You making out with that champagne, puss?'

'Yes sir, I finished.' The pale child stands up. The special look is still on his face. It is impossible to look at him. 'No hurry,' says Armand. 'I take it you're all dressed?'

'Yes sir, Uncle Benoir.'

'Well, sit down,' says Armand pleasantly.

Achille sets a chair. It is much too near, of course. Armand wanders away. He is getting into his underthings. The pure white silk pants and vest on which his initials and those of his mistress are intertwined.

Ouistiti is hopping about on the bed swearing at George. Armand bats at him with a palm leaf fan. 'Mr George don't care for you, fella. He got his own friends.' Hippolyte is helping him into his shirt. He holds his hands out for Achille to link the cuffs. 'How're you making out with Mr Castleton, puss? Does he give you good times?'

'O yes, I get good times,' breathes George. 'O, I do love Mr Castleton, Uncle Benoir.'

It is frightful the way he looks like Her, as if he were full up with love.

'Well, that's good.' The thing is not to look at him.

'But mama says I have not got to declare it all of the time.'

Armand says, laughing: 'Well, it could bore quite a few people, I guess.' He says, good-naturedly: 'It's all right if you want to talk about it with me.'

George calls out immediately: 'O, Mr Castleton is indulgent for me. O, he is good like bread.' He is standing close up to his uncle. Armand can actually feel his trembling with the force of his love. He says smoothly: 'So there are no complaints 'bout Mr Castleton, I take it? Stand away from me, pussy, you're getting me late. Seems mama picked the right article for you, eh?'

'O, yes,' breathes George. 'O, yes. He is like bread.'

Armand says suavely: 'So you said.'

George blushes scarlet. You aren't supposed to repeat yourself with Uncle Benoir.

'Well,'—Armand lights a cigarette—'I guess we'll have to
180

show Mr Castleton good times too, hein, puss? Show him around Benoirs?'

O, yes. Benoirs have splendid places. St Cloud, Mal Choisi, La Taquineuse. All the splendid delta places George loves so much. He says: 'Mama promised if I am good we can go to Taquineuse this fall, for my fête. There will be feux d'artifice,'—George says—'and everything.' He adds quickly: 'If I am good.'

'You be good, then,' his uncle tells him good-naturedly. 'We have to show Mr Castleton Benoirs.'

'Yes sir.' George says in a low voice: 'Uncle Benoir?'

'What's that?'

'I did not go to disobey mama.' Achille and Hippolyte are out of earshot now. George says: 'I did not go to do it, Uncle Benoir.'

There is a pause. Armand says coolly: 'I said that account was settled.' If George has any further problems he must put them to Monseigneur.

'Yes sir.' It is not any good to talk about it after that.

Armand says as if there has been no interruption: 'How's about showing Mr Castleton St Cloud?'

O, yes! St Cloud is such a splendid place with its great shadowy gardens full of oiseaux-mouches and its superb aviary full of oiseaux de Sénégal, the fruitsuckers and the violet-eared finches. 'O, I would like to show Mr Castleton all of our delta places. O, please can I, Uncle Benoir-chéri?'

'I'll do my best to satisfy you, puss.' He is now completely dressed except for his shoes. George knows that they will be the last things to go on because Uncle Benoir detests wearing shoes.

Mama told him they had the biggest battles to get him to wear them as a child.

George admires the small arched feet of his uncle, with the left ankle lightly shackled by a golden chain. George knows this is his 'heart foot' because Vivi done told him. It means he belongs to Mme Liane, Vivi said.

O, Uncle Benoir is droll! Everything is done and still he is sitting in his bare feet! Hippolyte has brushed his splendid hair, Achille has pulled a Cape jessamine through his buttonhole, even Ouistiti is riding astride Uncle Benoir's neck before he will permit them to put on his socks and shoes! O, he is enough to make a hornbug laugh the way he keeps on kicking their hands away like Bébé does when her mammy's trying to get her dressed!

George calls out suddenly: 'O, you are droll! O, I do love you! You have no idea!'

'Well, thanks for the testimonial, puss,' Armand points to a beribboned box. 'That's for you.'

O, Uncle Benoir has brought him special nougat from Paris because he knows George loves it so. O, George reckons Uncle Benoir is just about the most indulgent man on earth!

'That's all right, pussy. Don't eat 'em all before lunch. Save one for me.'

O, yes, he will! He will save the most beautiful piece of all for Uncle Benoir. The one which is most full up of amandes and pistaches and fruits glacés.

Armand is smiling round his cigarette. That was near. He has just managed to ignore the upturned face.

''Bye now, puss. Run along back to Viv and tell him he has to behave himself with you—he hasn't got to tease you, hear me?' Armand says. ''Bout time that case grew up.' He puts his hand out for George to kiss. Two more minutes at most and it will be over.

'Au 'voir, mon Oncle,' George says formally, touching the hand with his lips. He makes no further attempt to kiss Armand's face.

'Hey, take your bonbons.' Armand gives the beribboned box into George's hands. He doesn't seem able to manage it very well. He makes three tries before he is able to get a proper hold on the box. That right hand of his is trembling like a leaf. Armand snaps his fingers sharply. 'Set it down. Hippo will bring it up for you.'

Mimi, this time you've gone altogether too far. I'm going to strip you down for this, know that?

'All right?'

'Yes, sir.' George is taking himself off in a vague sort of way, mooning after Hippolyte as if he were lost. He is frightfully pale. Viv will love him up. He'll probably want to handle him as well, but it can't be helped. 'Breathe through your nose, puss,' Armand reminds him kindly. He is unable to bring himself to stand one more moment of his ordeal.

Directly George has left the room he tells Achille: 'Find Madame for me on the phone.' He sits smoking calmly, waiting to get through, with Ouistiti, happy to be alone with him, riffling possessively through his hair.

Achille puts the receiver into his hand and disappears.

Armand hears the serene voice of his sister.

182

'C'est toi, Armand? Bonjour, mon petit-frère chéri. Tu as bien dormi?' asks Marguerite.

Oh yes, he has slept superbly.

She teases him, laughing 'Don't tell me you have already put your shoes on?'

Oh yes. Today Armand has put his shoes on early especially to make a little promenade with her. 'A little tour of the garden,' Armand says. 'I have some news for you.'

She will be with him in exactly two minutes.

'Mimi, why d'you behave so badly?' Armand asks.

'Comment?'

He asks her: 'What have you specially got against decent be· haviour?'

16

The Cousins II

Bienville is on the last lap of his marathon when George gets back.
'Hey, that was quick.' Every trace of ill humour has disappeared.
The radio is going in a whisper and Bienville is in terrific form,
sitting on George's bed, smoking and laughing with his fiancée
and performing an intricate routine with his feet. He captures
George by shooting out an arm and raking him on to the bed.
'Well, was it bad? Did papa bawl you out?'

'No,' says George. He comes and stands close up to Bienville,
as if trying to get warm.

Bienville is making his goodbyes with his free arm round his
cousin's waist. 'Say au 'voir to Elaine,'—he hands the receiver to
George.

'Au 'voir, Mlle Elaine.'

Bienville directs: 'Send a big kiss.'

George kisses the mouthpiece solemnly and hands it back. He
stands with Bienville while he finishes talking, with both his arms
round his cousin's neck.

'Secours! I am being strangled by a revenant!' Bienville tells
Elaine.

'By a what?'

By a quelque chose dressed all in white. 'My cousin, Marie Benoir.'

George hears her astonished voice in French: 'It's a girl, then, Bienville?'

'Are you a girl?'

He tells Elaine: 'He says he doesn't know. Me, I think he's dead.' Bienville says: 'Sweetheart, we have to go. Marie is about to throw up and we're due down at this piss-awful lunch.' He sends her six kisses, one for every day up to and including Saturday, which is the day he will be back in Paris again. He lobs them over. 'All for you. None for the revenant all dressed in white who is clearly going to cat. 'Bye, sweetheart. Ring you tonight.' Bienville finally hangs up. 'What's the matter?'

'My face is cold,' says George.

He stands smiling at Bienville. He is frightfully pale. He is beautiful.

'I care for the mysterious smile,' says Bienville. 'You going to cat?'

'No.'

'Come here, then.' Bienville yanks George on to his lap. 'Want to be babied? Want me to love you up?'

'Yes, Vivi!'

'Well, stop those crazy shakes, then.' Bienville turns the radio up. 'You warmer now?'

'Yes, it is better,' says George.

'What happened, crazy?' Bienville wants to know. 'I suppose Herman pulled your ears for you or something and it hurt your goddam pride.'

'No, Vivi.'

'Well, what did happen, then?'

'I saw Ouistiti,' says George.

'So?'

'Uncle Benoir give me leave to hold him.'

'So?'

'I held him,' George says. He is still smiling. A tear slips quickly down his cheek.

'Is that all? You held Ouistiti and that is making you cry? Chrissakes, Marie, you sure know how to get on my nerves.'

George makes no reply. It's obvious he doesn't want to discuss his interview with Armand any more.

Bienville points to the beribboned box. 'Did Monsieur give you those? How come you ain't opened them even? You've usually ate half the box before you're up the stairs. Don't y'all want one now?'

George shakes his head. His eyes are so downcast he looks asleep.

Oh, Herman is getting to be a bore with that crazy attitude. As if Thingo can help it if he looks like mémère. Bienville reckons Herman pretty far out for his generation, but on this one count he is the Ultimate Square. Christ, so a person died. Even if she was your mother you couldn't go on mourning her for ever. Jesus, she was nearly forty when she died. However long did he expect her to live for, anyways? The Sioux stink, Bienville decides. And that pale Marie, that nut case with the shakes, now he won't even touch one single piece of candy because he knows Herman can't like him!

'Hey, wake up, woozy!' Bienville says roughly. 'Want a drag?'

'Yes, Vivi.'

'Get off my neck, then.' Bienville sticks the seven-inch holder into George's mouth. The child sucks on it eagerly, letting the smoke out through his nostrils in a steady stream.

'Hey! Since when you been inhaling?' Bienville takes the cigarette back. 'Café Society stuff, huh?'

You had to hand it to that case sometimes. Bienville's hard eyes are full of pride for this elegant pale child who is his favourite cousin. 'Want me to pet you?'

'O, yes, Vivi, please.'

'On your feet, then. You're getting heavy,' Bienville says. He spills George unceremoniously out of his lap on to the floor and walks towards the door.

'O, don't you dare lock it,' George calls out.

'Why ever not? I locked it the last time,' Bienville says.

'I know, but mama has disallowed it. I have not got to lock any of my doors.'

'What about the john?'

'I have not got to lock it.' George repeats: 'I haven't got to lock any door for any reason at any time on any pretext what so-ever.'

'Christmas!'

George says: 'It is on account of fainting spells.'

'Fainting spells! Christ, Marie!' Bienville sounds furious. 'You sure do pick the darndest things to have. Since when have you had fainting spells?'

'Since I been here I had one.' George adds proudly: 'I had one at Paris too. I think I am going through a phrase.'

'You're tootin' right you're going through one,' Bienville says. 'What in thunder do we do?'

'I don't know, Vivi.' George suggests mildly: 'Whyn't we just do like always only without we lock the door?'

'Now that I love,' Bienville says. 'That's the greatest of all. Whyn't we just go down on the street?' He calls to Albert sharply: 'Hey, you. Go on and stand outside the door. Sing out if anyone's coming. Hear me?'

'Yessir. This door, sir?' Albert says.

'What the hell door else d'you think I meant?' Bienville asks.

'O, don't be catawampus, Viv,' says George.

'That dope!' Bienville tells Albert: 'See you breathe through your goddam nose, mind me? I don't want to hear you blowing like a grampus whiles I'm in here.'

'O, Vivi, you are catawampus,' murmurs George, dreamily dangling his legs. He has only undone the ribbons of his sailor blouse.

'Chrissakes, Marie! Is that as far's you got?' Bienville sounds exactly like Marguerite.

'Well, I am fixing,' murmurs George.

'Here, leave me do it. We'll be forever in this dump.'

'O, it is not a dump,' George is being forcibly ejected from his blouse. 'Mr Castleton, he had it all made over special when he married mama and me. O, you are hurting!' calls out George.

'Christ,' says Bienville. 'You do talk more balls.'

'It is not balls. Mr Castleton is a very agreeable man. He has been very indulgent for me. So it is you who is talking them,' says George. 'For your information,' adds George, pertly: 'And if you want to know.'

'Hey, hey, sassy!' Bienville is wrenching off George's shoes.

'Well, you are always demigrating,' complains George.

'Marie! Chrissakes! We have to get down to lunch.'

'Well, you just catawampus becaise I got no permit to lock the door.'

'*Becaise*,' says Bienville. 'Christ!'

187

'Ain't my fault if I'm disallowed. . . .'

Bienville finishes in a terrible falsetto: '. . . Hit's on account of fainting spells!'

'O, Viv, you're droll,' George calls out. He is quite naked now except for his gloves.

'Hey, get *them* off.'

'No, leave my gloves,' says George.

'Hey, you gone crazy? What the hell kinda idea is that, going to bed in gloves? Marie, you paying me some mind?'

'No, leave my gloves,' says George.

J. Christ! He is not going to take them off. Bienville recognises the look. Force him and he will kick up like crazy, and that one-man menagerie outside the door will come pounding in. It is acute how this case will stick to a notion once he has made up his mind. No wonder Tante gets mad at him. It's enough to get a saint mad the way he looks at you with those black eyes of his like pious prunes.

'You want to drop a few of those fancy notions,' Bienville recommends. '. . . Don't, you'll find yourself being persuaded out of them by Tante.' He has thrown all his clothes off on to the floor. He switches off the radio and plunges into bed. 'Move over,' orders Bienville. 'Here comes Mr Viv!' He shudders pleasurably at the freshness of the bed.

The pale child latches on immediately, winding thin, elegant arms round Bienville's neck. 'O, Viv, I do love you. You are my favouritest cousin of all.'

'Better had be,' Bienville says drily. 'Ain't no one else.'

'O, there is Bébé,' George points out,

'Christ, don't remind me! That nit! I got to see her at my wedding.' Bienville groans.

'Will Uncle Beau be there too, Vivi?'

'You betcha.'

'Perhaps he won't be,' George says hopefully. 'Perhaps he'll be souffrant.'

Bienville says: 'Ain't the only one who'll be souffrant. J. Christ, I shall throw up if he comes.'

George asks nervously: 'Will there be beaucoup de monde at your wedding, Viv?'

'There will be plenty beaucoup.' The cookie way that case forgets his English the minute he gets worked up! Bienville predicts unpleasantly: 'The way it looks now, practically everybody in the entire monde will be there. Why?' asks Bienville sharply. 'You fixing to be shy, or something?'

'No, Viv.'

'You better hadn't. Hear me? You come that Up-State, Boy-Orphan-from-Sorgum-County act at my wedding, I swear I'll never speak another word to you long as I live.'

'O no, I will not come it,' George says quickly. He is playing with the gold chain round his cousin's wrist. 'You know I am not hardly shy at all now, Viv.'

He didn't know, but he is glad to hear it. Bienville says: 'It's getting to be a joke at your age.'

George leans forward quickly and kisses the medal on Bienville's chain. 'Is that St Bienville, Viv?'

'St Bienville!' He nearly chokes himself. 'Chrissakes, you are the wooziest concern! Don't you even know there ain't a St Bienville? It's St Xavier.'

'Well, I done kissed him anyways,' George says placidly. 'Will you kiss mine too, Viv?' He holds his medal out for Bienville to kiss. 'It is la Sainte Vierge.'

'I know it,' Bienville says. 'Whyn't we just go to Lourdes?' He touches his lips to the medal on his cousin's breast and then he kisses the two small nipples as well. 'Howzat?'

'It's nice,' says George, arching his breast for more.

'Hey, shameless!'

Vivi is kissing the way mama does when she is pleased with you. Kissing and kissing you on your mouth like she would never be satisfied. George parts his lips a little way. Mama will sometimes take a dragée into her mouth and smuggle it into yours between the kisses.

But Viv only ever slips his tongue in. George cannot say he is very struck about this thing Viv does, but waits politely till his cousin withdraws.

Now they are kissing-cousins, Bienville says. Now they can never fall out.

George says you can do it with figs. If you ate off a fig with another person at the same time as that other person ate off that fig with you, then that would fix it so you wouldn't ever quarrel.

'You finished?' Bienville wants to know.

George says: 'Mammy done told me. I mean to try it out with Dédé at Taquineuse when the figs is ripe in the fall.'

'Christ, Marie!' Bienville gives a yelp. 'You eat a fig off with that baboon you'll catch the leprosy.'

'O, I won't, Viv!' cries George. 'Dédé is my milk-sister.'

Bienville says maliciously: 'That's why. I bet you got it already. I bet you sucked it in with Mammy's milk. Yes, you got it all right,' Bienville tells him solemnly. 'That's why you're so white. Remind me to ring the leprosarium after lunch.'

'Oh, Vivi, you are stinking!'

'Well, get horse-sense, then,' says his cousin. 'Chrissakes!'

'Now,' begins Bienville. 'Marie, you listening to me or what?'

'Yes, Vivi.'

'You know that special kiss I gave you? That quite special one?'

'I didn't like it much,' says George.

'And *that* don't signify,' Bienville says, 'Because it couldn't matter less whether you liked it or not.'

'Well, I didn't,' says George.

The point, if he will kindly shut up, is that it has made them kissing cousins.

'Yes, you done told me.'

George says: 'I wouldn't want to drink anyone's spit ever, even if it was love-spit it would make me puke.'

'Well, you don't have to,' Bienville shouts. 'I done it for the both of us, and anyways it's better'n your piss-awful figs.'

'Well, I don't think it is,' George complains. 'Rooting around in my tonsils. It makes me want to throw up.'

'So what's different? You'd throw up anyhow.'

Bienville says good-naturedly: 'I'd sure admire to eat a fig off with you, fella, but I can't wait till fall. I'm getting married, remember? You're coming to my wedding next month.'

'O, my Redeemer,' calls out George in a desolate voice. 'Will y'all be away for long?'

Bienville says calmly: 'Around a year, I guess.'

'O, Viv,' moans George.

'You fixing to cry?'

'No, Viv.' He is rubbing a satiny cheek against his cousin's hand.

That's just as well, Bienville tells him, because he's getting married and that's how it's going to be.

''Bout time you shed that clinging-vine routine. You don't

190

know by now the way I feel about you, you ought to get liquidated, that's all.'

'Only there will be so many new people to love,' murmurs
George.

'Only I don't love 'em!' Bienville says, 'case you think I'm
fixing to love everyone in the whole world from Jesus to Ouistiti,
like you.'

Bienville calls out disgustedly: 'Aw, you stink!' He flounces
away from George. 'I'm going to get the hell out.'

'No, I will be your kissing-cousin,' calls out George.

'Big deal!' Bienville says contemptuously. 'Goddam unlocked
doors. Goddam nigger outside. Goddam gloves. It's going to bore
the piss.'

'O, no, I will be good for you,' cries George.

'All right.' Then he will say it one time more and not again.
'You are for me. You are for me and that is it. Compris?'

'Yes, Viv.'

'Vrai de vrai?'

'Vrai de vrai.'

'Okay.' He is looking intently at his cousin with his hard, handsome eyes. 'You going to be good?'

'Yes, Vivi.'

'Then get those gloves off,' Bienville says. 'Get 'em off, Marie,'
Bienville says quickly, 'they're putting me off.'

'O, Viv.'

'Come on, Baby.' Bienville says suddenly: 'Hey, you got something wrong with your hands?'

George murmurs something.

'I said you got something the matter with those hands? Hear
me, boy?' Bienville demands.

George murmurs: 'There is something on the backs.'

'Get 'em off.'

'Don't look, Vivi.'

'Let it happen!' Bienville says. He studies the *Picayune* comics
section while George is peeling them off. 'Okay?'

Okay. His hands are out of sight under the sheet. 'Say you
won't scold me, Viv.'

'Okay. Give 'em here,' Bienville says. 'I want to look. Give
your hands here, I said.'

'Well, don't you bawl me out.'

'I said "Okay", ain't I?'

'Well, don't you back down on me, then.'

'Well, thanks for those few trusting words! Christ!' Bienville says.

'Get 'em out! Lay them on top of the sheet. Christ, what's the hold up? Marie!'

'There is something on the backs.'

'What?'

'There is some meat or something broken on the backs.'

'Christ Jesus!' Bienville grabs George by the hands and hauls them over to him.

'You trash!'

His eyes are full of furious tears: 'You trash! You get yourself one other session like this I swear I'll kill you stone dead!'

'I will not get one, Vivi,' George says quickly.

'I will not get one, Vivi,' Bienville repeats. He is feeling the small hard palms. Christ. They are like crabs or something. They are all busted to hell!

Bienville says furiously: 'They will never get healed by my wedding. They will never get healed period.'

Bienville says: 'You can wear those stinking gloves for the rest of your life.'

He is white to the lips, a tear distilled from purest rage runs down his cheek. He hears the child's voice saying timidly: 'O, don't you cry!' But he lies rigid with his lip stuck out, washed over and over by the breakers of his rage.

That Tante! That Boche has let him have it with a soupir—one of those Christawful nigger whips Benoirs have had lying around ever since slavery. The delta places are practically crawling with them and Herman once told him they were for stripping uppity house-niggers with. Seems the attraction was you could tote a play toy like that in your vest pocket without spoiling the most elegant set and still get faster results than from a session at the Calaboose.

Oh, Bienville would like to frail her with that thing till all her nails got busted too.

And Bienville is going to bug that Benoir night and day till he finally gets off his butt and makes a Federal Act of it. Monsieur will only ever do this once in a million years, but when he does results are exceptional. No tears. No explanations. No redress. Just 'paid' put across that particular account once and for all. Like that time at Biarritz, he was about fifteen, and pretty raw with Maman over something. The pretty mister had taken it all in, then wham! he had let him have the whole thing for dessert in front of servants, guests, the lot!

'Yes, ma'am,' thinks Bienville. 'You are my favourite slave owner of all the world, but you sure been due for total liquidation an awful long time.'

He swings round suddenly and gives his cousin a hard triumphant kiss. His eyes look as if they had never shed a tear.

'What shall I do?' George asks him. 'Shall I put 'em on again?'

'Yes, get 'em on.'

'Don't y'all want to play? Shan't I accommodate you, Viv?'

'Accommodate! Christ, Marie, you do say the damnedest things!'

'What y'all laughing 'bout, Viv?'

'Far out thing!' Bienville kisses him abruptly. 'Come on, let's go!' If they are going to play they will have to be quick.

Actually, it is too goddam quick on account of being loused up from the start by those Christawful gloves. The best part of this particular session, as far as Bienville is concerned, comes at the end. That fabulous first-communion look on Marie's face, very intent and pure.

Bienville thinks: Marie, vous êtes comme une vase de cristal le plus pur. And that's immediately odd because he never ever does think in French.

'Was it enough, Viv?' George asks him fondly. 'Shall we do it again?'

'Christ, Marie!'

'Did I do it nice?'

'Yes, you did everything.'

George wants to know: 'Is y'all satisfied?'

'Jesus, Marie, you ain't supposed to talk about it,' Bienville says, laying his finger over George's mouth.

'Why, Viv?'

'Because.'

'No, why?' asks George.

Because it is a secret just for them. It has to do with being kissing-cousins, Bienville says.

George asks uneasily: 'Is it bad, Viv?'

'Course it ain't bad. I wouldn't want you to do it if it was bad, would I?'

'No, Vivi,' says George in a doubtful voice.

'Well, thanks for that touching testimony of faith.'

Bienville says: 'I thought you'd like to have us a secret together. Don't y'all want a secret with Mr Viv?'

O, yes, he wants one. George says softly: 'I could go right off to sleep this second. O, I could sleep good now, Viv, don't you know?'

Well, he can't, so that is all about it. 'We have to make it down to lunch in case you forgot.'

'Yes, Viv,' his voice is very slow and sweet.

'Come on, wake up!' Bienville taps his cheek. 'Hey, hear me? Wake up!'

'Yes, I am fixing,' says the languid child.

'You all right?'

'Yes, Viv, I'm sweating,' says George.

'I'll have Mammy sponge you over.' Bienville is out of bed like a bomb. George can hear him hollering orders at Albert before he slams the bathroom door. 'Have Mammy 'tend on Mr George tout de suite. And get that crazy case Hippolyte up here, I want a hair-trim and I don't mean tomorrow, compris?'

Mammy comes in and lifts George off the bed like a doll, setting him carefully down on the floor. 'Mon tresór, mon amour, mon p'tit amant! What Mr Viv done with p'tit m'sieu, Albert? Look at, she quite sweatin', she quite pâle.'

'Ain't mah fau't, maman.'

Christ, that crazy Créole talk! Bienville can hear their sweet crying voices through the bathroom door. No wonder Marie is practically a nut case with those two neurotics on his neck!

That is the first thing he and Elaine will have when they have kids—white nurses.

'You two 'bout finished in there?' He strides into the bedroom, shrugging on his coat. 'Chrissakes, Mammy, set him down! You going to baby him to death!'

She is holding George on her lap while Albert ties his shoes. He is decked out in his finery again, eating a piece of brioche with Mammy's handkerchief under his chin. Dédé, who has materialised from somewhere, is holding his free hand.

'What in creation you want to give him that piece of cake for?' Bienville wants to know. 'You want to get him in trouble at table or what? You know the way he finicks when he got no appetite.'

194

George Woozy Washington says immediately: 'I done asked nounou for it, Viv. I'm hungry.'

George says: 'It is like after the grippe.'

'Well, thanks for the bouquet.'

Bienville takes the brioche away and stuffs it into Dédé's mouth. 'Try talking through that! And stand away from p'tit m'sieu, hear me? You're dirtying up his glove!' Christ, three of 'em breathing over him. No wonder he's gasping for oxygen half the time!

The little girl detaches herself and stands eating brioche and staring at Bienville with awed eyes. He turns to Mammy sharply. 'He ready or what?'

Yes, he is ready to go down. Mammy says softly: 'Mr Viv done play too rough with p'tit m'sieu. He all tuckered out. Look at she sweatin' round the little neck.'

'Chrissakes, Mammy, he's all right!'

'Ain' all right, Mr Viv. You goin' to fetch on his faintin' spells Gran' Monsieur not goin' to be exactly pleased.'

'You mind your business!' Christ, that cow! Just because he's got her milk in him she thinks she's got an option on Marie.

'And Madame ain' goin' to be too pleased, neither, she know Mr George's room ain't been fixed yet. Christienne, she complain two times she cain't get in to fix the bed. Hit's gettin' on to be lunch time, Mr Viv.'

'Et quoi?' Bienville gives her a wicked look. It's getting to be something with that yellow cow. She don't watch out, he's going to mix it for her with Tante.

We'll see who's boss of this galère, Mme Vache. He hauls his cousin off Mammy's lap.

'On your feet,' he tells him. 'Hold on tight, Mr Viv going to whizz you down the stairs.'

There is an instant protest from Mammy. 'Oh, don' you do it, Mr Viv! P'tit m'sieu not strong enough for that kind of shines.' Bienville cuts her short by catching George round the waist and rushing him through the door and down the stairs in one long swoop.

O, it is like flying. His feet have quite lost touch with the ground. He has shut his eyes but Viv has got him tight. He finds himself swung round three times and deposited in the hall.

'O, Viv, O, don't!' shrieks George, gasping and clutching at

195

his cousin for support. He is reeling and trying to get his breath before Viv gets bored with him.

'O, wait for me,' gasps George.

'Well, straighten up then,' Bienville tells him. 'You look like the Hunchback of Notre Dame.'

George stands up cautiously. He feels a spasm pass through his chest. 'O, Viv,' he licks his lips and whispers voicelessly: 'O, I feel bad.'

'Aw, Christ, Marie!' explodes Bienville disgustedly. 'It's no good trying to give you any fun.'

It's unbelievable that running down a crummy staircase should produce this kind of effect. Those crazy violet circles round his eyes, when in creation did they happen?

'Chrissakes, Marie, you are a punk!' He is suddenly sick of the whole thing. This forever gearing himself to a kid cousin who can never quite keep up the pace. Being stuck with him like now. Bienville blames the Sioux directly for that. He considers it a typical piece of Sioux legislation that at nine years of age the Dauphin is still without a single kid of his own age and class to play with!

He is the Dauphin, the Moumou, the Souvenir and the rest of the crap, but all the Sioux can come up with is that coon comedy duo, Albert et Dédé!

He looks like he is going to throw a fit!

'You fixing to be souffrant like Uncle Beau it's going to bore the piss.' He puts out an impatient hand for George to hang on to. 'Christ, can't you move or what?'

'In a minute. I am coming.' George is looking intently at the floor as if he is reading off his answers there. 'Now I can, Viv.'

'Chrissakes, Marie. That the best you can do? You'll get me sold down river. Whyn't you say before you felt sick? You go into lunch like that, you'll have papa on my neck. You know whatever happens to you it is always my fault.'

'I won't say, Viv,' gasps George. His voice is very faint. It seems to be taking him all his strength just to stand on his feet.

Bienville says unkindly: 'Better hadn't with that voice. What in creation you keep looking at the floor for?' Bienville squats down mischievously, pretending to look too. He points out a vein in the marble with his finger: 'Hey, here's a good one! Hey, read that out!'

'O shut up,' George whispers furiously. 'It's bad enough without.'

'Without what?' He's crazy all right—that punk in the sailor suit! George is attempting to walk with a stiff, delicate, compass-like movement that strikes his cousin as the funniest thing yet. 'You look like a June-bug!' Bienville teases him. 'Hey, June-bug, you'll never make it before Gustave announces "Madame-est-servie".'

'O, I detest you!' George flares up suddenly. 'You stop away from me, you Viv! Tu m'en gazes! Tu m'en gazes! Tu m'en gazes!'

Oh, Marie is fabulous when he is mad like that. Bienville can see at least half the hall reflected in his eyes. 'O, you are disgusting for me,' George calls out. 'I feel so bad I could die. O, there is like cold water running down my arms.'

'Tell Mr Viv.'

'No, I will not tell you. You are méchant for me.' His small fierce face is stained a faint pink with temper. Bienville can see his heart leaping above the sailor blouse top. He says in a haughty voice: 'I wish to go alone into the salon, Bienville. I do not wish your aid, compris?'

Oh, Marie is out of sight. 'You're for me, boy,' Bienville calls out.

'Well, you are not for me,' screeches King Woozy, 'so fous-moi la paix and bloody push off.'

Oh, he is mad all right. It strikes Bienville that this time he has gone too far. For a brief moment he considers asking George's pardon, but then decides against it almost at once. It is not a thing that has ever been fashionable around Benoirs, to ask forgiveness of a child. Even you got punished without you earned it Benoirs will make it up to you some other way. Bienville decides the easiest way to settle his account is to pay it with a kiss. He catches his cousin round the neck and whispers: 'Hey, Bobcat! You still mad at Mr Viv?' It works like a charm.

'O, I am sorry,' calls out this ardent nut case, flinging his arms round Bienville's neck. 'O, I am sorry I was bad for you, Viv.'

It is utterly unbelievable! It takes this nut case to beg your pardon for something you have done! The sight of King Woozy in his celebrated sailor suit forgiving you like crazy is too much for Bienville. He just falls about.

'What y'all laughing at, Vivi?' asks Woozy, who is—but natch —beginning to laugh as well.

Say, that pale kid is chic all right. Bienville intends to make it up to him this very afternoon. He means to tease ol' Miz' to let him take him to a movie, though it would probably be easier to get permission from the Vatican. One of those Godawful nature films Thingo is kinky for. It will bore the crap, of course, and Marie will probably throw up with excitement at the sight of all those darling baby seals or whatever they are currently showing on the screen. Marcel will be detailed to drive them at this official 30 m.p.h. which has been set down by Sioux legislation for any drive involving the Dauphin. And that sad sack from the Agence will materialise, weighed down with Sten guns and hover during the entire proceedings in case of the attempted abduction of Dauphin Benoir. And Bienville will most certainly miss his late afternoon call to Paris because it will be a miracle if he can ever get out of the house before four-thirty on account Woozy's semi-sacred after-luncheon nap and also that macabre 'goûter' of sponge cake and a saucer of jam which Tante always subjects him to the minute he opens his eyes. And then the Grand Lever with Mammy and Albert getting him up fit to kill in his best blacks and Dédé only leaving go of him long enough for them to get his arms through his sleeves. And then that crazy chorus of farewells —'Au 'voir, au 'voir, moumou-chéri. Amuse-toi bien!' 'Au 'voir, au 'voir, nounou-chérie. Merci, merci!'

And coming back to routine interrogation by Tante Simon Legree: 'Bienville, why have you kept him out so late? I hope you didn't permit moumou to eat anything, Bienville? That would be all we need now, for him to catch an infection, Bienville!'

And Woozy at the dinner table still bemused by seals, with that serene, dreaming look on his face that always goes down big with Tante. He will get sent from table for finicking with his food and there will be the final bore of smuggling up some dessert to him and sitting on the bed trying to get through to Paris while Woozy sits up statching Mont Blanc and dipping into Bienville's brandy glass while he recaps the whole movie in a mixture of French and Ol' Kintuck. The whole prospect is torture in the last degree, but Bienville will do it for his favourite cousin, the pale, the ineffable, Marie Benoir with the beautiful new violet circles round his eyes.

He spies approaching, with his hard bright eye, the figure of Gustave, that uppity Maître d'hôtel of Tante's, crossing the hall.

'Hey! Where you going?' asks Bienville in his best slave-owner's voice. Gustave is nearly white, and Bienville has it specially in for him.

'I am announcing lunch,' declares this scented coon, his white blood mantling, or whatever it's supposed to do, in his cheeks.

'It's a delusion,' Bienville tells him and jerks his head towards the dining room. 'In there, hear me? You can announce lunch in ten minutes' time.'

Gustave tries standing his ground, but Bienville asks trickily: 'You fixing to get slung out or what?' He takes a running jump at Gustave and slams the dining room door in his disgruntled face. 'Do as you're bid, nigger. Hey, good looking'—he snaps his fingers at George—'there's a splendid dessert in there. Viv's fixing to get you two servings of that nice thing. Fair deal?'

Vivi and Woozy are going towards the salon like lovers with their arms round each others' waist. At the doors of the salon Bienville detaches himself from George.

'Okay, Gumdrop. See you at the top.'

He runs a cool, proprietary eye over his cousin. 'Breathe through your nose, boy,' says Bienville, who can be a Sioux with the best of them.

He goes into the salon and thinks directly: hey, it's happened. The pretty mister is wearing his most inscrutable smile, and Tante's face is an education on account she has extremely recently been declared a disaster zone.

Yes, ma'am. The Sheriff sure 'nough caught up with you. It's going to be an interesting lunch!

The British Punk, Bienville notes with satisfaction, is nowheres around.

Bienville hopes the gentleman has beat it for Punksville, then they can all get back to Paris and start living.

17

Zero

Castleton is saying as far as he is concerned that is a LOAD OF OLD LUMBER.

'What is the matter, Armand?' whispers Liane.

There are signs that the talk is breaking down. He hopes it is only temporary.

He wants another cigarette. She takes the long slim holder from him, refits it, lights the fresh cigarette with her own and puts it back into his mouth.

'He can be difficult, your brother-in-law,' Liane says. 'We shall be here forever.'

They have been lying on her bed since after lunch. At four o'clock Benoir had made the call on an impulse. He has been put through to his brother-in-law at his office without difficulty, but Vince is taking an unexpectedly tough line. Benoir has had to make a quick reappraisal of the situation. It is quite likely there will be some hard bargaining.

While waiting for the British comeback he reacquaints himself with his mistress's breast. 'Let me see, Li, where are the cicatrices?' he asks her, curiously. 'Where did he make the cuts, your plastic fellow?'

She guides his small lemon-coloured hand.

'Tiens, one can hardly feel them. He is formidable, your fellow.' He kisses the high, stiff lilac-coloured nipples and tells her: 'It is still too high, but when it has dropped a little it will look completely natural.'

She kisses her small lover with amused affection. He always gets such pleasure out of anything new. Benoir is like a child in that respect, thinks Liane. She indicates the telephone with her head. 'What is happening there, if anything?'

They have come to an impasse, Armand tells her. He still hopes it is only temporary. She hopes so too. 'What is he waiting for, your Castleton?'

His Castleton is waiting for her Benoir to come up with an offer. A kind of Versailles Treaty, to be exact. So far the terms have not been acceptable. 'Why don't you make some sort of compromise, then?' Liane wants to know. 'Why must you always complicate everything?'

He merely points to his cigarette holder. When she has given it to him again, she urges: 'Tell him, tell him that Mimi is enceinte and that the little boy is fretting for him. Pauvre petit bonhomme! He will go back at once,' predicts Liane. 'Armand, where is the difficulty?'

There is no difficulty, but he will not do it. 'I will not catch anyone through their emotions.'

'But if it is the truth? He loves Mimi and he loves her boy. It is your duty to tell him if they need him.'

'I shall not do my duty,' he assures her. He asks instead: 'What does de Chassevent say to the new bosom?'

Nothing. 'He paid for it,' says Liane.

Benoir makes a dismissing noise. 'He is abysmal, your husband.'

Liane looks admiringly at her vivid little cockbird of a lover who is lying with one of his legs flung over hers, and his monkey asleep directly above his head on the pillow. She takes his hand which is so much smaller than her own and starts to kiss the fingers. 'Armand, do it for me,' she asks him.

He smiles at her, but his eyes have taken on a listening look. Negotiations have reopened. She hears the loud English voice saying: 'What's the position?'

The position is precisely where they left it.

'The ball's in your court,' says Castleton.

Mon dieu, what an expression.

'Oh, tell him, tell him,' Liane urges. 'Armand, it is taking too long. Yves will be back. I must start dressing.'

He holds up an imperious finger. 'Less noise.'

He tells his brother-in-law coldly: 'I made you a certain promise, Vince. You haven't told me yet whether you accept it.'

'What promise was that?' says Castleton, vague on purpose. Bloody Benoir pride. It is half killing him to have to say it again. Let him come out with it. He hears the prideful voice of his brother-in-law saying with difficulty: 'I give you my word that there will be no repetition of a certain incident.'

He sounds like the Dauphin at his most maddening. 'It's not enough,' says Castleton before Armand has finished. He asks him roughly: 'How are you anyway, you silly old prick?' He still very much likes Armand. He has unaccountably just had a vision of his brother-in-law as a child hopping so hopefully in and out of his sick mother's bed.

He likes him enormously. Armand says in a concerned voice: 'How are you making out, Vince? I rang the St Charles but it was full. It seems the whole town is in the grip of this terrible Cotton Convention.'

'Yes,' Castleton says. 'I'm at the office.'

'My God,' exclaims his brother-in-law. He sounds acutely embarrassed.

'Don't be an ass,' says Castleton quite civilly. 'There's a suite. Are you speaking from 38?'

He doesn't say from home, thinks Armand. 'No, I'm with Li.'

Castleton can just see him 'en grand lit', as the Dauphin would say, with Madame de listening in between the passes on one of those bloody extensions.

Armand says: 'Do you want something from home, Vince?'

'I want Bone to send some of my gear round,' Castleton says. 'I'll get the office to ring him.'

'Who?'

'My man,' says Castleton. 'I'll get the office to do it.'

Armand says: 'I can pass a message to your valet, Vince. Tell me what you want.'

'No, scrub it,' Castleton says. 'Does he ask about me?'

'What do you think?'

'I suppose he's worrying everyone's guts out.'

Benoir says: 'Fretting is something the Dauphin really understands.'

They both laugh, and Armand says: 'We have told him you are on a business trip. Like that you can make it either long or short.'

'Clever stuff.'

Benoir says: 'Make it short, Vince.'

He is immediately furious with himself for having said it. He flushes so that Liane calls out: 'Oh, for goodness' sake, Armand, your pride is quite ridiculous. Tell him the truth and start to dress or Yves will find us like this.'

'Let him,' says Benoir. 'I am just in the mood.'

Liane insists: 'I find you horrible. You wouldn't sacrifice one particle of your pride for that poor child who is crying like that for his father.'

'His father is dead,' he tells her coldly. 'You mustn't let your sympathy confuse you.'

But she sweeps on. 'Even Yves has more proper feeling. He telephoned Marguerite this morning to ask after his godson.'

Benoir says laughing: 'Better look out there, Li. If there's a divorce, de Chassevent will sling you out and try to press his suit on my wretched sister.'

She says hotly: 'My God, you are hard, Benoir. You are as hard as your sister.'

He says: 'Don't speak of what you don't understand.' He hauls Ouistiti down from above his head and dumps him on her belly. 'Amuse yourself with your small lover.'

'Ah, Armand, you are a pig!' calls out Liane. 'He will pinch me, you beast.' She jumps out of bed and flies into her dressing room shrieking.

Armand says into the phone: 'That was Li. Could you hear her?'

'Yes.'

Armand says: 'She has had her pubic hair dyed to match the hair on her head. I find that fantastic.'

Ouistiti has rolled himself up into a fast-breathing ball in the hollow of Armand's neck. Castleton can hear his brother-in-law murmuring: 'Vite, vite, fais dodo, mon chouchou.'

Castleton says: 'When you've quite finished.'

Armand says tenderly: 'He is asleep now, Vince.'

Well, hooray. 'Are you alone now?' Castleton wants to know. 'Apart from your beastly ape?'

'Yes. Is it private?'

No, it's not private but it could take a long time. 'Depends on what you've got to offer,' says Castleton, the British trader.

Benoir says: 'Nothing. I have already given you my promise.'

'Look, don't give me that again,' Castleton says at once. 'Just don't bloody annoy me.' He feels astonishingly cheerful and laughs outright as he hears Benoir say in the guarded tones usually reserved for blackmailers: 'What do you want, Vincent?'

'The lot,' says Castleton. 'Liberté, Égalité and Fraternité—less stick for the Dauphin.'

Benoir says: 'I cannot promise for my sister.'

'That lets me out, then,' says Castleton.

Benoir says: 'You must remember Mimi's nerves.'

'You do it,' says Castleton.

Benoir points out: 'She is his mother, Vincent.'

'I know,' says Castleton. 'Have you seen his hands?'

'No.'

'Then shut up,' says Castleton.

Miss Shuter comes out of the inner office and in a whisper says she is going to order something to be brought in for him. 'You've had no lunch, Mr Castleton.'

'No. It's all right, thanks, Miss Shuter.'

Armand says immediately: 'You haven't eaten yet, Vincent?'

'So what? I'll go out and get some dinner later.'

That silly prick Armand is carrying on alarming. His pride and his conscience and his affection for his brother-in-law are all giving him hell together. 'Mon dieu, Vince, you can't eat out like that in restaurants.'

'Why not?' Castleton says. He has picked a very good place for restaurants. 'New Orleans is famous for 'em.'

'No, seriously,' Benoir says. 'Let me give orders for meals to be sent to you from home. Marcel will bring them to you.'

'Don't you dare,' Castleton says. 'I'm delighted to be shut of those dinners.' If he comes back that will be one of the first things to go. *If* he comes back. He asks his brother-in-law bluntly: 'D'you want to hear the conditions?'

Yes, he will hear his terms. Benoir says coolly: 'I will do my best to meet you.'

Castleton assures him: 'There aren't a lot. It's just a general anti-slavery bill.'

There is a Benoirish pause. Castleton says: 'Are you with me, old darling?'

Yes he is listening.

'One,' says Castleton. 'One A, One B, One C. Two,' says Castleton, 'Two A. Three.'

'Is that all?'

'No. Keep your bloody son off my stepson, Benoir. He's a disgrace. If I ever catch him round George I shall give him the biggest bloody hiding of his life.'

Benoir says coldly: 'My son is getting married. It will be at least a year before he sees his cousin again after his honeymoon.'

'Hooray,' says Castleton, rudely.

'For the rest . . .' continues Benoir.

'Yes?'

'I am afraid I cannot meet you.'

'Why not?'

'I cannot make promises for my sister to which she will almost certainly not agree.'

'You can, you know,' says Castleton. 'Don't give me that, Benoir.'

'No. This is between you and Mimi. If you care to discuss it in a civilised way with her that is a different matter.'

'No fear,' says Castleton. 'I'm not going anywhere near your beastly sister.'

Benoir says: 'Is that final?'

'Yes,' Castleton says. 'I think I'll pack it in, anyway. I don't think I could take any more.'

'Am I to tell that to my sister, Vincent?'

'If you like.'

Benoir says in unmistakable tones: 'I hope you understand, Vincent, that I am on my sister's side completely. Marguerite is a splendid mother and her son adores her. If she seems a little severe at times it is because her nerves have still not recovered from the shock of her husband's death . . .'

'I'm not dead yet, old dear,' Castleton says.

'. . . and the strain of her disastrous marriage to that fanatic Davis.'

'Don't perjure yourself, Benoir,' Castleton says shortly.

205

The actual talk has come to an end. There is an exchange of civilities. Armand says: 'Will you sell the house, Vince?'

'Oh, good Lord, yes. Directly I've wound up here I shall go back to London.'

Armand says affectionately: 'Let me know when you decide to go, Vince, and I will put you on to my agent. He is a Jew, but he is completely honest.'

In all seriousness, he is actually saying it! Good old Benoir!

'What are you laughing at, Vince?'

'Benoir, you're gorgeous!'

Armand says wryly: 'My poor Vince, you are stuck with all those bidets.'

On the contrary, the Benoir improvements will bump up the value of the property enormously. 'I must remember to send Mim her cut,' says Castleton.

There is a cool pause.

'Don't be an ass, Benoir,' says Castleton.

Benoir says diffidently: 'I shall see you then, Vince, before I leave for Paris?' He sounds exactly like Mim's chap.

'Shall I see y'all, papa darling?' the pale, shy Dauphin with his bold touch.

'Yes, rather,' says Castleton warmly. 'When d'you leave?'

On Wednesday. 'Viv's wedding is for Sunday, you know.' Armand says: 'We have decided to fly puss over in a mask.'

We.

Castleton says: 'I suppose Mim and the boy will be living with you?'

No. He intends installing them at the Georges V apartment. His Marie and Marguerite are better apart. Armand adds quickly: 'They love each other, of course.'

Of course.

Armand says: 'Vince, I shall try to have your house vacated for you as soon as possible. It may take another week till everything is clear. There are seventeen servants to send back to Paris, you know.'

'I should hire the *Égalité*.'

Armand says: 'Vince, I will never be able to repay you for what you have done. Perhaps when we meet next week we can talk about it again. It might still be possible to reach an agreement.'

'I shouldn't think so,' Castleton says. 'What about the Harem?'

'The Harem flies with us on Friday.' Armand says: 'Poor puss.'

'What are you going to tell him?'

At the moment he has no idea. Benoir adds typically: 'We will think of something.' He asks his brother-in-law: 'Where shall we meet, Vince, on Monday?'

'How about the Lafayette bar at the St Charles?'

Ah non, not at an hotel.

Of course not. Castleton says: 'I was forgetting the Benoir purdah. What about here, then, in my private suite, where you can't be got at by Miss Shuter?'

D'accord. He will be at the office at three o'clock next Monday sans faute.

Sans faute. Castleton says: 'I'll have the champagne really cold for you.' He adds: 'Give my love to Mrs Castleton. Tell her I recommend a refresher course at the new Chantilly stable.'

'What's that?'

Castleton returns vaguely: 'I thought your cousin's training policy forbade the use of the whip?'

Benoir rings off immediately. A flush washes over his face and neck. He waits until it has subsided, then he calls out: 'What are you putting on in there, Li?'

She calls from her dressing room: 'It is my green dress, Armand.'

'Do I know it?'

'No, it's new.'

'At once come here and show it me.'

She comes in presently, preceded by a heavy, heady scent. She sees to her astonishment that he has finished with the telephone. Her dress is of a parakeet green.

He says smiling: 'You have good taste, my Li.' He kisses her. 'That is a good dress.' He is quiet and smiling. She asks: 'What has emerged, Armand?'

'Nothing.' He says: 'I am going to take a bath.'

She follows him into the bathroom, aghast. He tells her: 'He asked too much. Nothing more can be done.' She notices he does not add 'for the moment'.

'So it is final?'

207

Yes, it is final. He advises her: 'Don't sit there, my darling. You will wet your pretty dress.'

She is beginning to sob. It is the wrong thing to do but she can't help herself.

Benoir says quietly: 'Eh bien, Li.'

Liane calls out: 'Oh, what will he do? What will he do, Benoir?'

He observes softly: 'My darling, I am wet.' She is trying to put her arms round his neck. 'Oh, that poor child, Benoir. What will he do?'

'What should he do? He will get over it.' He is looking detachedly at her tears. 'Come, Li, don't cry any more. Your face looks like a sunset on the Delta already.'

She says incoherently: 'He is so sweet, Benoir. He is so adorable when he looks at one over his tartine with those big eyes.'

All kids are sweet, he tells her, with or without tartines. 'Even that cannibal Viv was sweet when he was small.' He is very pale. A line of white is showing wickedly under the pupils of his eyes. He rises from his bath. 'Alors, c'est terminé, Li?'

She nods. He is folding himself in a huge white towel. 'You must stop, my dear. Everything is coming off.' He picks her eyelashes gently from her left cheek and hands them to her. 'Only the Dauphin can emerge unscathed from Floods at the Delta.' He gives her a cool kiss.

'Oh, Benoir,' whispers Liane. 'Oh, Benoir.'

'Quoi Benoir?' He tells her: 'Here, take your foot and dry it nicely for me.'

He puts his small left foot into her lap. The slender gold chain round the ankle has been soldered on in imitation of a slave's shackle. There is a small name plate dangling from it inscribed: 'Property of L. Laurent de Chassevent.'

Nothing could be further from the truth, of course. Liane thinks compassionately: he doesn't belong to anyone, my poor darling. She dries the small foot, powdering it lavishly and kissing the instep and the sole. He asks her in mock surprise: 'Have I provoked this rush of maternal feeling, Li?'

'Armand.'

'What is it, Li?'

She can see that her messed-up make-up and unequal eyelashes are already getting on his nerves. She says as quietly as she can: 'She is so hard with him, your sister. She is so severe, Armand.'

He says in a cold voice: 'Stop it, Li.'

But she can't stop it. She calls out impulsively: 'Now he has no one to stand between him and your sister. Oh, she will lead him a dog's life, that poor child.' She says: 'Please stand between them, Benoir. Do it for my sake.' She says: 'He is my godson, Benoir. I love him so. Do it for my sake.' She says: 'He is so sweet, Benoir.'

He looks at her musingly for a long while. He thinks: she is probably imagining the Dauphin is our child. Then he says, not unkindly: 'Life is a boring business, Li. Don't make it worse.'

That is the big danger with Benoir, of course. You have only got to really bore him once to get 'The Key'.

'The Key' is your own latch-key dipped in gold. Sent back with a brief but charming note, it marks the end of an affaire absolutely. Several of her friends have experienced 'The Key' and Liane will not deceive herself that she would be the exception.

He takes both of Liane's hands in his. Li's 'proletarian hands', he calls them.

They are white, with strong turquoise veins. Beyond that there is nothing to recommend them.

The thumbs turn back slightly, which is amusing, but the much manicured nails are really bad.

He kisses her finger tips which she has always kept a rosy pink since the day at Le Touquet when he had asked her if she had been picking strawberries.

He says very gently: 'You can look happy, Li. I have no intention of abandoning him.'

'Ah, Armand!' exclaims Liane, kissing his hand.

Benoir remarks: 'You know, you look charming when you are compassionate, Li. Your caste gives you a heightened tenderness. I find it extraordinary, that.'

He drops his towel. He says: 'I suppose it is too late to do anything about it now. What a pity you are dressed.'

18

Naval Chat

Directly he comes off the line from Armand he asks them to have a
personal call put through to London.

Commander C. A. Castleton.

He doesn't particularly feel like coping with the affectionate
yelps of his sister-in-law at the moment. Old Syb is a dear and all
that, but her point-to-point gush is pretty hard to take at the best
of times. It amazes him now to think that before his marriage he
had considered that kind of voice to be quite normal.

While waiting for London he stares out at the curious shadow-
less day, with the whole of New Orleans dissolving under a milk
white sky. It is oppressively hot already.

That stiff-necked prick of a Benoir and his ruddy loyalties!
Needs a bomb under him. Mim's dead lucky to have him for a
brother. He still smiles when he remembers the way that ass had
slammed the receiver down, when he'd recommended the refresher course for Mim.

He asks the office: 'What's happening to my call to London, if
anything?'

Miss Shuter answers archly over the intercom: 'We did have London, Mr Castleton, but we've lost them. I'm afraid they're being rather naughty.'

No hurry. He's quite happy to wait. 'It's only for a chat with my brother.'

She's a decent stick, Shuter. It's a bind she's keen on him, but she's managed to keep it in proportion to the last. This winding up business must come as a bit of a blow to her. It can't be much fun to have to go back to Mum or a bedsitter at Purley or wherever. Actually there's no earthly reason why she shouldn't stop on in New Orleans, and Castleton intends to see what he can do towards bullying his successor into taking her.

Perhaps he might do worse than emulate Benoir and make a gift of Shuter to Ferdy Meresdale. Who knows but what he might turn out to be 'chouchou' for her.

Bloody Benoirs. He has had his marriage in the biggest possible way and doesn't want to go back to any part of it.

Miss Shuter is saying: 'I think we're getting warm now, Mr Castleton. Any minute now and we're in business.'

There is another what Miss Shuter likes to call 'delayette' during which she asks him: 'When are we going to see Mrs Castleton at the office? I think she's absolutely out of this world. The Paris branch sent me every single cutting of your wedding. It's made quite a little book.'

Miss Shuter says: 'I'm abject about this delay. Shall I have something sent up while you're waiting? You must be absolutely starving.'

No thanks. He has only this one call to make and then he's going.

Miss Shuter says: 'How's Mrs Castleton's little boy? We were absolutely thrilled to see him the other day. The whole office went mad about him. Isn't he the image of his mother, though? Oh, yes,' Miss Shuter answers herself with enthusiasm. 'Oh, yes he is!'

There had been a memorable visit to the office by the Dauphin a few days ago at Castleton's instigation. The carry-on before and after it had been unprecedented.

'What d'you want with moumou at your bank, Vincent? There is nothing for him there. He will bore you with his questions, voilà tout.'

'I want to show him off to everybody. I can't get over him. You come too, darling. I can't get over you, either.'

'*Ah non, vous savez! Spare me your office. I shall send moumou to you after he has made his nap, at four o'clock.*'

'*I had thought of driving him down in the Bentley, darling. She's as smooth as cream. I promise you I'll stick to thirty.*'

'*Just the same it will make him sick. He is not accustomed to your driving.*'

'*Chance is a fine thing.*'

'*Comment?*'

'*It's an English saying, darling.*'

'*I shall send him to you then, sans faute, at four o'clock. With Deckers. Like that there is less danger of the press becoming a nuisance. Benoir will be furious with me if there is a picture. I shall send Mammy with him too, Poilu. When you are sick of him you can throw him out and she can bring him home again.*'

He had replied dryly: '*Thanks, darling. It's going to be fun.*' To which she had answered: '*It is vour wish, Vincent.*'

It had been a washout, of course. Though not total. He had enjoyed his punch-up with the press.

At a minute to four he had gone down in the street to wait for the boy, watched, needless to say, by the whole bloody building.

The flash bulbs had started flickering like heat lightning the minute he had shown his nose. Bloody newspapers and their damn impertinent questions. He had been delighted to show them the greatest non-co-operation.

At four o'clock precisely the famous white 'Ambulance' flying the tricolour had driven up and had started the cameras whirring like lawn-mowers when Deckers had leapt out, seized the Dauphin by the scruff and hurled him at his stepfather like a mailbag. They had Mammy bundled out of the car and had bulldozed their way through the lobby into the lift with a newspaper held in front of the Dauphin's face before a picture could be taken.

Three cheers for Deckers of the Agence.

A few triers who had tried a bit too hard had got their fingers caught in the lift. And that's all right. That's for their bloody libellous cartoons. Any time, chaps, as far as Castleton is concerned.

The Dauphin had been led off to be tarted up like royalty, and then led back to the boardroom by Miss Shuter and the pretty brown woman who is his nurse.

Mammy had said in her soft respectful voice: 'Sir, Madame say for p'tit m'sieu to keep she coat on, 'case she catch de courant d'air, sir.'

All eyes had been turned on the pale princeling, dressed all in white, with his mother's impeccable taste and an almost arrogant simplicity.

Bloody spoilt brat of Castleton's.

He could see them thinking it. He had said promptly and nastily: 'Look, no smoking, please. Mrs Castleton's boy can't take it.' The 'please' had been the rudest thing about it.

They'd put their smokes out resentfully and Ferdy Meresdale had said in his ventriloquist's voice: 'Castleton with Young. Ha, Ha, Ha. Bloody inconsiderate bounder.'

Mim's beautiful chap had been very good, climbing on to Castleton's knee and climbing off again immediately to be introduced. Doing the social round and shaking hands with everybody, including Castleton, in his efforts to be polite, and obviously creeping all over at the very sight of Ferdy Meresdale, Ian Carrington-Clarke, Tommy Scott, 'Bwana' Feilding, Weston-Burt, et al. And sitting good as gold, trembling ever so slightly, in his pretty white reefer coat which is collared and lined with white mink, no less, with the mercury standing at eighty.

'Are you cold, darling?'

And the air-conditioning switched off without a by-your-leave by Castleton, the Inconsiderate Bounder.

Starting to sweat. Eyelids, upper lip and neck all coated with silver.

'Are you too hot, darling?'

And everything switched on again, regardless.

Bloody gales. Papers flying all over the shop.

Silly bugger.

Have a heart, Castleton.

And the reefer coat eased off by degrees to reveal the full glory of his white sailor suit and the mad violence of his heart skipping and bounding in the top of his blouse.

Sipping ice-water throughout the meeting . . . doesn't he ever want to pee, Castleton? . . . from a sterilised crystal tumbler which has been specially brought from home.

He is on no account to drink from other vessels, Vincent.

Assuaging his unassuagable thirst, breathing through his nose, obeying Christ knows what other injunctions from St Charles Street H.Q. The pale, shy wizard from Martinique, with his wild regard and his sweet creepy smile which never fails to strike alarm in the beholder, and which is nothing more than shyness.

He had sat staring unwinkingly at the lot of them, which had done Carrington-Clarke's nervous tic a bit of no good.

'Pourquoi fait-il des grimaces, ce monsieur là?'

The wizard's English, Castleton has noticed, is always a bit rocky, probably because the wizard only appears when Mim's chap's in a bit of a flap. The remark, of course, had only been for Castleton's private ear. *Personal remarks, moumou, one doesn't make them.*

And coming off Carrington-Clarke at last with a pleasurable sigh, and on to Ferdy Meresdale with renewed vigour.

Old Ferdy, who is as near an albino as dammit is to swearing, had been a perfect godsend to the novelty-loving wizard who had spent at least half-an-hour taking in the conical head with the queer glassy hair like white nylon, the vivid rose complexion, the almond-shaped eyes with their great palpitating pupils of an almost navy blue. But the thing that had utterly intrigued had been Meresdale's hands which are red and scaly like fowl's feet, with the middle and index fingers of the right dyed to a bright mahogany with nicotine.

He had scarcely been able to drag his eyes away to whisper: 'Il est bien curieux, ce blond monsieur, vous ne trouvez pas, papa-chéri?'

And Meresdale suddenly shooting out a mahogany finger and saying out of the corner of his mouth: 'Think you'll know me next time, young Benoir?' Which had completely taken the wind out of the wizard's sails.

'And don't give us that shy stuff, here. It won't wash, yer know. We've got yer number, young Benoir. You can speak English all right when you want ter, can't yer, eh?'

'Yes, sir.'

'Oh, ah. Then speak it. Don't bugger about.'

And jabbing the bright rufous finger in Castleton's direction: 'What d'yer make of him, eh? Bloody awkward blighter, isn't he? Bit of a mauvais teep, what?'

And little Benoir's cool reply: 'I think you are un mauvais type,

214

vous-même, if you ask me. D'abord c'est honteux de se promener avec des mains comme ça. It should not be impossible for you to wash your hands properly at your age.'

This unexpected comeback had got a roar from everybody except Weston-Burt, and Bwana Feilding had called out: 'Thanks for saying what we've all been thinking for years.'

After this sortie, Mim's chap had sat back calmly, every inch a Sioux, with half the office furniture reflecting in his eyes.

'So yer like him, eh?'

'Naturally I like him. He is my father-in-law.'

To which Ferdy had replied rather wittily: 'How's yer wife?'

This sally had provoked much girlish laughter among the ladies who had been sitting by their bosses in case anything needed taking down, and Miss Shuter had fluted out: 'Lord Meresdale's teasing you, isn't that a shame?'

Little Benoir had retorted calmly: 'It is not important to me what he does.'

After that Miss Shuter, Miss Glaze, Mrs Brodrick and Miss Copley had started handing round the tea, to the immense satisfaction of the Dauphin. He had been very organised, setting out his cup and saucer, plate, spoon and napkin which have been sent from home in a small picnic case to be brought into him at the proper time by Mammy. A similar case, with the Dauphin's toilet things had already been placed in Castleton's washroom.

This case, Castleton had been told, would contain a hypodermic which had bothered him quite a bit in spite of Mim's calm assurances. 'It will almost certainly not be needed, but if it is it will be quite easy for you to give it him. My poor Poilu, don't look worried. He will keep perfectly still. I have told him he must let you do it.'

Tea had been a great success, with the Dauphin allowing the cushiony Mrs Broderick to tie on his napkin.

'C'est presque comme un fif o'clock, n'est-ce pas?' And telling Mrs Broderick, to whom he had taken a fancy, that at the fif o'clocks of his Tante Marie, while tea was the 'boisson de rigueur', coffee and chocolate were also invariably served, as were petits fours secs, liqueurs, gâteaux assortis, sandwiches and bonbons sur choix.

Mrs Broderick had said rather dazedly 'how nice' when the

Dauphin had further honoured her by a lightly sketched-in outline of his Tante Marie's indisposition. This had fortunately been in French, which Mrs Broderick understands only slightly.

He had helped himself joyously to four lumps of sugar, remarking: 'C'est bon, ça, j'adore le thé Anglais!'—and to the wan Carrington-Clarke he had said kindly: 'You must drink it while it is 'ot. It will cheer you up. You are a little triste, if one may say so.' And engaging him in a conversation, the gist of which Castleton couldn't quite catch because of making small talk with Miss Copley. But the glazed look in Carrington-Clarke's eye had indicated that he was either getting Shiloh and the Davis boys or one of the gamier exploits of 'my cousin Viv at Paris'.

Blowing wholeheartedly into his own tea: 'Ah, merde, c'est chaud alors,' he had explained: 'This is what my Uncle Benoir does when Ouistiti is impatient for his soupe.'

This had led to an exchange of notes on monkeys with Bwana Feilding ('they are chouchou' had been the Dauphin's contribution). It had come out that old Bwana had kept three of them during his term on the Gold Coast (the first the office had come to hear of it).

'Jolly interesting little blighters.'

And the rude Meresdale calling out: 'Oi, Wis*titty*!' and throwing Bwana a biscuit.

Mim's fellow had accepted his allotted share of biscuit (a Huntley and Palmer's petit beurre) with great enthusiasm— 'Tiens, c'est un biscuit Anglais? May I please keep half for Dédé, papa darling?'

And the resultant outcry: 'Why can't he have a whole one to himself?'

Christ, Castleton.

What's the idea?

Mean bugger.

And Mim's fellow supping tea and ice water both at the same time to everyone's fascination until Castleton had firmly put his glass away, which had immediately precipitated cries of

Let him have it, Castleton.

He's thirsty.

Poor little blighter.

His popularity had taken a further plunge when Mim's pale chap had refused Miss Copley's offer of a second cup of tea, explaining regretfully in his sweet languorous drawl: 'Thank you, ma'am, but I am not only ever permitted to have just the one,' and looking straight up into Castleton's face.

He had not enlightened them as to where this veto had come from, so they had probably been left with the impression that Castleton is a flinty-hearted bastard and a general purveyor of schrecklichkeit.

After tea Mim's concern had gone docilely with Miss Shuter to wash his hands again (he is as fastidious as Mim) and then to visit the outer offices and the American and Foreign Exchange departments where he had been voted a dish and a sexpot in his white sailor suit, and presented with a box of chocolates as big as himself.

It had never been opened, of course, but sent immediately, if not sooner, to a children's hospital.

There is a strict 'Mim' embargo on all outside gifts which runs, if he remembers rightly, something like this: 'If one accepted one present, one would be obliged to accept them all.' She had added: 'Can you imagine, Poilu, what it would be like if an immediate stop had not been put to this practice?' And he had answered rather rudely: 'No, I can't, darling. You tell me.'

According to Mim no present to her chap is ever bona fide, but are all made by crafty types wishing to curry favour.

He had come back from his visits in bad shape, his heart wagging furiously in his throat and loquacious with relief. He had made straight for Castleton's knee, chattering his head off and looking the dead spit of Armand. 'O, now I have seen everything, but everything in your whole bank, don't you know?'

Tommy Scott had scored a tremendous hit by remarking gravely: 'I hope you didn't take him anywhere near the vaults, Miss Shuter, or we'll be missing a few thou in the morning.' Which had struck Mim's fellow as the most priceless joke he had ever heard.

His wild high shrieks had pierced everybody's ear as he had called out in a perfect ecstasy of mirth: 'O, will y'all imagine if I done stole that money, Mr Castleton? O, I would got to keep it in my pot d' chambre like Dadee does at Mal Choisi.'

Dadee is Mammy's husband, he had informed the room at large: 'My cousin Viv says every time Dadee wants to piss he has to take his money out of the bank'—which had gone down a treat with the men but had a little nonplussed some of the ladies.

After this sally he had gone quiet, thinking no doubt of the report he would have to give of himself when he got home, because he had said quite suddenly: 'Mr Castleton, I was shy but I think it didn't show.'

A slight shaking had seized his limbs and Castleton had wound up the meeting without further ado, to the annoyance of Pip Weston-Burt who is not only not a family man, but will see himself further first. He had sat eyeing his blotter and muttering:

Bit arbitrary, Castleton.

Not good enough. Dim view. Bloody inconvenient.

I mean, what's the upshot?

I mean, one wants to be in London by the weekend for Aintree, *if* it's all the same to you.

He had ignored this protest completely and had silently dared the rest of them to exhibit, by look or word, the slightest surprise at his stepson, who by this time was saying goodbye to everybody with tears streaming down his face, as if it was the most usual thing in the world.

Of course everyone had behaved as if nothing was happening, though Carrington-Clarke's tic had suffered hideously in the process.

Old Bwana had offered: 'Want any help and so forth?' and had gone down with Castleton to deal with any lingering press. Together they had laid the weeping child on the back seat of the Rolls with his head on Mammy's lap, and piled him with robes.

Bwana's cheery 'He'll be all right now, old boy,' had clearly given Castleton to understand that he, personally, didn't give the poor little blighter very long.

The situation had worsened rapidly on the drive home. There had been endless stops while Mammy had held his head, and Castleton had held his head, and Deckers had screened him from public view with his villainous mac, while he had retched his heart out, clutching his stepfather and calling out: 'O! O, my Redeemer. O, I am splashing your shoes,' and finally bringing it all up, tea, water and the somehow pathetic remains of his share of the petit beurre.

Mim's face had been an absolute study when she had seen the cortège come in.

It had been impossible to tell which had annoyed her most, the giant box of chocolates or the unexplained half of an English biscuit still clutched in the hand of her half-dead child.

But the strangest reaction had come from the kid himself. He still regards his visit to the office not as a harrowing experience best forgotten, but as a delightful red-letter day to be discussed in detail again and again, and second only to *Woodland Friends* in popularity as a pre-dinner topic on the gallery. Especially the fresh-faced portrait of the Founder, Henry Cecil Castleton, his hands laid protectingly, if a trifle smugly, on the heads of a negro boy and girl, to whom the Dauphin has taken a liking and insists on alluding to as 'M. votre père' despite the bag-wig and muslin cravat.

Castleton is on the point of saying 'This is no bloody good' when he hears the London operator say: 'Putting you through now. Sorry to have kept you,' and London voice says: 'Can Commander C. A. Castleton take a personal call from New Orleans, Canal?'

He can hear old Cecil, as usual, delightedly bellowing before the final connection has been made, and then the office being told to 'Go ahead, please, Canal.'

The line is so good that he can hear the Knightsbridge traffic, but old Cecil has got to shout.

'Vin, old darling, where are you, what?'

'I'm here,' says Castleton shortly. A terrible nostalgia for London has gripped him.

His brother is shouting joyously: 'Not in London? Don't tell me you're in London, old cock?'

'I'm not telling you. You're telling me. I'm in New Orleans,' Castleton says.

Old Cecil says archly: 'I say, temper, what?'

There is a puffing pause while he lights a cigar prior to getting down to a bloody good natter with his favourite brother.

'Be with you in a tick.'

There is a bellow which means he has chucked the lighted match into the waste paper basket as usual. The silly clot is roaring his head off about it.

'You really are one, aren't you?'

'How's darling Mim?' Cecil wants to know when he can speak again. 'Is she sick of you yet?'

'Yes,' says Castleton.

'I knew she'd rumble you. When's the divorce?' asks Cecil, who goes in for this kind of naval chat.

'I don't know yet,' says Castleton.

'How's the Wrong 'Un?' The Wrong 'Un is Cecil's name for George. 'I bet Mim bashes him about.'

'She does an' all,' says Castleton.

'Oh yes,' old Cecil says knowingly. 'I bet she treats the poor old Wrong 'Un somethin' shockin'.'

'You win,' agrees his brother.

'What about havin' a few words with him, then? A few mots en français avec le Wrong 'Un?'

Last time, when he had spoken to Cecil from home, he had induced his shy stepson to have a word with his brother. The poor little sod had stood speechlessly clutching Castleton's ring whilst having his ear affectionately blasted by Cecil's Admiralty French.

Castleton points out: 'I'm at the office, ducky. Do get organised.'

Oh Christ, of course. He always forgets the difference in time. Cecil demands: 'Let's have yer dirt, old darling.'

'I've had the Sioux,' Castleton says. Just for kicks. Just to see if he will get it. If he gets it he can always make a joke of it. He doesn't get it. He asks instead: 'I suppose it's pretty warm in New Orleans already?'

Castleton says: 'Fairly. What about you?' He wants to hear it's pouring in London.

'It's bloody pouring here,' says Cecil. 'Haven't you packed 'em off yet?'

'Who?'

'Mim and the Wrong 'Un. Hot weather's no good to Mems and kids.'

Christ.

Cecil says: 'You're no good as a family man. Got any roses into his cheeks yet?'

'Not really.'

'You're no bleeding good.' Cecil says: 'Send him to us. Mim too. We'd soon get the roses into their cheeks at Ashwater. Fresh milk. Fresh air. Bags of everything. What about it, old boy?'

Castleton is seeing the great South Terrace at Ashwater on a golden April evening. The rainy air is loud with birdsong and there are sheaves of daffodils everywhere.

And on their very first evening Mim in a stunning get-up is saying coolly: 'It will not be possible to stop here long, Vincent. The draughts are phenomenal . . . moumou will never survive it,' and adding for good measure: 'He is charming, your brother.' Not a word about Syb, of course.

Castleton says: 'It's going to be a bit orkard just now, old darling. This bloody winding up is taking a bit of doing. And we've got to be in Paris for Mim's nephew's wedding by the twelfth. And after that the kid's due at the Clinic for his tests.'

Cecil comes out of the Naval Chat department and says: 'What about Crombie?'

'We'll have to write him off,' says Castleton.

'Why?'

'Mim's agin him,' Castleton says. 'She's got her shirt on the Frenchman.'

Cecil says without the slightest hesitation: 'Then he's the bloke for the job, old boy. You may depend on it. A mother's instinct, never wrong. Bless 'em,' says Cecil. His deeply felt conviction is causing his voice to break in an open, manly, eighteenth-century sort of way. It strikes Castleton as a waste that Cecil couldn't have married Mim. He'd have gone down a treat with the Dauphin.

Old Cecil is putting the lid on by saying: 'What a blessing darling Mim has got you to share her little chap with.'

'You're gorgeous,' says Castleton.

He adores his brother who is the kindest, most altruistic creature on earth and, bar his stepson, probably the naïvest.

Cecil says: 'Isn't he any better, then?'

'Not really.'

'But he's no worse?'

'No, I suppose not.'

'Then that's the thing to hang on to,' Cecil tells him.

'Yes,' Castleton says. 'It's a right fuck-up.'

After a pause he asks: 'What goes on at Wilton Place?'

He is thinking affectionately of the tall, ugly house full of draughts and dogs lying about all over the loose covers. At this time of year it is always filled to bursting with spring flowers from Ashwater.

Daffodils.

The news from Wilton Place, as far as Castleton is concerned, is good. Darling Syb is away in Ireland. It seems her father, the seventy-eight-year-old Earl of Dunrraine, is booked. Cecil says tenderly: 'Poor old Dundy.'

'Yes,' says Castleton absent-mindedly. He is thinking about Cecil's innate kindness and generosity of spirit, and how lamentably short his elegant ruffian of a Mim is of both these commodities.

Cecil says: 'I'm flying over tomorrow.'

Bill and Alistair, Syb's two brothers, are already there. 'Do the old boy a power of good to have the family round him,' Cecil says. 'I wish you could come too, old darling. Cheer him up no end. He thinks the world of you.'

The Castletons, Castleton has just discovered, are every bit as close knit as the Benoirs.

He asks his brother: 'Have the Littles gone with Syb?' The Littles are the very much younger section of Cecil's brood of five. Three of them, all born in Hong Kong in quick succession, after a hiatus of nearly nine years. It is from the Hong Kong born Littles that Castleton hoped to recruit playmates for Mim's chap.

'Is Sammy there?' Sammy is Miss Samantha Castleton and a hot favourite with her uncle who hopes to be in business with her regarding the Dauphin quite soon.

She comes rushing up to the phone shouting: 'Where's George? Can I speak to him, Tosh?' and making a confounded noise in his ear with a ginger nut.

Sammy had annexed the Dauphin within two minutes of clapping eyes on him at the wedding. 'I think he's smashing. When're you going to bring him to see us, Tosh?'

Castleton says shortly: 'It depends.'

It is affecting him strongly to hear young Sammy's cheerfully disrespectful voice. It reminds him of the dismal fag ends flung to his stepson after Mim has finished her own conversation on the phone. 'Say what you have to say. Be quick. You can't expect papa to waste his time with you.'

And the elaborate breathing before the languid voice says timidly: 'Bonjour petit-papa chéri,' which is about all he ever manages to get out before Mim tells him: 'That is enough. Give papa a good kiss and finish.'

Sammy is seven but she is a whole head taller than Mim's concern and at least a stone heavier.

She is exclaiming: 'Oh, *Tosh*! You're so *vague*! *Why* can't you bring him? He's not *ill* again, is he? Oh *crumbs*! What a *bind*!'

She is disappointed in her protégé and is making no bones about showing it. 'I think he sounds *soppy*.'

'Well, he's not.'

'I think he sounds a *drip*.'

'Well, he's not. So you'll just have to take my word for it.'

'Robin says he calls you "petit-papa"—does he?'

'Yes.'

'What a scream.'

'Why? It just means stepfather in French.'

'All right. Keep your hair on,' Sammy says. 'Can't he speak English yet, then?'

'Sort of.'

'What d'you mean, *sort* of? Oh, Tosh, you are *maddening*!'

'He speaks Ol' Kintuck,' says Castleton.

'What on earth's Ol' Kintuck?'

'You'll know when you hear it,' says Castleton, uncommunicatively.

'You're a *Pig* and a *Beast*,' Sammy says. 'D'you ever speak French to him?'

'Sometimes.'

'Crumbs, I expect the poor mutt thinks it's Chinese.'

'On the contrary,' says Castleton, 'he thinks I'm perfect. In every way,'—says Castleton—'so sucks.'

She says jealously: 'He sounds an awful nit. Robin says he's not going to take the slightest notice of him. He says he's going to spend all the time you're at Ashwater in the stables reading, and only come in for meals.'

'Jolly good idea.'

Robin sounds pretty foul just now, by what Castleton can make of it. He seems to be going through what Mim's fellow calls a 'phrase'.

Sammy says: 'I shall probably do the same. What're you going to bring me from N.O., Tosh?'

Castleton says simply: 'Nothing, after that.'

There are howls of 'beast!' and 'stinker!'

'I was only kidding. Honestly, Tosh. Liddy'n' me'll look after him.'

Lydia is the youngest Little and well-known for her comfortable

223

and motherly disposition. She will probably want to spend all her time combing the Dauphin's hair.

Sammy says: 'Will Aunty Mim be coming too, Tosher?'

'Of course she will.'

'Robin says if she thinks he's going to call her Aunty she's got another think coming.' Sammy says: 'I think she's absolutely fabulous.' She says generously: 'Tigger'll be pupping in a few days and George can have any puppy he chooses, and I'll keep it for him. Only he'll have to choose an English name because Robin says he's not going to have a pup of Tigger's called by a French name. Robin says he's off the French completely. So you won't forget to tell him, will you, Tosh?'

'That Robin's off the French?' (He's got something there.)

'*No!* About the *puppy*!'

(What hopes.) Castleton says: 'No, I won't forget.'

Sammy says: 'Only you *are* a bit vague.' She says suddenly: 'I wish you were here. I'm growing my hair. I miss you, honestly. It's rotten your being married, Tosh.'

'Don't give me that.'

'It *is*. Don't you miss me, Tosh?'

'Not on your nelly. I'm in clover with George. No back chat. Anticipates me slightest wish. Get off the line, young Sammy. I want a final word with your Pa.'

'Oh, you and Cecil,' Sammy says, 'Don't forget my present.' Sammy says: 'It's got to be something absolutely smashing.'

'Get off the line, matey,' Castleton tells her.

He can hear Cecil expostulating. 'Darling, you're *not* supposed to *ask*. I don't know what you kids are coming to.'

He says dotingly into the phone: 'That kid. She's practically a commie.'

Castleton says grumpily: 'Your lot don't know they're born.'

Cecil says at once: 'What's up?'

'Nothing. It's just this winding up. I don't particularly want to go and live in Paris, either.'

He's dotty. Paris and London. Only two hours apart. They can pop over and see each other every week-end.

Only they never will.

'What's up, old darling?'

He would give anything to dump the whole thing. He just says: 'In-laws. I never think it works.'

Old Cecil says at once: 'But you get on all right with Mim's brothers, don't you?' (Needless to say, he gets on with Syb's two crashers like a bleeding house on fire.)

'Armand. I don't know Baudouin Benoir. Thank God. From what I saw of him at the wedding.'

Cecil says civilly: 'It's quite remarkable how Mim's family carry those fantastically good looks. Armand Benoir must be quite the best lookin' feller I have ever met.'

'There's nothing wrong with his looks,' says Castleton, gloomily.

'But you do like him? What?'

'Yes,' says Castleton. 'Worse luck.'

Cecil remarks amiably: 'I saw in *The Times* that young Benoir intends to get the Chantilly stable going again. Important event for the French turf if he does.'

'Yes. I think he's going to Ireland this summer to look at horses.'

Cecil says instantly: 'He must stay at Dunrraine. I'll tell Alistair and Bill. They'll be delighted.'

'I shouldn't bother. The Sioux are all hopeless out of their own homes.'

'What's he like, young Benoir?'

'He's the original shit,' says Castleton.

'I say, I say,' Cecil says mildly. 'Might be an interest for the Wrong 'Un, eh, if his cousin works up the racing?'

'It might. If he lives long enough.'

Cecil wants to know: 'What's the Wrong 'Un say to it?'

Say? Castleton says brutally: 'He's not asked, chum. He does what he's bloody well told and likes it.'

He is suddenly and relievingly angry. There is a silence which may or may not mean that Cecil is getting the picture. Castleton says quickly: 'Sorry about that.' His anger has relieved him completely. No need to unload.

He says: 'It's that blasted Clinic that's getting me down. He's so absolutely terrified of it.'

'Not now he's got you as well as Mim to back him up,' Cecil says. 'He'll feel quite different, old darling.'

He really believes it. He is saying: 'Mothers are too tender hearted, bless 'em. Now he'll feel your strength behind him.'

Which is very funny.

Castleton can hear Mim's cool voice (they will be installed at the Avenue Georges V apartment by that time, waiting to get into some bloody house or other): 'No, Vincent, I shall not take his nerves into account. I have seen that done at home to a degree where only the invalid was considered. He is only making a fuss because you are here.' And in the special animal trainer's voice she reserves for her son: 'Plus d'histoires, c'est compris? Si non, je te donnerai une bonne claque en de plus, mon très cher.'

Cecil is blathering on about 'our girls', by whom he means Syb and Mim, presumably. Castleton cuts him short by asking: 'How's the garden?'

The daffs at Ashwater this year, it seems, are absolutely magnificent. 'There's no other word for 'em, old chap.'

'Well, hooray. Some compensation for Hong Kong.'

Castleton is thinking about his wife. Her beauty and her harshness.

'I wish you could see 'em.'

'So do I.' She is the least kind creature he has ever met, Castleton thinks. Her unkindness is beyond everything. He is listening attentively to every word his brother is saying.

'Two miles of daffs. Took us nearly a month to plant 'em.'

Mountains of heavy bulbs heaped into farm carts like mangolds. Castleton is seeing two miles of daffodils. One on each side of the peaty drive. He can see the silken white bark of the birches fluttering loose in the sun.

Two miles of daffs. It is almost too much.

He can see them green, pointing closed muzzles straight up at the sky. He can see them yellow, their frilled jaws wide, bending towards the earth as if they were grazing.

Cecil is saying: 'They all came out together day before yesterday. We had a bit o' sun. It was like a miracle.' The day before yesterday had been a day of high wind and glaring sun in New Orleans. And all the time Mim had been on the rampage the daffs at Ashwater were coming out in their thousands.

Castleton says abruptly: 'I shall have to hang up now, old darling.'

He has suddenly made up his mind to go home.

But it's not so easy to get shut of old Cecil, who is protesting: 'Half a mo'. What a chap you are.'

Love, the Castleton answer to the Big Kiss of the Benoirs, is being sent in vast quantities, especially to Mim.

'She's a wonderful wife and a wonderful mother, bless her.'

'Yes.' She's a brute and a childbeater, but he just says yes.

Miss Shuter is hovering in her street make-up which, since her arrival in N.O., has taken on a mysterious Egyptian look. Or perhaps it's just meant to be Créole. Whichever way, it lends an odd Mephistophelean cast to the mild Shuter features.

Miss Shuter comes forward and unobtrusively places a telephone number on Castleton's desk. From where he is standing he can see it is a St Charles exchange number, but he can make nothing of it. There is something else written at the bottom of the card which is probably a name.

He tells his brother: 'I shall have to go now, old duck. Something's cropped up. I shall make a point of seeing you sometime this summer. I shall probably buzz over to Antibes. I may have to come alone. It depends.'

It depends. That covers everything.

'Well, anyway, let's 'ave yer.'

Cecil complains: 'Never see you nowadays. Or that sod Robin. He gets so stuck into his work at that fucking ICI place. Christ alone knows what he does there.'

Castleton says: 'We'll know soon enough.'

'When we all go up in smoke,' agrees Cecil. He says as a parting shot: 'What about Christmas at Ashwater? Can you make it?'

'I'll try. I'll get on the blower again as soon as things are clearer.'

He is seeing the churchyard at Ashwater under snow, with the luckless Dauphin, beset by cramp, staggering about under a giant gamp of Cecil's. There are dark wet patches of grass showing through the snow like spinach on a tablecloth, and the leaves on all the evergreens are pointing down. The frozen green of the churchyard. The crimson jollity of the house.

Not if I know it, thinks Castleton.

He says: 'Goodbye, old darling. Look after yourself for once and let your ruddy lot get on with it.' He says, pretty sharply: 'What's up with young Robin? He sounds in urgent need of a clout.'

Cecil says comfortably: 'I think he misses Hong Kong. All the Littles do, poor dears. They've had such shockin' colds since we've been back.' Cecil says: 'If you could see their poor little red noses, Vinnie, it would break your heart.'

'I shouldn't think so for a single moment.' Castleton says callously: 'My ticker's not so easily broke.'

He is thinking of Mim's fellow and how he has seen him cry at least once every day since he came to New Orleans. He says: 'Give me respects to Wonky.' Wonky is Ah Wong, Cecil's Chinese cook and by far the best, in Castleton's opinion, of the pretty poor bunch which is Cecil's Ashwater staff and which consists of the usual disgruntled Couple and a bossy old battle-axe of an ex-nanny plus the usual daily local impressment.

Cecil says slyly: 'Want a word with Nanny, old dear?'

'No fear,' says Castleton, rudely. He can't be doing with Miss Edie Pratt who for him typifies the worst in British Spinsterhood and who, if she had her deserts, would have been sent packing years ago with a flea in her ear.

Cecil admits she is a bit of a pill.

Then why keep her?

Castleton has no patience with what he considers a typical Castleton carry-on.

Cecil is saying: 'Anno domini, yer know. It comes to all of us. Can't just throw 'em out.'

Which in view of the Welfare State is just plain bloody ridiculous. They order these things better in Mim's family where anyone who doesn't pull their weight is out. It strikes Castleton that this is the only thing he and Mim ever see eye to eye about.

He tells his brother: 'You're a B.F. but you'll get your deserts. Ashwater will become a repository for dreary old ghouls, all knitting their heads off and laying down the law.'

Cecil says mischievously: 'Nanny is knitting herself cuckoo for when the Wrong 'Un comes. Vests, according to Pratt, are what the well-dressed Wrong 'Un will be wearin' when he visits Ashwater, if ever.'

Castleton counters smartly: 'That's out for a start. Tell the silly bitch that Waxen William is allergic to wool. We have to have all our little sailor suits with silk throughout. Si non, on est malade comme billyho.'

Cecil says: 'You've cheered yourself up.'

It's true. They have achieved exactly nothing, as Mim would say, but hearing old Cecil's voice and the Knightsbridge buses have done him a power of good.

Miss Shuter is apologising profusely for disturbing him. He is looking at the card.

Mme de Chassevent, eh?

'Only she did stress it was very urgent, Mr Castleton.'

Mme de having a spirited go behind her lover's back to see what she can do towards persuading him to go back.

'She rang up several times but you were still speaking to London,' Miss Shuter says.

'Yes, we did go on a bit,' Castleton says. 'Thank you for waiting. I hope I haven't kept you too long.'

'Oh, no,' declares Miss Shuter, who has a touch of the Casabianca in her make-up as well as Mephistopheles. 'Shall I put you through now?'

'No. I'll do it from home.'

He thinks of Liane de Chassevent: she's had her wish, so let her hear the good news from Benoir. He turns to go. Shuter is still there. Still in the office whence all but she have fled. He says genially: 'I wonder if you would do me a favour?'

She is all teeth and attention. 'I wonder if you would go downstairs and pick out a book for my stepson? I think they're still open. Anything about animals or flowers. Lots of pictures, not too much to read. If you can get fairly large print, all the better. He's just learning to read English.'

She looks at him raptly, obviously seeing Mim's beautiful fellow learning his letters at his stepfather's knee and improving himself like nobody's business.

Castleton says mildly: 'He's not very bright. We plod along, you know,' and hands her a five-dollar bill. With any luck he will be in the washroom when she gets back and she can leave it on his desk.

She is there, when he comes out, with a little square package and the meticulous change. She hopes that she hasn't been too long and that she's picked the right thing. 'It's about birds.'

Then it's the very thing. He is mad about birds. 'It's most awfully good of you. I'm sure they'd have been closed by the time I got down.'

She doesn't seem to be going. He smiles at her genially. He very much hopes that she is not going to press her suit on him or even thank him for proposing her to Lord Meresdale so forcefully that she can now stay on in New Orleans if she likes. It's not that he has anything against the girl, it's just that he wants to get back to his dear old Southern home before he changes his mind.

'Mr Castleton . . .'

Here it comes.

But it is only Shuter the decent stick, asking permission to ring up home and get them to send a car for him. 'Do let me, Mr Castleton. You've had nothing to eat all day. You must be absolutely exhausted.'

Good old Shuter. He smiles at her with real affection and says robustly: 'Good Lord, no. I'd rather drive myself home. Do me good. Can I drop you anywhere?'

She tells him roguishly she has a date. Her first in New Orleans.

Oh, good. That lets him out, then.

He'd really like to ask her to a meal at No 38 before they pull out of New Orleans, but he can't do that because he's married to the inhospitable French who live in a perpetual state of je m'enfoutism as regards the rest of the world, and couldn't care less if it would give decent sticks like Shuter immense pleasure to be invited into their bloody homes and eat their bloody dinners. He can hear that ruffian Mim saying: 'What an idea. I certainly have no intention of being bored by your secretary, mon vieux. I hope you haven't caught this terrible urge to be hospitable from living here. It's an American disease.'

He'll have to think of something else to mark the occasion. He gives Mephisto Shuter a gentlemanly smile and makes for the lift.

19

Meanwhile at Thirty-Eight . . .

He comes out of the air-conditioned building into the milk-white evening and drives through the warm glassy streets, thinking.

They've taken the hood down and it's reasonably cool. He is going home eventually but there is no immediate hurry.

No, indeed.

He is thinking, for instance, of the intense relief which would be felt if his brother-in-law had the faintest inkling that Castleton was (even eventually) coming home.

Silly clot! Let him sweat it out. He's bought it with his bloody face-saving. He grins at the thought of the sweat Armand must be in at this moment, thinking 'all is kaput', or whatever Benoirs think on these occasions, and that he will have to resume responsibility for Little (there is a Reason why I cannot love him) Benoir.

Seeing Mim's beautiful beggar say twice a year. *Le Fairplay. Vince has a certain right to see him, Mimi. One will be in London in any case to visit one's tailor. I shall bring puss to see you at your bank, Vince. It will be best for you to meet on neutral ground.*

The Sioux would rough it for three days at Claridge's . . . *One cannot remain longer, Vince, the food is impossible . . .* and Mim would, of course, remain in purdah in their suite. No nonsense about remaining friends after divorce with Mim.

Seeing the pretty little skeleton, which would undoubtedly be all that would be left of his ex-stepson, Georges-Marie Benoir. *He is a little pale, Vince, his nerves have taken a switching.* Hearing the sweet high drawl. *You must forgive him, Vince. He has forgotten his English.*

And Floods at the Delta of a stature that even Benoir would not be able to ignore. *Hey! Twelve years old and acting like a baby. What's Mr Castleton going to think?*

The goodbyes. *Turn Mr Castleton loose, puss, hear me? Take his hands down, Vince.* No need to call him papa, now.

The promises and bribes. *You'll see Mr Castleton again before we leave for Paris, fella. I'll tease mama to let you come. Want I should ask Mr Castleton to leave you have his handkerchief? Let him have it, Vince, it will make him happy.*

The quick confidence when the boy is out of the room . . . *Go get washed up, puss, or mama will want to hear a reason for those eyes . . .* with Armand drawing his arm through his ex-brother-in-law's. *It need make no difference to our friendship, Vince. There is someone for Marguerite's hand. I know you will be happy for her. Personally, I do not find him sympathique, but he could be the right man for her. We must hope so. Her nerves are not good. About puss I am not optimistic. They can be very cold, these Argentinians. If a child isn't reeking from their loins they have absolutely no interest in him.*

(That bastard 'Baby' Pererez, of course.)

And finally: *My sister wishes you to know she is carrying your child. She will write to you later through her lawyers. Naturally she wishes you to have complete jurisdiction and will do her best to fall in with any arrangements you may care to make.*

This last bit of the fantasy is making Castleton laugh like a drain, and two people turn round to look at him.

He accelerates slightly and, for the first time, sets a course for St Charles Street and Number 38.

He drives the Bentley into the courtyard of his dear old Southern home, where all the brilliant flowers have been freshly sprayed for the night, the callas and the cannas and the belles de nuit, and the begonias and the bignonias and the cherokee roses, and where the fountain is splashing away like fun among the palmetto fans.

And who should be standing at the gallery rail but his old pal Waxy Willie, all got up in white from head to foot, straining his weepers for a sight of his dearest friend whom he (sagacious infant) has got an idea that he will never see again and enjoying an illicit snivel in the friendly Southern dusk.

Yes indeed.

His little right hand is still encased in its snowy glove, and the pretty lilac patches under his eyes pay touching tribute to his constancy. The tap, at a moderate guess, cannot have been turned off for more than twenty minutes at a time since Castleton's departure thirty-six hours ago.

He shouts up cheerfully: 'Hullo, ducky. Are you waiting for Pa?' He is holding his arms out because of course the dear little chap will throw himself at you regardless of distance or height. This is partly due to an affectionate and trusting nature, but also to the incontestable fact that when horse sense was being given out, Mim's beautiful little fellow was behind the bloody door.

He comes hurtling down into Castleton's arms, shrieking: 'Papa! Papa!' and exhibiting every sign of love, affection and respectful what have you. Tears of joy are simply sliding down his face like water down a florist's window.

'Christ, George! Have a heart, ducky! I've only been away thirty-six hours!' He is searching through his pockets for another handkerchief. Mim's fellow is a glutton for them. He keeps on sobbing! 'O, it has been forever. O, I thought you would never come.'

'Why on earth not, you silly noodle? Blow.' He has had to take the child's own pocket handkerchief out of the bosom of his sailor blouse where his heart can be felt scrambling about like a bird in the fragile cage of his breast. 'You really are a prize one. Whatever made you think I wasn't coming back?'

He touches a solemn finger to his blouse and says: 'I felt it here.'

Castleton says briskly a bit less of his ticker and a bit more of his loaf would have been more to the point.

'Wouldn't it, what?'

O, yes, he will use his loaf more for the future. But George hopes there will not be any need. 'O, it was so shocking without you, papa darling. O, we couldn't none of us eat our soupe we missed you so.'

Soupe is the Benoir word for grub.

The sight of his stepfather endlessly signing cheques has evidently impressed him deeply because he now declares: 'O, we would rather eat pain sec for all our lives, maman and me, than have you leave us pour gagner des gigots.' He has got both his arms round his dearest friend's neck and is positively raining tears on him.

'Oh, do for Christ's sake shut up, ducky.' Castleton has got him on his knee in a darkish corner of the gallery and is effecting repairs out of sight of the salon windows. Any moment now the soft voice will be calling: 'What are you doing out there, moumou?'

'Can you pack it in now, darling?'

Pain sec and gigots are still in brisk supply and creating a shortage of dry handkerchiefs.

'Come on, let's get you mopped up. I want to say hullo to mummy.'

Summer is coming fast. Already there are silver flashes in the thick black gloom under the palms. The creature reports between sobs that this is the second night that the fire flies have appeared, and also that today he has discovered a humming-bird's nest under the cucumber tree. It is shaped 'tout à fait comme un porte-monnaie. Un tout petit porte-monnaie, vous savez, papa?' This purse-shaped nest is causing him to sob quite wildly.

'Now then, now then, less of it.' Castleton wags an admonitory finger. He is holding Mim's chap very tight. There is less of him than ever. Thirty-six hours and virtually only eyes are left.

Which all goes to show, says Castleton, that his stepson is a Total Loss.

O, he is saying all the delightful British things like 'Turn that ruddy tap off or I'll do you!' and 'Don't bugger about.'

George permits his dearest friend to wipe his face for the last time, and says in a satisfied voice: 'I am quiet now.'

'How about this, then?'

'This' is the richly coloured little book entitled *Colibris and*

Humming-birds, bright fruit of the last minute raid on the bookshop by Miss Shuter after he had finally decided he was coming home.

'Now you'll be able to find out what built that little nest.'

'O, is it for me, papa? A present only for me?'

He is delightful to give anything to. He is pleased with everything. He is completely unspoiled, and the words 'What have you brought me?' have never crossed his lips.

Mim has seen to that.

'It is quite unnecessary to bring him something every time you come home, Poilu. Moumou is delighted to see you back. I assure you that is sufficient pleasure for him.'

He is in the act of being thanked ecstatically when the cool voice from the salon demands: 'Whom have you got out there with you, moumou?'

'C'est un monsieur,' shrieks the creature, clapping his hand over his stepfather's mouth. '(You are not to speak. You are not to speak.) C'est un monsieur qui veut prendre le dîner avec nous, maman-chérie.'

'Ah? Do I know him?'

'O, yes'm,' the creature calls out, ill-advisedly as well as incorrectly. 'He is kinfolks to us, don't you know?'

'Speak French,' says the cool voice at once.

'Yes'm,' he is shrieking in a whisper. 'O, my Redeemer. O, she will never guess. O, you will be a surprise for her.'

He has squashed his stepfather's face against his thudding heart and is kissing the bridge of his nose in his excitement.

'He is English, mama darling. You will like him. He is very nice. Please may I bring him in to dinner?'

'Is he big? Will he eat a lot?'

O, she is funning.

He is large, but not excessively so. George is confident that there will be soupe enough for all. Si non, they will all gladly share it with him.

'Speak for yourself,' the cool voice tells him. 'And don't mix French with English.'

The owner of the voice is at the gallery doors. 'Where is this person I am supposed to share my soupe with?'

'He is here.' O, she is funning, she is funning.

'Where? Show me.'

'He is here. O, you are looking at him, mama darling.'

235

'C'est celui-là?'

'Oui, maman.'

'Pas de problème,' says Marguerite. 'You may invite him to dinner.'

She is coming towards him. That cool, cruel, ineffable Mim.

'Hullo, Mrs Castleton.'

'So you didn't go to England after all, Vincent?' She sounds completely composed, but she is kissing him as if she would never stop.

Mim's bit of goods is cavorting about exclaiming: 'O, he will never leave us again, mama darling. Not for a single moment. O, we will be able to eat our soupe tonight.'

She catches him cleverly by the blouse and pushes him at Castleton. 'Kiss him, kiss papa hard. Hard, I said. Little feeble thing, d'you call that hard? Puth! Papa will think it is a fly on his nose. I'll show you how to kiss him!'

They are both of them kissing him now, fighting for his face and laughing and screaming and tickling each other like a couple of out-of-hand children.

Gay Mim is calling out: 'Keep still, stupid! If you try to escape, we'll only give it you worse!' and using what practically amounts to commando tactics.

The boy friend is, of course, by far the gentler of the two. 'O, look, maman, look this poor man, we have undone his tie! O, we have quite ruined his hair for him, O, my Redeemer!'

They are shrieking with laughter, both of them nearly on the floor as Castleton defends himself as best he can. He is laughing too. Laughing uproariously. Really shouting out loud at this fantastic rough-house that is like nothing on earth.

Mim's sprightly boy friend keeps sliding off his chest and shrieking: 'O, I cain't hol' him, don't you know. O, he jest being plain bad. O, il m'échappe toujours!'

But experienced Mim is showing him the ropes. 'Petit incapable, fais comme moi! Prends-le dans tes bras. Prends-le, donc! Enfin, c'est ça! Serre-le, alors. Fort, fort, plus fort qu'ça! Put your two arms round papa's neck and hold him tight. Now take his mouth. Timid thing, take his mouth! I give you full permission.'

They have really got him now, both of them pinning him down while they attack him silently, going for his mouth in a perfect transport of love.

He has never experienced anything like this concerted attack, but finds himself quite enjoying it in a weird sort of way.

It's pure rape, of course. A kind of Benoir Blitz. It's impossible to tell t'other from which as they lie on his chest in a scented heap, exclaiming Benoirishly: 'Je vous aime! Je vous aime! Vous êtes ma vie!'

It may be rape, but tout de même one does not 'tutoyer' one's victim.

It's astonishing how those two comics can keep it up. It takes quite a while before they are satisfied. Mim's hair is halfway down her back and her boy friend's hair is plastered to his head with sweat before they let him go.

'Ça va! Assez, assez, va laver ta gueule!' She is gathering up her hair and panting and laughing. 'You can imagine what went on with that one while you were away, Poilu. The whole household was swimming in his tears.'

'J'ai pleuré comme un veau,' remarks the creature complacently. His mouth is actually puffed with violent and prolonged kissing. 'J'ai hurlé comme un loup.' His arms are still tightly round his stepfather's neck.

'Did you an' all?' says Castleton, kissing him.

Marguerite says: 'I told you to go and wash your face, moumou. Unless you prefer to have dinner by yourself on papa's first night at home?'

O, no, he doesn't at all prefer it. He will go wash his face at once.

He makes for the gallery doors, *Colibris and Humming Birds* clasped to his heart, telling them both: 'O, I will eat my soupe tonight. J'ai tellement faim, vous savez. C'est fou comme j'ai faim ce soir.'

Papa and she will hold him to his word. She calls out after him: Hé, toi! If you really polish your plate you may claim a reward!'

'Par exemple?'

Anything he pleases.

He threatens saucily: Ça vous coutera cher, Madame.'

'Petit voyou!'

'Vous m'avez dit "anything". Oui ou non?'

'Non!'

'Si!'

'Non et non!'

237

'Menteuse!'

'Voyou! Polisson! Marchand de Cacaouettes!' She is pelting him with abuse, threatening him with her slipper and laughing at his cheek. 'Little Jew! Wait till I catch you. I'll make you laugh on the other side of your face!'

She is finding him deliciously funny, her son. Everything is funny tonight because Vincent is back. Funny and delicious.

She comes back to her husband, affecting to limp, one slipper still comically in her hand. 'You have really made him hungry, Poilu. It's a miracle. You've no idea how much he loves you, that stupid thing.' She seats herself deliberately in his lap. 'D'abord you are extremely popular with les Benoirs. Did you know that, my darling?' She is smiling into his eyes.

He had an inkling.

He dislikes her flirtatiousness enormously. Her whole attitude is a typical piece of 'Mim'.

'I think I'll go and shave.'

She remains smiling at him, very much at ease in his lap. 'Are you still angry with me?'

'Yes.'

She assures him: 'You needn't be, Vincent. He has forgiven me. Completely.' Marguerite says: 'That little stupid, he has a better character than Madame sa mère.'

He quite agrees.

She says: 'He hasn't one shred of vindictiveness in his whole nature. I find it quite fantastic, that.'

He is quite sure she must.

She bursts out: 'Oh, Vincent, don't start, please. I have had nothing else to listen to but reproaches for my terrible character and my faults and how badly I behave.' She says: 'I know I have been bad to him, Vincent. It was excessive what I did. But Benoir carries his disapproval to a point where the whole thing simply turns into a joke.'

She's running pretty true to form tonight, is Mim. If this is supposed to be an expression of her regret it certainly won't uproot any trees. We'll have to have something better than that from you, chum.

*   *   *

238

She is clasping him to her, both arms tightly round him under his coat. 'Oh, Vincent, it was so horrible while you were away. You can't imagine what an atmosphere of gloom. Benoir has been quite detestable. D'you know that idiot hasn't spoken three words to me since you left? Only in public! Even my nephew has taken it upon himself to pontificate about the proper feelings of a mother! I suppose he thinks because he's going to get married it gives him the right to criticise. Tant pis! I've become bored with the whole business.' She says: 'I got so sick and tired of those two always preaching at me I was on the point of phoning Bic to come and fetch moumou and me away. We would have spent the summer with him at his place in the Ardennes.' Marguerite says: 'Would you have minded that, Vincent?' She is smiling up into his face.

'Not really,' says Castleton, genially. He is smiling down at her. Apart from her beauty there is bugger all to see.

Marguerite says it would have been solely to escape from that idiot of a brother of hers.

'Seulement pour emmerder Benoir,' she says: 'He is so angry with me he walks about looking exactly like Napoleon. It's terribly funny,' says Marguerite, who is actually laughing about it. 'I had no idea he could be such a bore.'

Oh dear, oh lor'. It really is incredible.

She says: 'I'm still in deep disgrace, of course. With Benoir these things go on forever. The whole household have taken their cue from him, now. Naturally, it was too good an opportunity for them to miss. Not one has dared to open their mouth so far, but I can read their opinion of me in their eyes.'

Marguerite says if this state of affairs continues she will instigate a Putsch and make a few examples. That may induce a few of them to forgo the luxury of criticising Madame. If that doesn't help she will make a clean sweep. 'It wouldn't take much for me to sack the whole rabble.'

She seems delighted at the prospect. She really is extremely nasty.

'What are you looking at me like that for, Vincent? That stupid nerve is jumping in your cheek.'

As well it may with horrid Mim going on gaily: 'Of course I had to endure a long lecture from "les Soutanes". Two lectures. One from Monseigneur and one from Father Kelly.' She says: 'That's another thing I won't forgive Benoir for in a hurry, pushing those two holy crows at me. Mon dieu! I thought their

239

sermons would never end. I was practically given to understand that I am anything but their favourite daughter-in-God! In fact,' —this hardboiled girl is saying—'I was left with the strong impression that only vast sums of Benoir money stand between me and the Divine Wrath!'

Crikey.

'D'you know what that pumpkin-face of a Father Kelly told me, Poilu? That the lowest and humblest of Our Lord's Creation have more compassion for their offspring than I have! The effrontery of that Irish peasant.' She begins to laugh. 'I told him he had set me so many penances that if I did them all I should have no time left in which to perform my wifely duties!'

'I wish you could have seen that bumpkin's face!' cries Mim, the sans-culotte who gets a kick out of reviling the cloth which clothes the ministers of the God who permitted the crash at Chantilly.

'He got so red I thought he would burst! He was tout à fait gonflé comme un boulefrogge!' cries Marguerite, who is mixing French and English like mad, and looking exactly like her son who is, of course, forbidden to mix French and English on pain of 'pas de dessert pour toute la journée' and all the rest of it.

'Je m'en fiche des Soutanes!' the fearless girl is crying. 'Let them keep their opinions pour effrayer les mangeurs de crucifixes. There will always be plenty of fools for them to impress! Like my sister-in-law, Marie!'

For Mim the Beautiful Bolshie there are only two opinions worth having. Her brother's and her husband's.

'Have you done, old Duck?' asks Castleton mildly. For while she has been surpassing herself he has been taking quiet stock of his wife, the lovely Marie-Madeleine Marguerite Castleton, very much née Benoir, and has come to the conclusion that he doesn't like her.

He is probably still in love with her, but he doesn't like her a bit.

Mim née Benoir isn't going to lose any sleep over that, of course. She's such a mess that ordinary standards don't apply, but for the high-falutin Castletons the outlook is not excessively jolly.

She is saying: 'I adore that thing in your cheek.' Which is completely true. She adores every fibre of him. She says: 'I was like moumou. I would have died if you hadn't come back. Would you have minded, my darling, if we had both died?'

'I'd mind about moumou,' says Castleton impolitely. 'Push off. I want to shave.'

'He was so certain you weren't coming back, my little silly.'

'That's right, I wasn't,' says Castleton, cheerfully. He is making off towards the gallery doors with Mim hanging on to his coat at the back like the Dauphin does.

'But you came back because you love me, Poilu?'

'Get your hair done, Mim,' Castleton says.

Yes, she will get her hair done and she will let him shave, and then they will all have dinner together. It is the first time he has called her Mim tonight.

'Are you hungry, my darling?'

Yes, he is hungry, come to think of it. He has just remembered he has had no lunch.

Then they will eat at once. They will not wait, as Mim is so charmingly putting it, for Benoir to finish 'se puter avec Liane'. There is nothing her brother detests as much as dining before nine o'clock and she will be delighted to pay him back, even in such an inadequate way, for his filthy behaviour towards her.

She would never dream of putting dinner forward by a single second for her son, of course; only to spite her brother.

'Get in,' says Castleton, pushing her into the salon. She is speculating happily: 'I wonder what that little Jew will claim as his reward for eating his dinner properly. I wouldn't put it past him to ask to come into our bed. He would like nothing better than to sleep between us, little sly thing.' Marguerite says: 'If he does, I shall cheat him, Vincent. I shall fob him off,' declares Mim the Sharper gaily, all agog to pull a fast one. 'Nothing shall come between us tonight, my darling, not even my son.'

'Shut up,' says Castleton in a disgusted voice. As they cross the hall she orders Gustave in clipped military tones: 'Tell them to put the dinner forward. You may announce it immediately Monsieur has completed his toilet. We will not wait for Monsieur Benoir. And send Philippe up immediately with the drinks to Monsieur's dressing room. C'est entendu?' asks Marguerite, who is not only incapable of saying please to a servant, but has the gift of making French sound the rudest language on earth.

'Très bien, Madame.' Gustave is holding the lift gate open for them, his eyes politely disregarding her disordered hair.

'And tell Philippe he is to use the stairs, d'you hear? In case he thinks the lift has been installed especially for his benefit.'

241

'Très bien, Madame.'

Gustave who, unlike his mistress, is a person with proper feelings, says courteously that he is very glad to see Monsieur back home again and hopes Monsieur has had a pleasant trip. 'P'tit M'sieu sure goin' to be happy now he got she papa back. Man, he di'n' stop to cry since Monsieur went away.'

Castleton is about to say something civil when guttersnipes Mim pushes him into the lift from behind. 'Quickly, Poilu, before another ovation starts.'

She presses the button, shooting the lift up swiftly from Gustave's astonished face.

'Mon dieu, these people with their terrible speeches!' She is kneeling in the small armchair that has been put in for her sick son. 'As if it mattered whether he is pleased to see you or not.'

He doesn't bother to answer her. He just gives her an absent-minded smile.

'What are you thinking of, Poilu?' She has slipped her hand into his trousers pocket along with his. He takes his out. He can't be doing with any of that.

Actually he is thinking what a pity it is she can't be more like her brother, Armand Benoir, but takes, it appears, almost entirely after his late father-in-law who was such a little shocker that even the deeply pious Dauphin is leaving him to make his own way out of purgatory as best he can without the benefit of his prayers.

The Dauphin had blacklisted him with Courvoisier, 'Ce sont des ordures, vous savez, Mr Castleton.'

Old Mim should head the ordures list. No two ways about it.

Oh, Vincent is being tiresome and English and won't tell her what he is smiling about.

'Poilu . . .' The lift has stopped at their floor.

'What?' He is holding the gate for her to get out.

'You aren't very nice.'

'No,' agrees Castleton. 'Get out.'

As she gets out she says quickly: 'I have some news for you, Vincent.'

He hopes it isn't news about the cadeau, but it is. She is standing in front of the lift smiling at him with her magnificent sombre eyes, and in her smile—the strange, shadowy 'Mim' smile that gets him every time—he reads the glad tidings that the grey-eyed cadeau is on the way.

'Are you pleased with me, Poilu? Is it a good surprise for you?'

She has got hold of both his hands and is pressing them against the part behind which the wretched cadeau is supposed to be lurking.

'I want him to feel his papa's hands. Kiss him, Vincent.'

It's vintage Sioux, of course, but a bit touching as well. He feels it won't be stretching his resources too far to give both her and the cadeau a decent kiss.

'You are not to be angry with me any more, Poilu.' She is holding her head ingratiatingly, like her chap does when he is begging: 'O, don't, mama darling, don't scold me any more.' (Only she always does.)

Poor old Mim. She's in for a thin time. The English have gone off her, probably for good, and she has completely forfeited the regard of the French.

He can just hear Benoir saying gravely: 'You have transgressed beyond the limits of condonance, Mimi. Your callous and unnatural behaviour towards your son has completely forfeited my regard,' and looking exactly like the young Napoleon.

Only Mim's boy friend, the beautiful-natured Dauphin, will go on loving her come hell and high water, because she is his 'petite maman-adorée'. Which may not say much for the Dauphin's I.Q., but is bloody lucky for Mim.

Mim is going on about the cadeau to him in a special voice that is making him want to laugh.

'He will make you forget this whole stupid business, my darling.'

The cadeau as a douceur. 'Don't be a bore,' advises Castleton, patting her kindly on the arm.

The first blush he has ever seen on her washes over her face. Tears—probably of rage—are glittering in her eyes. She looks exactly like her son.

'Do I bore you, Vincent?'

'Of course you do. Frightfully. Except in bed.' He tells her: 'Piss off and get your hair done.'

'Vincent!' cries Marguerite.

'Piss off,' says Castleton.

Oh, Vincent is in a mood. If he and Benoir intend to keep this up it won't be very gay. Vincent is taking this whole thing about moumou as if he were the father. In a cool defensive voice she remarks: 'It hasn't even made him afraid of me, Vincent. You are a fool if you think it.'

'Shut up,' says Castleton.

Marguerite says: 'Nothing has changed. He loves me as much as he has always loved me.' She says in a satisfied voice: 'He is chic, my son. Only that stupid paw of his is taking so long to heal. I'm sure if Benoir wasn't continually being confronted by that glove he would already have forgiven me.'

It's the most disgusting thing that she has said tonight. She hasn't one single ruddy clue of how to behave. He walks straight into his dressing room and slams the door.

20

Marguerite

She stands looking after him for a moment. He is completely mad, that English husband of hers!

They are all mad in this house, but he is worse than all the rest of them put together. She would never have dreamed that Vincent could make such dramas! So much for the vaunted sang-froid Anglais!

Only her son has shown any sense at all about this wretched business. He has forgiven her completely, and long before that stupid paw of his has healed he will have forgotten all about it. Incidentally, it was really amusing while Vincent was away, he was almost like a little husband to her. He knew I was unhappy, Marguerite thinks, smiling. He simply can't stand it when Benoir is angry with me.

She steps quickly through her bedroom into her dressing room and rings for her maids. She will keep her finger on the bell until those three idiots come falling over each other in their hurry to answer. She will make them dance for their soupe tonight. She will make them change her dress, her coiffure, her underthings, the maquillage for her nails, shoes, stockings, scent, jewellery, everything. In one short quarter of an hour everything must be done. And done to her complete satisfaction.

She will put on the same face that Papa always made when anything displeased him. The whole household had quailed under his terrible eye.

Marguerite had adored the small martinet whom everyone is always telling her she resembles. That fool Benoir has often reproached her with it, but she is only happy to resemble Papa.

Papa would never have tolerated for a single moment even one half of the slackness and insolence with which she has been confronted lately.

She is naked now, and being sprayed with her special scent. The scent that Vincent likes especially. It is unfortunate that she should have been wearing it on that afternoon, because now that little fool of a moumou will be almost certain to take against it. She has noticed that he has already taken a dislike to the salon. He would never breathe a word, of course, but he will not go in there unless he must, and then he will escape to the gallery on the slightest pretext.

Mon dieu, she will be glad when they can clear out of this horrible house and get back to Paris.

Bienville's wedding can't take place too soon for her. Her bureau she has already arranged to have sent back to La Taquineuse. It would be pointless to have it shipped to France, monsieur would only take an immediate dislike to whichever room it was put into.

She knows the workings of his mind so well. Nothing, but nothing, could now persuade that little donkey to look at his beloved medallions. Tant pis, it is a thing that they must leave to time.

That fool of a Sidonie is inundating her with scent. 'Enough! I said enough! You idiot, what are you drenching me like that for?'

Sidonie puts the spray down.

It is unbelievable. One has only got to ask to be lightly sprayed to be soaked like a baba au rhum! 'Fetch a towel,' says Marguerite. 'You fool, not a damp one! Are you quite out of your mind? A damp towel will only fix it.'

Dry towels are brought.

'Now wipe this sirop off you have squirted over me. My legs as well,' says Marguerite. 'Go down on your knees and wipe my legs properly.' Marguerite says: 'I have no intention of walking about smelling like a poule de luxe to save you the trouble of getting down on your knees, in case that's what you think.'

They are getting her into her dress now, two of them, working with silent concentration on the almost invisible fastenings.

She will wear Vincent's rubies tonight. The dress is perfection, and she would much prefer to wear nothing with it, but she will put on his rubies to please him, though he certainly doesn't deserve it in his present mood.

For herself she has no feeling for rubies, apart from the fact that these were Vincent's first gift to her. She has dismissed them privately as typical 'Cartier-for-the-English-taste'. It is so typically English of Vincent to think that rubies must suit her because she has black hair! In actual fact they couldn't be less her stone.

Tant pis, she will wear them a few more times as they are, and then she will have them reset. The centre ruby of the necklace might even be worth recutting. The colour is good. It would lose in size, of course, but that can't be helped. She will get de Jong's opinion on it directly they reach Paris. He is quite the best man with rubies, at least according to Liane who, since her latest change over from mauve to tangerine hair, has taken to wearing a lot of them.

The best idea will be to ask Benoir about de Jong because, as usual, it is Benoir who is paying for this new craze of Liane's. She will have to wait, of course, till Monsieur her brother has stopped regarding her as a criminal. Vincent, she feels, will probably like his rubies even better when they have been reset and given the correct treatment. He has uncultivated but instinctive taste for the uncluttered.

She thinks a sautoir, extremely simply mounted, will probably best release the full beauty of the colour. The ear-rings, with their smaller stones, can, she hopes, be tactfully forgotten.

Oh, she loves him so much she can hardly wait till these three fools have finished with her to run like the wind to her husband's room and watch him shave!

That slyboots moumou will have stolen a march on her! He'll be in the front row now, that sly sleek moumou with his newly washed mug and his well brushed 'Sunday' hair that shines like violet silk!

His hair is the only thing that little donkey has taken from the Benoirs. The rest is pure Bienville. Oh, that drawl! That awful drawl that comes straight from the Delta, from those fat aunts of Georges'!

Georges had laughed every time moumou had opened his mouth. 'Mimi, come quickly, Tante Zélie wants to say "bon zour" to you!'

It's extraordinary, Vincent and Georges couldn't have been less alike, but her little rubbish had amused both her husbands. She thinks, Vincent is very sweet with him, his little 'ducky' as he calls him. She thinks amusedly, mon dieu, what a name!

Her hair is done at last, thank God! Sidonie is holding the handglass for her to study the back and sides. The effect is good. She really knows her job, that big-boned peasant. She is the best maid Marguerite has had since that impossible Berthe, that temperamental Parisienne, had walked out on her at Biarritz without a word, in the middle of a house party.

The whole arrangement has been excellently carried out, and the style is supremely becoming to her. The main interest centres on the back of the head where the rich hair has been gathered and laid in inky swathes of an almost violet black. In front the hair has been drawn quite simply away from her face, displaying the delicate purity of her features. She looks like a girl who has just jumped out of her bath. Vincent will like it.

Sidonie says: 'It's quite remarkable. Madame looks like a young girl with that hair. It is a most demanding style on account of the extreme simplicity of the line, but Madame can wear it to perfection.'

'Are you finished, or what?' It's difficult to know what she means, Sidonie's compliments or her hair.

That Créole! thinks Sidonie. Even her hair is Créole. It is superb, but it is not European hair. She has seen plenty of black hair in her life, but this one's is blacker than the devil!

Sidonie says: 'I hope Madame is satisfied with her coiffure?'

'I shall be satisfied if it holds up,' says Marguerite.

'It is quite firm, Madame.'

'One must hope so,' says Marguerite. 'It generally starts to come down before one is halfway through dinner.'

What is she talking about, that bitch? It is completely and utterly untrue!

Sidonie thinks, if she starts anything with me tonight she'll get as good as she gives. My God! She'll hear the truth for once in her life! After last Wednesday I've had about enough of her. She says: 'It is quite firm, Madame.'

Pauline and Nicole are redoing Marguerite's nails, one to each small authoritative hand.

My word, the things she's done with those hands, thinks Sidonie. She has seen that Créole catch both her little son's stick-like wrists in one hand and hit him with the full weight of her rings on his poor little naked arms.

Sidonie asks: 'Is there anything further that Madame requires?'

The answer is a dismissive shrug that implies everything up till now has been done in such a slapdash way it would be a waste of time to ask for anything further.

Sidonie says with a half-smile: 'I hope Madame is not implying that I don't know my job?'

'You do not know it,' Marguerite assures her. She isn't even half-smiling. She has no more notion of putting up with an impertinent servant than with a disobedient child.

Sidonie says in that case it might be better if she left. She finds her voice is slightly more raised than she intended.

'Exactly,' Marguerite says. 'I was on the point of giving you your notice.'

Nicole goes quickly towards the bedroom. 'Where are you going?' asks Marguerite.

Nicole comes back into the dressing room.

Marguerite says: 'Perhaps there are others here who would also like to take this opportunity of leaving?'

There is complete silence. Marguerite says to Sidonie: 'Start to move, Poisson!'

That bitch! She has given her her notice! She has seen to it that she got it in first!

Sidonie says stiffly: 'If Madame wishes to make a replacement I can wait till Madame is suited.'

But not at all. Madame will take Christienne to do her hair until they get to Paris. Voilà tout.

'But Christienne is a chambermaid, Madame.'

'Et quoi?'

She is getting quite red in the face, that Norman turkey-cock. Marguerite says: 'There is nothing you do which any chambermaid cannot do as well or better. In case you think you are indispensable.'

Marguerite thinks, she looks like Liane when she is furious like that, with those crimson blotches on her neck. They all look exactly alike, these dish-faced Normandes, with their three-cornered noses and their blue pigs' eyes. She probably has a disgusting white body like a cochon-de-lait! Phoui! How a fastidious man like Armand can bring himself to touch a body like Liane's passes her comprehension. Papa always said the Normans are the most unreliable race in France and he would never take one into his service. Well, this is certainly the last time she will employ one.

She says briefly: 'Walk. Get Mme Poitou to pay you whatever is owing to you, and take yourself off. If you haven't completely disappeared by midday tomorrow I will have you thrown out.'

There is an involuntary exclamation from Pauline.

'What did you say?'

'Nothing, Madame.'

Pauline is busily putting the manicure things away while Nicole is searching the carpet for an object that has never been dropped.

Marguerite thinks, I hope that has finally silenced you, Madame. But not at all. Porky is launching into one of those impassioned appeals to Heaven and Justice that seem to be the standby of dismissed servants.

She is calling on Heaven to witness that never in all her twenty-five years as a lady's maid has she been treated like this, and dropping her Parisian accent all over the place. She looks too funny with her arms flailing like windmills and that face like a well slapped behind!

'I have held posts with the best families in France and England and four and a half years in New York and I have never heard a single word except of praise for my work and only the highest possible references when I left.'

'You will not get one here,' says Marguerite.

'I don't need your reference,' Sidonie calls out. Even her arms are scarlet now. She is trying to get her apron off and the strings have tied themselves into a knot.

'Madame forgets I was two years with Madame la Duchesse de Rochefort.' (Only she calls it Roquefort.)

I must save that one for Bienville, he will adore it, Marguerite thinks; when we're on speaking terms again! It is fantastic how this thing with moumou crops up at every turn and spoils everything!

'She was a most sweet lady, très dévote,' the Poisson insists, 'she was quite in despair when I left.' (Only she calls it dissipair.) 'I never would have dreamed of leaving her, only to oblige my cousin Rose who, as Madame well knows, has been nearly twelve years in the service of your revered sister-in-law' (she has really said it) 'who is a most sweet lady, très dévote' (what, another one) 'and an example to all by reason of her sweet acceptance of her souffrance and her admiral fortitude which causes the hearts of all to bleed on her behalf, especially at certain periods.'

Mon dieu! 'Admiral fortitude' is still funny, but the whole thing is already threatening to become a bore.

'And to oblige Monsieur your brother, who at the time was most anxious to secure the services of a really first class maid of impeccable references and the highest possible reputation to accompany Madame on her honeymoon.' (The good Poisson? But naturally! Who else?) One would think she would have talked herself out of breath by now, but not a bit of it. 'Monsieur Benoir is a most polite and charming gentleman and it is a pleasure and honour to be able to oblige him.'

Tiens, she had no idea Poisson was obliging. There had been no hint of it here, of course.

She decides suddenly, I've had enough of this Norman cow. 'Écoutez, ne m'emmerde pas trop, hein?'

She is smiling, not at Poisson, but because she has suddenly thought of her beloved brother, Armand, at his most Napoleonic, saying: 'I don't propose to tell Marie about this business of puss, Mimi. She has no knowledge of this sort of thing and it could make her very unhappy. For my wife Motherhood is still an ideal of tenderness and compassion, and it would be pointless and cruel to disillusion her, especially in her present enfeebled state of health.'

My wife! Enfeebled state! She had been unable to resist smiling even while he was saying it, which had thrown him into the most terrible rage! She thinks tenderly, Armand, mon petit frère-chéri! He is adorable when he is pompous like that. He has a most sweet 'disisposition', as the Poisson would say! What is she bawling about now, that peasant? She seems to be back with her Roquefort again, making a proper meal of it, as Vincent would say, calling herself every sort of a fool for leaving an idyllic position in her beloved France to slave in foreign parts for a tyrant who hasn't a good word to throw at a dog and who is incapable of making anyone happy.

Marguerite asks serenely: 'Is it me, this charming portrait you have just finished painting?'

'Yes, it is you!'

Oh, how she is looking at her now, that Créole in whose wicked eyes the whites are showing dangerously.

Sidonie says: 'I have never been so unhappy with anyone in my whole life as I have been with you. I have only to hear your voice, I am unhappy. My heart bleeds for your husband and for your son, that poor sick little boy whom you treat with such brutality. My God, what a life you lead him!'

'Be careful what you say, Poisson,' advises Marguerite.

No, she will not be careful! Sidonie shouts out: 'It was a shocking thing you did, to beat a poor defenceless child like that!' She thinks: she's not French at all, this one. She's not even a Créole. She's a sorceress. All the Benoirs are sorcerers. Even the little boy has those terrible eyes.

That poor ill thing who looks so pale one is afraid he will drop dead at one's feet. She hadn't believed it possible when his bonne had come begging her to keep the little Dédé for her while she tried to do something for him. She didn't want the little girl to see the condition of that poor thing's hands.

What a thing! The bonne said she had beaten him so unmercifully that he had lost control of his bladder. When she undressed him to put him to bed he was soaked. It is the first time he had ever done such a thing. The bonne said he was a most clean and fastidious child. What a thing! That poor child was in such misery that he had called for his dead father. 'And you call yourself a mother,' Sidonie cries.

Marguerite enquires: 'Perhaps you would care to repeat what you have just said in front of Monsieur?'

'If Madame likes,' Sidonie says stoutly. 'I have nothing to tell Monsieur he doesn't know already. Everyone in this house knows what you are, only they are all afraid to tell you because of your filthy temper,' Sidonie says. 'You are an inhuman brute and I wouldn't stay here not if you were to pay me five times my money.'

Oh, now she is going to say that boring thing about money not being everything!

'Money's not everything,' Sidonie says. 'A million francs couldn't pay me for staying with a monster who beats her own son with a whip that was meant for blacks!' It's true! The bonne had told her she had used a whip that was only for blacks. What a filthy thing! To use a thing like that on one's own flesh and blood. 'For blacks!' Sidonie keeps on repeating. 'What a filthy thing!'

Marguerite observes softly: 'It's lucky for you that my nails are not yet dry, Poisson, or you would get my hand across your face. It is exactly what you need, une bonne claque, forte et ferme, across that peasant's clock of yours.'

Ah, here comes the tears. Poisson is crying at last, loudly and lustily! It is doubtful if even the good Roquefort would recognise her pet in this roaring crimson-faced wench.

She tells Nicole: 'Ring down and tell them to send Deckers up immediately to fetch this person away. She is making a nuisance of herself.'

To Pauline she says: 'Fetch me my handkerchief and be quick about it. I am late as it is with this farce.'

Mon dieu, believe it or not, Pauline and Nicole are crying now. They are all three of them howling together. It is unbelievable! What a nuisance this nail on the little finger of her left hand is still wet, tant pis, it will have to dry on her way to Vincent's dressing room. She refuses to stop one moment longer in this bedlam of howling females.

She is on the point of leaving when a rumpled-looking Deckers presents himself to fetch Poisson, the usual copy of the *Figaro* sticking out of his coat pocket. He marches straight up to the still lowing Normande and steers her out of the room by slapping her on the rump with the newspaper like a recalcitrant cow.

It strikes Marguerite that the slaps are more familiar than official, and the accompanying growls and imprecations are not really meant.

They are probably sleeping together. Deckers et sa Fesse! That suit looks as if he goes to bed in it, but in any case it probably wouldn't jolt the Poisson's delicate susceptibilities if he made love to her in his hat!

Marguerite thinks, if Deckers weren't so good at his job I would let the Agence know my opinion of them for sending me an apache like that.

Directly Poisson is out of hearing she says: 'Telephone my hairdresser immediately and tell them to send André to me twice a day till further notice.'

(It was all rubbish about letting Christienne do her hair, of course. That had merely been to enrage Poisson!)

'He is to report at nine sharp tomorrow morning—and I don't mean a quarter past, c'est compris?' says Marguerite. She isn't talking to anyone in particular. She is simply giving an order. So that is that business settled. But what a delight to escape from that room! What a bore! There seems to be no end to the repercussions with this business! All the same, she has to smile when she thinks that it is her son, her good little moumou who would never knowingly cause her an inconvenience who has just lost her the best maid she has ever had.

Oh, it is all the biggest nuisance, but she is happy in spite of it. Happy because Vincent is back and she is free now to go to his room. If only he doesn't keep his silly mood too long, Marguerite thinks. Otherwise it will not be good for the pregnancy.

She is convinced moumou is as he is because Georges and she had been so much in love while she was carrying him. He was replete with love before he had opened his eyes to the world, like a plump bourgeois waking from his nap after his good Sunday dinner.

Her petit souvenir de Georges! Nobody would think, to look at him now, he had been such a little fatty!

Oh, she is happy to be carrying Vincent's son. And she will make him happy. If he makes her fat, tant pis, she can run about at Auteuil like a farm girl and not a soul will bother her. She knows Vincent isn't keen to live in Paris, but she will more than make it up to him, and once he sees his son he will feel completely different about everything.

21

The Green and Purple Dream

He's had quite an audience, one way and another, to watch him
shave, thanks to the indefatigable efforts of his stepson who keeps
darting from the dressing room to the gallery, and back again,
with minute by minute reports on individual reaction to Castleton's return.

All, all have been unanimous in welcoming him home. According to the Dauphin there hasn't been a single exception. The latest
bulletin is that Maurice and Marcel are delighted, and so is
Gustave.

'Gustave says he has already had the honour of speaking with
Monsieur since his return,' gasps the Dauphin who, as usual, is in
imminent danger of knocking himself out.

'Oi,' Castleton catches him on the hop and dumps him down
on the bed. 'Let's see you sit on your bum for five seconds.'

'Give yourself a breather,' says Castleton who's being shiver-
somely reminded of the *Cri de Peuple* Kitten as the pretty bag of
bones stares at him with enormous eyes, murmuring ingratiatingly: 'Jules is also pleased you are back.'

'Well, jolly good. Who's Jules?'

'O, papa, don't y'all know who Jules is, papa?'

'Not really.' He still doesn't want to call me that, thinks Castleton, and lists a row with Mim about it, along with other coming-shortly attractions.

It turns out that Jules is none other than his old pal Deckers of the Agence.

'Fancy,' says Castleton, amiably.

'Yessir. Jules says that for an Englishman you are not at all bad, and he is not a type who makes compliments easily.'

'He's not, eh?'

'No, sir. Jules says for all of him the entire British nation can go sleep with their sisters, but for Mr Castleton he is willing to make an exception. Jules says he considers you to be the example classique of an old English gentleman.'

'So there,' says Castleton.

George has to admit that Jules is no Anglophile, but adds consolingly: 'He detests the Yanks even worse. I have shown him your book, papa,' reports the Dauphin, in the tones of one who has conferred inestimable favours. 'I have shown it to Dédé too, and I am going to read it to her. When I am less excited,' explains the Dauphin. 'It wouldn't be any good to read it now.'

In the meantime he intends holding his book himself. It's doing him so much good and there will not be the least need for him to relinquish it later as mama has given him full permission to take it in to dinner with him.

'It's doing me so much good, you see,' repeats the Dauphin, rather strangely.

He is holding *Colibris and Humming-birds* (there's a difference, apparently) with his left hand only. His gloved right hand has retired unobtrusively somewhere beside him on the bed.

'Papa.'

'What?' That glove will have to go. It's slowing up the healing process. It's probably being worn by order of Benoir to save his ruddy sister's bacon.

George says: 'Dédé will come and watch you shave as soon as Mammy has made her presentable.' He adds: 'With your kind permission, of course.'

'Righto.'

'I have asked for her hair to be tied with white ribbon as nearly as possible for Mass. In fact I think you will not hardly notice any difference,' says George.

He is watching his stepfather lathering his face with great attention. 'Be careful of your eyes, my darling, if soap gets in it could be bad.'

'What rot!'

'It is not rot at all!'

The Dauphin dotes on cautionary tales. It seems a bod named Felix once got soap in his eyes (it has since been confirmed that he was shaving) with the result that he is now obliged to wear spectacles for the rest of his life. 'That is the Net result,' repeats the Dauphin, who likes to exercise his taste for the dramatic, except when Mum is around, 'and in conclusion it has made him the laughing stock of the kitchens. So that is in case you still think it is rot,' finishes the Dauphin smartly.

'Who's Felix, anyway?' asks Castleton, blobbing a bit of lather on his stepson's nose.

'Felix is mama's sous-chef. And don't pretend you don't know because your ignorance will not get you anywheres. And don't you dare to come near to me with that brush!' shrieks out the Dauphin, who finds this kind of jape hilarious.

'O, you are tickling me! O, my Redeemer! O, you will finish up by getting soap on my blouse and Bob will be your uncle!'

'Moumou!'

Mim shoots in, wearing, of all dotty things, his rubies. 'Are you mad, Vincent, letting him scream like that?'

But she's so glad to have him back that there is only the faintest whiff of leg-irons in her tone. 'You really have no control over him, Poilu.'

She walks straight up to Castleton and smiles at him in the glass. 'I am not even going to ask you what that stupid mood was for. I am just glad it has passed.'

He grins back at her through Father Christmas lather and starts to shave.

The rubies are a yell. Old Mim showing willing. He hasn't seen the damn things on her since the day he gave them to her, almost. She probably thinks him too obtuse to have noticed she doesn't like them. Le thique skin Anglais! Her frock is absolutely charming.

'O, don't Mlle Mimi look beautiful!'

257

The boy friend is shaking his fingers about as if he'd burnt them. 'O, mama, that is my most favouritest dress of all.'

She blows him a cool kiss. 'What are you gasping like a fish for?'

Castleton says crossly: 'He's been farting about telling everyone I'm back. I want him to sit still.'

Marguerite says at once: 'You hear what papa says?'

'Well, I am sitting,' retorts the Dauphin mildly. 'I can't be more sitting than I am. O, papa, don't y'all adore mama's dress?'

'Yes, does it please you?'

Marguerite says, smiling: 'Or is it too plain for the English taste?'

'It's all right.'

'Thank you for nothing!'

What a gallant she has married! Phoui! She will go and sit with her son. There will always be a warm welcome for her in that quarter. Moumou is never in a mood.

They sit together on Castleton's bed, like brother and sister, arms round each other's waists, elegant legs kicking over the side.

'Mlle Mimi?'

'What?'

He is completely absorbed in watching his stepfather shave in what he considers a delightful and highly entertaining way. He is far more amusing to watch than Uncle Benoir, who lets his valet do everything.

'Well, what?' His mother tells him: 'You start to speak and then you don't finish what you have to say.'

She has found his left hand, Castleton notices in the glass, and is privately caressing it, fondling and fingering the good 'un which has healed to a satiny ribbon of a pretty, new-looking pink.

They are laughing together about it, whispering so that Castleton shouldn't hear.

'Is this all you have achieved, you fool? You promised the other one would be ready for Viv's wedding and you are still wearing your glove!'

'O, no, it will be ready,' promises George. Mim is making him giggle so that he can hardly even whisper.

'Looks like it! Hurry up! Stupid thing! You will get me into trouble with the men! Papa will sling me out!'

'O, mama, you are droll! O, mama!'

Well, I give up, thinks Castleton.

'Mama,' George whispers, 'does he know about his present? O, now he looks like Père Noël. O, look, mama.'

Yes, she has told papa, if that is who he means. 'What has one told you about personal remarks?'

That one has not to make them.

'Then is he happy?' George wants to know. 'O, if he knows he must be very happy, I think.'

'Ask him yourself,' answers his mother, giving him a little push. 'You might be luckier with his answer than I was.'

Yes, he will ask him. He gets off the bed and asks his stepfather shyly: 'Êtes-vous content de Madame ma mère?'

'Say it in English and I'll tell you,' says Castleton, chucking him under the chin.

'Are you pleased with your present? Was it a good surprise for you?' asks George.

'Oh yes, oh rather. Mind my razor, old love.'

What a farce. And what an answer!

That little idiot it quite satisfied with it, of course. 'O, he is really pleased with you, Mlle Mimi. He didn't say much because he is English, but we can certainly take it he is pleased.'

She thanks him for elucidating. 'Drink your porto and try and get a little colour in your face for a change.'

Yes, he will drink it. He can't say he is madly keen but he will drink it all the same.

He tells his stepfather earnestly: 'I am not going to be turbulent while mama is enceinte. It could disturb my little brother, don't you know?' He announces piously: 'O, we are all going to love him very much because he comes from God.'

If there is no upsurge of music it is certainly not the Dauphin's fault.

'My God! My son!' ejaculates Marguerite in comical despair.

She tells him: 'Take yourself out on the gallery and watch for Uncle Benoir. And take your halo with you.' She finds this room a little small for so much piety.

'Take your glass with you as well, moumou. You are not to leave a drop. Otherwise you will find yourself celebrating papa's homecoming by yourself upstairs.'

'Here you are, love.' Castleton opens the gallery door for him and immediately a loud wild ringing fills the room.

'Shut the door! Moumou!' Marguerite calls out. 'What are

259

you mooning about for? Either come in or go out, but make up your mind.'

He comes back into the room again. 'O, can y'all hear the cicadas, mama?'

George explains happily: 'They live for seven years under the ground and only come up for three days to make love before they die. Father Kelly told me. Only the gentlemen sing, he said. That is supposed to be their love song, that we are hearing now.'

George says: 'To me it is bizarre that only the gentlemen can sing.'

'Many thanks for your valuable information and kindly shut the door behind you.'

Marguerite says: 'Those things can drive one mad. If one remained here one would have to have the entire courtyard treated. It wouldn't be possible to stand that noise for a whole summer.'

'Oh, I dunno,' Castleton says.

'Papa had all his properties treated regularly. Even in France where the cicadas aren't at all loud by comparison. Of course on the delta places it was hopeless.' Marguerite says tenderly: 'Poor darling, he couldn't stand the slightest noise.'

'Hard luck,' says Castleton.

My God. She really hopes that dinner will do something for his temper otherwise the outlook will be the reverse of gay. Luckily, despite short notice and the usual non co-operation from the kitchen, she has managed to order a menu that will be exactly to his taste.

She jumps off the bed. 'Haven't you finished cutting your throat yet, Vincent?'

'Just about.'

She is standing directly behind him. He goes over to the wash basin to splash his face and finds her waiting for him.

'Well, blow me down,' says Castleton cheerily, 'if it isn't Mrs C.'

She says, seemingly out of the blue: 'You know, Vincent, Papa could be very hard with Armand sometimes. There was a period when he was really unjust to him.'

'Really?' He's groping for a towel. She gives it to him and says: 'It never changed his feelings for our father. Armand knew Papa did his best for him according to his lights and he will always honour him for it.'

'Thanks,' says Castleton, giving her back the towel. He knows

260

what it's all leading up to, but he's blowed if he's going to meet her halfway. At least, not at this stage.

Marguerite says: 'I didn't understand it at the time but now I can see that Papa loved Armand best of all his children. He was his first born and he was such a beautiful and intelligent boy. Papa was terribly proud of him and always wanted him to be perfect in everything because of the important position he would have to fill and that's why he was sometimes so strict with my poor brother. Can't you understand that, Vincent, even a little?'

'Not really.'

She says in a low voice: 'Mon dieu, has one really got to beg and pray?'

'I expect so,' Castleton says equably: 'I bet George begged and prayed.'

He feels her arms drop from his waist, and a good job too. It's a sort of do-it-yourself apology. She brings you the component parts and you're supposed to fit them together for her. Well, nothing doing.

Bone comes in with his shirt, and Marguerite turns away abruptly. She walks over to the gallery door and stands looking out at her son.

'Good evenin', madam,' Bone greets her affably. 'Glorious weather we're 'avin. Summer seems to have come on all of a rush.' As usual he can't take his eyes off her. 'Properly caught us on the 'op this time, 'asn't it? My word!'

She doesn't even bother to open her mouth. She finds the English preoccupation with the weather quite tedious enough without having to hear it from a servant.

Just now she has other worries than the weather. Vincent can really be horrible! I bet George begged and prayed. She turns her head and tells him coldly: 'Armand is here in case it interests you.'

She has just seen the car drive in and raps the window sharply. 'Don't run, moumou!'

Mon dieu, that child collects hangers on! He has got half the household out there with him. If he keeps it up at this rate by the time he is twenty he'll be lucky to be left with a piece of bread in his hand!

His hand.

She turns back into the room. There is no point in her going to meet Benoir.

Marguerite thinks: And that will be another one in a bad mood, I suppose. Unless Viv changes his mind and comes in to dinner the only amiable face at table will be moumou's.

She can hear his shrieks now, greeting her brother with the jubilant news that Vincent is back and Benoir's voice, almost as excited, answering him above the ridiculous 'noises off' from the crowd which has collected to watch.

'Oi,' shouts Castleton, opening the door. 'Hullo!'

The wild loud trilling invades the room at once.

'Shut the door, Vincent!' calls out Marguerite.

He flaps a cheery towel at his brother-in-law. 'Hullo! Be a duck and send George in, will you?'

He tears in, breathless, and finds himself being firmly escorted to the bed. 'Sit down and stay down. I mean it.'

'He has just gone to telephone Mme Li,' gasps George. 'It is quite natural he should want to tell her, papa darling.'

'Well, hooray and all that, but keep your bottom on that bed.'

Castleton says: 'You'll go off pop, you will, rushing about like a maniac.

'Oh dear, oh lor',' says Castleton, winking at him.

George announces proudly: 'I have told seventeen persons up till now. When I have told Sidonie I shall have told every single person in this house except Viv.'

'Don't talk so much,' says Marguerite.

George says: 'I couldn't tell Sid because it's her free evening, Nicole said. So I have kindly requested Nicole to let her know in case I am already in bed when she comes home. It is quite possible she will be late tonight, Nicole said.'

'You have been told not to talk so much,' observes Marguerite.

'Yes'm, I'm sorry.'

'I love Sid.' George says: 'I think she is a most gorgeous girl.'

'George,' says Marguerite.

'Well, I am not the only one, mama. Jules thinks she's gorgeous too. They are fiancés. Only Sid is married.' So now he only has his cousin to tell. 'Mama, may I go out on the gallery and wait for Mr Viv? When I am rested, may I, mama, please?'

'No, Mim, he's not to,' Castleton says. 'I won't have him rushing about any more.'

'You hear what papa says.'

Marguerite kisses him. 'Bienville will hear your good news soon enough. In any case you'll be seeing him tomorrow morning before he goes. Now be quiet.'

Benoir comes in, arms held wide and openly delighted to see his brother-in-law back.

'Good to have you home, fella!' He is kicking him joyously on the shins. 'So the bank didn't need you in London after all?'

'No,' says Castleton, keeping it up.

'Tant mieux pour les Benoirs alors, hein, puss? Merci, Philippe.'

He is accepting his first glass of champagne with a slight air of puzzlement. He asks his sister coolly: 'Can anyone tell us why we are drinking in here? I suggest we take our drinks downstairs and leave your long-suffering husband to dude up in peace.'

She answers him as coolly. 'I ordered apéritifs to be served in here because dinner will be early. I have told them to announce it as soon as Vincent has finished dressing.

In Heaven's name why?

He hopes his sister has no designs for inflicting that dreariest of American institutions, the early dinner, on her luckless family.

She has no designs of any sort.

She tells him briefly: 'Vincent is hungry, voilà tout.'

'He didn't ate lunch,' puts in the Dauphin.

In that case it is not necessary to say another word. 'Get your trash on, Vince, and we'll go eat.'

All three Benoirs are sitting on the bed now, with Marguerite in the middle. Benoir leans over suddenly and kisses her on the cheek. 'Alors madame, ça va?'

It is the first time he has kissed her since their quarrel and she feels quite light with relief as she kisses her beloved brother back.

'Bon soir, Armand, mon petit frère-chéri.'

It seems that in the general rejoicings over Vincent's return, free pardons are being given out and she makes no secret of the fact that she is vastly relieved at having secured hers.

It's no fun being in Benoir's black books! Mon dieu, he certainly understands to make his displeasure felt, this little brother of hers whose heart is so tender that he can't bear to hurt a fly!

She still feels hot when she remembers what he had said when he had sent for her about her conduct to moumou. She realises now that she had never seen him angry before. It was horrible when he had addressed her in that formal voice as if she were a stranger.

'I hear that your son called for protection from his father yesterday, Marguerite. If this is true one must really hope that there is nothing beyond the grave and Georges has been spared all knowledge of your behaviour.

'If I didn't know that it would defeat its end by making your son unhappy, I would certainly force you to beg his pardon on your knees.

'I have asked Monsigneur to speak to you this morning. Perhaps as your confessor he will better be able to bring home to you the enormity of your conduct. That is all I have to say to you. Go and prepare yourself for him and have the goodness not to keep him waiting.'

It was Mammy, of course, who had reported the whole business to him. It's well known she reports everything to Benoir.

Like that time in Washington when her marriage with Davis had gone completely to the devil and Armand had suddenly appeared in the middle of that terrible heat wave they were having and had quietly ordered them to pack her things. They had left immediately for Paris with just sufficient luggage for herself and the child.

And in the plane he had told her in that same dry voice: 'I have absolutely no intention of letting your son pay for the mess you have made of your marriage, my dear.'

It's quite true the child had suffered. It's no excuse, of course, but shut up with that madman Davis in that dreadful hole in Mississippi she had been nearly out of her mind. And moumou had been like a mad thing after Georges' death. Insufferably spoiled and refusing point blank to accept Davis. She can see now it had been his illness that was already coming on, but then there had been terrible scenes between them.

She is convinced that Mammy had been at the bottom of that affair as well, and had reported the whole thing over the telephone to Paris.

God knows, Benoir may have even given her orders for a daily bulletin of the situation at Shiloh.

She would put very little past Benoir—and Mammy, of course, would never miss an opportunity to make herself indispensable to him. God knows what kind of a settlement he has already made on her and her brats.

Marguerite thinks: That was one of the very few mistakes our father ever made when he chose that Créole for what was virtually my brother's first mistress. Now, of course, nothing can shake an association begun when they were both fourteen. Even if Benoir were willing, Mammy would cling with all her strength to a position which gives her the right to live like a grande cocotte and asks practically nothing of her in return.

It's true she loves moumou, but even that is more in the way an animal loves its young.

She had once quite openly confessed that if she had had her way she would have postponed his sevrage till he was three!

Well, they will see what Benoir intends for moumou. Personally, she will fight like a stag before she will let a similar situation develop with that cretin of a Dédé. And she won't hesitate to enlist Vincent's help either!

Vincent, of course, will come in on moral grounds only. Who cares, as long as he comes in on her side! She loves her brother, yes. But she loves her son better and she will do everything in her power to prevent him being bogged down with that kind of liaison.

She'll start the campaign at once. As of tonight that ridiculous practice of sharing his dessert will be discontinued. What an idea in the first place! Needless to say it had been introduced by Benoir for the purpose of inculcating altruism and democratic ideals!

And just exactly as if she knows when one is thinking about her, there is a soft knock at the door and Mammy glides in, leading that idiot of a Dédé by the hand.

My God, what on earth has Madeleine been doing to that child's hair? She looks like the bride of Ouistiti!

The little girl's queer hair has been braided with white ribbons, and a pinafore of sheerest lawn trimmed with lace, and elaborately tucked and pleated, veils the bright yellow and scarlet plaid of her dress.

Marguerite says coldly: 'Has anyone given her permission to come in here, Madeleine?'

George says at once: 'I did, mama. I wanted she should come and watch papa shave. Please may she, mama darling? It will do her so much good.'

Happily for the rest of them his ideas of hospitality and hers don't coincide. For her taste there are already far too many people in this room.

As she expects, Benoir says: 'Let her stay, Mi. What harm is she doing?'

Then for five minutes only. 'D'you hear, Madeleine? Collect your daughter in five minutes.'

By that time they will all have had more than enough of her. She asks the little girl severely: 'Have you forgotten what to say?'

'Bon soir, madame.'

'Et puis?'

'Bon soir, patron. Bon soir, monsieur.' Her smoky eyes are fixed on George.

Mammy says, smiling: 'She seen her gallant over there. What y'all do to show polite, Dédé?'

She drops a terrified curtsey at no one in particular.

'Bravo,' says Benoir, pinching her cheek. 'Madame will understand that it was meant for her.'

Mammy directs her—'You go on over an' stan' by p'tit m'sieu an' don' you fidget him, hear me?'

The little girl runs straight to George and buries her face in his lap.

'Charming,' says Marguerite. 'A good beginning.'

Mammy apologises: 'She don't only got eyes for p'tit m'sieu, that one. Dédé, don' y'all know better'n to show yo' back to madame?' She's trying to turn her daughter round to face the room but the child remains obstinately with her head in George's lap.

'Dédé!' Her mother is trying to prise her loose from George. 'Dédé! Fi donc! Dédé! Bad thing!'

Quite charming. Especially as by now she is meddling with moumou's hand, actually fingering the place on the palm with her narrow inquisitive monkey's paws. Marguerite calls out sharply: 'What is that child doing over there? Doesn't she know she is not to touch petit m'sieur, Madeleine? Take her away if she can't behave herself.'

George says kindly: 'She is a little shy, but it will pass.'

It will not get the chance, Marguerite assures him. 'Remove your daughter, please. We don't need that kind of display in here.' She calls out after Mammy: 'If you want to do her a kindness you will give her a good smack. That child has been spoiled till she has lost all sense of proportion.'

Dédé lets out a roar.

Benoir says quietly: 'Bring her to me, Mado.'

266

She stops crying at once, staring at him from her mother's arms.

'Did Maman make that pretty apron for you?'

'Dit "oui, patron",' says Mammy.

'And aren't you even a little ashamed to make such an ugly face with such a pretty apron on?'

'"Oui, patron",' Mammy says.

'C'est ça, alors. Now Maman is going to ask if Achille can find something nice for you in my room. I have an idea there is a pretty box of nougat for her, Mad, but of course only if she doesn't cry.' He takes her from her mother's arms and sets her on the floor. 'Is that a bargain between us?'

'Oui, patron.'

'Then make a nice curtsey and run along. A really nice one this time, especially for madame. Bravo, now one for all of us. Bravo again. And don't forget to save a piece of nougat for your flirt. He's sure to give you some of his caramels. Two caramels to one piece of nougat is the correct rate of exchange, if I remember rightly.'

She rushes off and back again at her mother's instruction. 'Merci, patron, pour mon joli cadeau.'

Not at all. If he has given her pleasure, that's all he asks.

'Mon dieu, Benoir,' Marguerite is laughing in spite of herself.

He replies, smiling: 'As long as she doesn't come back again. I have run out of compliments, I'm afraid.'

He's terribly good with kids, Castleton thinks. He went to no end of trouble to make her happy, and only the slightest dilation of his nostrils showed he was yawning his head off.

'That child has been spoiled rotten,' Marguerite declares. 'I hope that will be a lesson to you, moumou, not to invite that imbecile into the house any more.'

Benoir says, good-naturedly: 'Puss wanted her to share our pleasure at having Vince back.'

And meanwhile they have all had their ears split by that squalling brat!

'Come and sit along of Pa.' Castleton lifts his stepson on to his knee. ''Ow's yer pore old back, then? 'Ow's the rheumatiz?'

'O, it is rather chronic, don't you know?' returns the Dauphin promptly.

The rheumatiz is a joke between them.

'Well, that's no good, is it?' says Castleton, giving his back a rub. 'We can't have that, can we?'

'O, no, we cain't,' agrees the Dauphin.

He has the most damnable pallor on him tonight that Castleton has ever seen. A kind of semi-transparent sugary look like those sweets Mim has sent over regularly for him from France. They're made by the nuns at the St Esprit Convent and are flavoured with an essence of roses grown especially in the convent grounds. They are snow-white, semi-transparent and stamped IHS right the way through. The Dauphin adores them. They are the only sweets he is allowed to eat in any quantity.

'Have a drop of whisky, old dear. Do your pore old back a power o' good.'

'Only a sip, Vincent.' Marguerite speaks sharply. This stupid game about rheumatism really annoys her.

It's nice to sit on Mr Castleton's lap sipping his whisky which, though not exactly good, isn't bad either, and in any case about one million times better than that stinking bière de la Meuse, though it is nearly warm on account Mr Castleton don't like ice which George finds curious.

Still, he is very obliging and never tells you to continually sit up, which makes him a very restful person to sit on.

Mama will take you in her arms when she is saying goodnight, but she don't care for you to lean against her a lot in the daytime and anyways he couldn't tonight, on account of that perfume she is wearing.

O, Viv is the best of anybody when he babies you, but he ain't always in the mood, and then it will only last about five minutes before he lets you drop through his legs on to the floor. George thinks proudly, my cousin Viv can get more fed up of anything quicker than anyone in the whole world.

He very much hopes his cousin will be at dinner tonight. Even you aren't allowed to speak, Mr Viv can be more fun. If not George will have to make do with catching Mr Castleton's eye. Each time you do this he winks at you, which isn't exciting but is the next best thing to Viv for relieving the tedium till dessert.

He feels quite hungry and is really looking forwards to his dinner, which Gustave has told him will be very good.

There is not going to be any foie gras or anything like that, so it shouldn't be too difficult to eat up everything that is put on his plate.

He knows exactly what he is going to ask for, but he won't

think about it now because it is making his heart thump. He yawns and puts both his arms round Castleton's neck.

'Don't go to sleep,' his mother tells him. 'We are going in to dinner in a moment.'

'O, no, I won't.'

He feels deliciously sleepy. If he lies still his green and purple dream will come.

It isn't at all complicated and only takes about five minutes to dream because it is incomplete.

It consists of walking down a street which looks exactly like a street in Paris but which George knows is Algiers because of a glinting bright veil of suspended dust which is hanging over the pavé and has been raised by the slippered feet of many black veiled women who George always pictures as looking exactly like French war widows, although his parrain has many times assured him they do not. These slippers keep up a loud whispering which mingles with the cries and bells of sweetmeat men and lemonade sellers and the excited yapping of taxis on the boulevard at the far end of the street and with the loud wild ringing of bicycle bells as the carpet vendors swoop past with their fringed and richly coloured wares over their shoulders.

About halfway down the street is a small public park with acacias and oleanders and a French war memorial which is also a fountain where linen is sometimes washed. It is opposite the park that the actual dream takes place, in a courtyard which he is entering now by an opening so narrow it looks like a crack in the high blind wall of a house.

The centre of the courtyard, which is surrounded by tall modern flats hung with hundreds of little balconies on which radios are always broadcasting very loudly in French, is filled with an enormous tree that is bigger than the biggest tulip tree at Shiloh, only parrain has told him that this is a pistachio tree so old that it was there long before the flats, perhaps even before they built that part of the city. Parrain had said one could not give a more certain age because this might be inexact.

The branches of the trees are loaded with pistachio nuts which George has never seen growing but thinks will be the same heavy purple as the permanganate coloured water Felix had once showed him when he was blanching pistachios for his favourite glace à la pistache.

The great tree is also loaded with bulbuls, which are quite

hidden in the thick foliage and which parrain has told him are birds which only sing at night, but in his dream they sing by daylight as well.

The song is very loud and beautiful and is a proper tune like the singing at the Notre Dame for midnight Mass.

The shade of the pistachier is purple on account of the nuts, and also a very lovely and singular green because of the tremendously thick foliage, and where the two colours meet is the place where he has to wait for the best part of his dream to happen.

He must stand motionless in this bi-coloured shade, his eyes fixed on the opening to the court where the dust is suspended like a glittering curtain and the slippers of the women and the vendors go flipping by and then suddenly over the loud song of the bulbuls and the radio broadcasts and the taxi horns and bicycle bells, he will hear a French voice calling 'mou . . . mou . . . mou . . .' as if it was calling a cat, and immediately he will rush out of the shadow into the arms of his young father who loved him dearly and couldn't speak a word of anything but French except for the few words of English he spoke with his jockeys.

That is the end of the green and purple dream which is quite short because that is almost everything about papa that George can remember. Except that he looked like Viv but that may be only because mama has told him. Like the loud shrilling of the carpet vendors' bike bells which is really the noise of the cicadas and comes from outside and doesn't belong to the dream at all.

George calls out: 'They are quite harmless creatures and Father Kelly says we shouldn't despise them but try and profit by the example of their diligence.'

He's surprised to find he's sitting bolt upright in Mr Castleton's lap and talking very loudly. Everybody is laughing at him.

'You fell asleep, you silly thing,' his mother tells him.

'Wake up, ducky.'

Castleton is laughing in spite of the fright he's been having. He still looks pretty IHS but nothing like as bad as when he was asleep.

There was one moment of sheer panic when he seemed to stop breathing and the only way you could tell he wasn't dead was that Armand and Mim had gone on talking.

'Are you all right?'

O, yes, he is all right and ready for his dinner.

He's been telling them that for so long they are beginning to believe him.

Marguerite is getting up. 'Go and take your place at table.'

After that last statement they will all expect him to turn in a brilliant performance.

Armand says, smiling: 'I have a feeling that puss will walk away with the honours tonight. Mama tells me there's a big prize out for cleaning your plate?'

'Yessir, Uncle Benoir.'

'I hope you've thought of something splendid to ask for?'

O, yes, he has.

'Bravo, puss.'

It's an extraordinary thing that he should still have these dreams. That thing he had just now on Vincent's lap could have been nothing else. This is extremely disappointing.

He asks his brother-in-law tranquilly: 'By the way, Vince, did Mi ever get the chance to tell you her good news, or did puss get in with it first?'

No, Mim told him.

Marguerite puts in dryly: 'He is delighted of course.'

Armand says: 'Puss has been really chic about it, Mi. I was so jealous when I knew you were coming I bit papa and got pan-pan for the first time in my life.'

He puts his arm round his sister: 'You see, Vince, how bad your wife is. Even before she was born she was making trouble in somebody's paradise.'

He takes his sister's face between his hands and kisses it. 'You don't deserve it, madame, but I love you.'

'O, I do too,' agrees the Dauphin stoutly. 'I don't like pépère, though.' The Dauphin confesses, to be quite honest, he don't think pépère was nice at all. 'As it is, I pray for him as little as I can, though it's not always possible to avoid it altogether. Mama?'

She is beckoning him to her.

'Yes, mama?'

Marguerite asks him: 'D'you want to be sent straight to bed?'

O, no, he doesn't want it.

'Then don't you ever dare to speak of pépère like that again or I will send you up instantly.'

'I'm sorry, mama,' says George.

He will not say it but he will think it in his heart. He will not *ever* like pépère. Mama has told him that pépère was a beautiful man but George thinks if his looks had matched his nature he would have looked like the most hideous toad.

'Don't daydream, George,' his mother tells him. 'I shan't tell you a second time. Go and take your place at table at once.'

She herself is going with her brother who has got his arm round her neck and is whispering into her hair with an amused look on his face: 'I see you have the famous rubies on, my dear. They don't go with your dress, but never mind, it's a very good idea.'

They race each other to the dining room and he has already seated her as Castleton comes in.

She is buttering a roll for her son: 'Here! Something for your famous appetite! It will be another nine days' wonder, I suppose!'

22

Li'l Marie

Dinner's a bit of a rum do. Not the meal. The dinner itself is the usual masterpiece, as cleverly planned, superbly cooked, impeccably served as always. It's the set-up that's so quaint, with all the Benoirs very animated and Castleton silent, not to say glum, and poor old Armand suffering genuine torture at having to eat so early, and forkfuls of this and that being passed round amidst Gallic cries of "goûte-moi ça!'

All bans are off. No sooner had they seated themselves at table than Mim had flipped a bit of bread at her chap. 'Tu peux parler, toi! Mais pas à haute voix, c'est compris?'

Whether he clears his plate or not she means to grant him this small favour, her good little thing who was the first of any of them to see Vincent tonight, and to bring him back to her.

So there is the Dauphin chattering away like a starling and dipping his beak into his champagne (Benoir has declared 'no Vichy' tonight) and listening raptly to the grown-ups' conversation, his frightful pallor deepening, as it seems to Castleton, with every minute.

The topic of the moment is, of course, the cadeau. A topic in which the bizarre Benoirs take the most passionate interest. Gustave is handing round the *homard thermidor*, closely followed by Victor with two splendidly contrasted sauces (Benoir can't abide anything dry) and Philippe is about to serve the first wine of the dinner, a pale green, deliciously chilled Moselle, when Mim explodes her bombshell by casually announcing her intention of feeding the cadeau herself.

The effect on her brother is electrifying. He is in the act of dismissing the Moselle (only champagne, no German wines for Benoir). 'Mimi, are you completely out of your mind?'

Not at all. She is chivvying her boy friend, who is still dreaming over his *melon rafraîchi au Frontignan*. 'Hurry up, old daddy, or you won't get your reward.' There is only one thing she would like her brother to tell her: 'Where can one find a reliable wet-nurse today?'

Benoir replies imperturbably: 'A person will no doubt present herself. You have eighty-seven departments to choose from, my dear. You will on no account commit this stupidity, Mi. I hope that is understood?'

They will see.

They will not see. 'It is the biggest nonsense and I forbid it.'

She makes a face at him. 'You are only furious because you have been obliged to eat your dinner an hour earlier than usual, mon vieux.'

What nonsense. Vince was hungry and that is an end of the matter.

He is transferring some of his lobster on to Ouistiti's plate and removing the lobster leg which Ouistiti is busily dipping into his champagne glass and sucking. 'In the first place your child will be better served by a professional nurse. *Non, j'ai dit non! Petit salaud! Un autre verre ici.* And for the second thing you will completely spoil the shape of your breasts. *Mange, mange, mon chouchou.'*

'Mange, mange, mon chouchou.' She is watching her son tackling his lobster and taking off her brother at the same time. 'Chouchou doit manger vite, vite son homard, si non chouchou n'aura pas un petit rein d'un rien, ce pauv' p'tit chouchou.'

O, Mlle Mimi is funny. O, he can hardly get the breath to tell her he has eaten up everything, he is laughing so much.

'Show your plate. Lift up your knife and fork.'

Benoir interjects stiffly: 'You may be quite sure that there will be no deception with your son, Mi. There is no need for puss to show his plate. We are not in Germany here.'

She calls out comically: 'But I don't trust your puss, Benoir. He is a sly animal, your puss!'

She gets a cold stare from her brother, who returns to the subject under discussion, remarking gravely: 'I'm sure your husband already appreciates that you have sacrificed yourself sufficiently by bringing a second child into the world.'

Any woman having more than one child is looked upon by Benoir as a child-bearing machine. (The things we subject these poor creatures to, Vince, in our selfishness!)

'Georges would never have permitted you to feed his son, and Vince will not ask it of you either. We are all delighted that you show such concern for your unborn child, Marguerite, but you mustn't exaggerate. Now permit us all to continue our dinner in peace. This lobster is quite excellent, Mi. Your chef is a splendid fellow, and I hope I shall be allowed the pleasure of thanking him personally afterwards.'

Marguerite exclaims: 'Oh, not that boring thing of toasting the chef!'

Her brother returns tranquilly: 'Don't sulk, Mi. It's your own fault. If you weren't so irresponsible and had let us know in time we could have arranged something with Madeleine. Like that, Vince's son would not only have had the advantage of her splendid milk, but it would also have strengthened the bond between the half-brothers. You are a feckless creature, Mi,' observes her brother, putting a well-sauced morsel of his lobster direct into her mouth.

She calls out with her mouth full: 'D'you hear that, you half-brother? What are you mooning at me for, you half-a-brother?'

The Dauphin has fallen into a kind of trance at the mere thought of his mother having milk like any ordinary woman.

He asks her shyly: 'Will you really have milk, mama darling, when you have my little brother?'

Naturally she will have milk. 'And I will feed you too, you little baby, if you aren't careful and eat your soupe.'

He answers promptly: 'O, I will like it. I don't care much for ladies' milk, but I will like yours.'

She declares herself honoured by his preference. 'Little force-ripe, what can you possibly know about it? You can't remember Mammy's milk.'

O, no'm, he doesn't. This was from Bébé's mammy, the milk he means. 'She had so much she said it hurt her so Viv made me drink some off. I didn't like it. Viv squirted it in a cup.'

His mother tells him: 'You are a perfect little pig.'

He answers calmly: 'Viv had some too, mama. He said he liked it. Viv ain't bothered with a cup.'

She is delighted to hear it. She thinks Baudouin will also be delighted when he hears what kind of a creature has been engaged as his daughter's nurse.

Her brother says: 'You aren't going to tell Beau anything, Mimi. The poor fellow has enough on his plate as it is. It is in the past and one has only got to look at Bébé to know she hasn't suffered in the slightest from a harmless prank on the part of a young and high-spirited nurse.' He tells his brother-in-law: 'It is amazing what splendid health that little girl of Beau's enjoys. It is a thousand pities she can't give some of it to puss.'

'Yes.'

If Vince becomes much more silent it will be difficult to carry on a conversation with him at all. If he has said three words since they sat down at table it will be a lot.

Marguerite says: 'I hope you are satisfied, Benoir, with the way your son behaves with servants, and with the kind of example he is setting my son.'

He is neither satisfied nor dissatisfied. 'It's typical of Viv's behaviour at sixteen, voilà tout. As to the bad example, we can take it puss has survived. We must be boring your husband badly, Mi. The poor fellow is quite silent.'

He tells his brother-in-law pleasantly: 'You have met my brother Baudouin's little girl, of course. She was at your wedding with her father.'

'Yes.'

Mon dieu!

Benoir says, smiling: 'She is a nice little kid, a little spoilt perhaps, but still a nice little thing.'

'O, she is motherless,' chirps up the Dauphin out of the blue. 'O, can y'all imagine, papa darling, what a shocking thing?'

'You. You're a juggins,' says Castleton.

It is a fact that puss can always make Vince laugh. Thank God. Vince can be really heavy going when he is in a bad mood. It's still this thing with puss, of course. Poor Mi, it could be quite some time before her husband takes her in his arms again. This isn't good. If Mi has behaved disgracefully she has also been adequately punished for it. One can exaggerate with these things as with everything else. He smiles as he says a little dryly: 'Sounds like puss thinks papas are quite a good thing to have around, but mamas are irreplaceable. That right, pussy?'

'O yes, O yes,' calls out the Dauphin, who can always be relied upon for this sort of thing. 'O, I love mama best of all the world, Uncle Benoir.'

Well, bravo, pussy. So that is in case Vince ever imagines that what has happened has made the slightest difference to his feelings for Mi. She is still his mother, whatever she has done, and he will love her just because of it.

Vince should know how to dissociate himself better. If he were the father that would be altogether different. He is thankful for the diversion created by Bienville putting in a noisy appearance just as the *caneton à la presse* is being prepared, plumping himself down between his cousin and his aunt, and disrupting everything as usual.

'Hey, what goes on? I looked for you in the salon and they tell me you are eating already. It's only a quarter of nine.'

'A place here for Mr Viv,' says Marguerite at once.

No, Mr Viv has got to go and dress. He has promised Monique de Saussures he would collect her at nine. They are dining at the Boulangers' and then they are all going on to the Cajun to dance.

'Hey, how's your child, Tante Mi? Have you started to eat for two yet? It's the done thing, you know. Unless you eat for two it's not a recognised pregnancy. Hey, leave me breathe, will you, Marie?' He is pressing his leg down hard against his cousin's.

'Viv, papa is back,' shrieks out the Dauphin. He has wrapped both arms round his cousin's neck. 'O, papa is back, Vivi.'

'So what?' is the frank reply.

Bienville favours Castleton with a coolish stare. 'What's all this, anyways? Since when has Marie been allowed to talk at table?' It turns out it's a hoedown on account of the British Punk is back!

Christ!

His cousin, the nut case, is telling him proudly: 'I have permission to talk throughout dinner, and I am to drink only champagne!'

Christ, the Sioux are absolutely kinky for the British Punk! Of all the cookie ways to act! First they give it around that the Punk is on a business trip. And that's official and has been specially dreamed up pour kidder les domestiques. Now, when the Punk is back, the kick-up is so hideous it must be obvious to a moron the Sioux thought they were never going to set eyes on him again!

He tells his cousin: 'You'll get pissed as a priest.'

'No, I will not get pissed,' retorts the Dauphin smartly. 'So do me a favour and get lost.'

'George,' says Marguerite.

'Hey, sass,' says Bienville, shooting a bread pellet at his cousin's nose.

'Well, Viv is bugging me, mama.'

She says at once that if he is going to take advantage of his permission to talk by being impertinent to his cousin she will withdraw the privilege at once. 'You will remain silent for the remainder of the meal and you will most certainly not get your reward afterwards.'

'What reward?' Bienville wants to know. 'Hey, Thingo, what's this reward?'

George says in a muffled voice: 'It was to have been for eating my dinner properly.' He has already relegated the whole thing to the past.

Marguerite adds: 'And if you are crying you may leave the table now.'

Benoir observes: on the contrary, if anyone is going to be sent from the table it will be Viv who is, as usual, the trouble maker here. He turns to Bienville and says courteously: 'Don't let us keep you from your rendezvous.'

Ah, ah Papou se fache!

This sobriquet, originally bestowed on Benoir by the *Cri* after a law case, and now his popular name in France, exactly fits the handsome mister in what his son thinks of as Hermie's 'Mood Créole'.

Bienville wants to know: 'What's woozy going to choose for his reward, Tant' Mi?' He adores this aunt, who was only eight when he was born. She is the biggest fun, and her frock tonight is fabulous, but why she keeps on marrying macabre citizens like Davis and Castleton is anybody's guess.

She has no idea what George is going to choose. She hopes it will not be something boring, but one never knows with him.

'How's he making out? What's the score?' demands Bienville, suddenly on fire with excitement for the game.

So far he has eaten everything. She sees her pale child anxiously following the preparations for duck *à la presse*, the leaping flame reflecting hellishly in his eyes. The stupid thing can't bear the crunching of the bones.

'Mama.'

She says immediately: 'If you don't like it, you may leave it, ma souris. Gustave will find you something else.'

She is annoyed to find the three men looking at her as if they can't believe their ears. Those fools probably think it's easy for her to be severe with moumou all the time. It isn't easy at all, it's quite horrible, but someone has got to force him to make the effort to get some flesh on those bones.

Oh, if he would only always eat like that and there would be no need for her to force him!

Gustave has found him a nice little dish of quails in pastry that will be perfect for him.

Marguerite says: 'You must eat two. Two with some salad, c'est compris? You may take them in your fingers, moumou. They look good, your *cailles en chemise*.'

The little boy calls out at once: 'O, don't y'all want some, mama darling?'

No, she is going to eat some duck with papa and Uncle Benoir. 'Not everybody is as silly as you.' She gives him a kiss. He is really pale tonight, that child. 'Begin to eat, old daddy, or you will still be eating your *cailles en chemise* when we have finished our dessert. We are all waiting to hear what you have chosen for your reward.'

'Yes, what're you going to ask for, woozy?' Woozy looks fabulous tonight, Bienville decides. Just as he likes him, spooky as hell and deliciously ready for the mortician.

'Hey, j'adore ça, *cailles en chemise*.' Bienville is finishing the dish up, pushing them whole into his mouth.

'You must make me a wedding present of your chef, Tante Mi. Papa is giving me Hippo. Comme ça, I shall have a splendid dot to match the one old daddy de Grenier has no intention of settling on Elaine.'

'Papa isn't giving you Hippolyte at all,' remarks Benoir. 'I have already told you if you want Hippo you must take Achille. I will not separate those two. They are brothers.'

'Et après?' his sister wants to know. 'What are you speaking in that holy voice for? Really, Benoir, sometimes I think you are a bigger fool than my moumou.'

She can think what she likes. 'Throw me a quail for Ouisti, Viv. He has been making eyes at them for at least five minutes. Anyone but you would have noticed.'

'They are too good for your gorilla,' Bienville protests, but he throws one over all the same. It lands in Castleton's plate.

'O, my Redeemer,' calls out George, shocked and delighted by his cousin's audacity.

'Bravo. You have surpassed yourself,' remarks Benoir. 'Apologise at once.'

'It's all right,' Castleton says.

'He can speak!' Bienville announces in tones of awed discovery. 'Tant' Mi, your hubby hasn't got lockjaw after all!' He adores the word hubby—which, he insists, exactly fits the British Punk.

'Apologise,' repeats Benoir, who by this time, his son decides, is looking somewhat like Napoleon.

'Ay'm awfully sorrah, deah oeld chearp. I trust you will forgive mah.' He finds his imitation not at all bad. Everyone is laughing, even Punky, in spite of gravy on his shirt. Only Nap isn't finding it funny. He is dealing out perishing looks and showing the celebrated whites of his eyes.

'It is a quarter of ten, Bienville,' Nap is saying coldly. 'In case it interests you, Bienville.'

Yes, he is going. Bienville can feel he isn't wanted here. Bienville confesses he finds the extreme harshness of his father's attitude towards his only child totally incomprehensible.

'Here is your poor Mr Viv with only a matter of hours left in which to enjoy his family, and papa can't wait to throw me out.'

D'abord he finds that all the Sioux have behaved towards him with the utmost callousness. Tante Mi has been his greatest disappointment. She has refused point-blank to give him her splendid chef, when she well knows that the de Grenier cooks are all barbarians from Outer Gaul lured into Paris by the de Greniers with rotten horseflesh.

'Have I said I wouldn't give you Louis, you fool?' cries Marguerite, laughing.

She is leaning to kiss him across her son. 'I simply refuse to inconvenience Vincent for your sake, voilà tout. I will see what I can find to train in his place when we get back to Paris and then I will make a present of my Louis to you and your Elaine. You are both welcome to his temperaments. You will very soon find them more trouble than his cooking is worth.'

Never. He is a genius trained by a genius, and she is inconceivably chic to give away her pearl to his shiftless bride who is completely indifferent to household matters and quite incapable of training a flea.

'You are darling for me, and I adore you,' Bienville declares. 'You will enjoy training your new chef, Tant' Mi. It will be a stimulating change for you after the Dauphin. That is the trouble with the Dauphin, you know. After nine years he's getting played out. But your new fellow will be fresh and full of fight. He'll probably also suit your hubby better. At least at first. He won't be quite as expert as your Louis, and a few burnt sauces are more compatible with the British way of life.'

'Well then, they just are not,' puts in the Dauphin smartly. 'The British don't care for burnt sauces. For your benefit,' says the Dauphin, 'and just in case you think you own the world.'

'George, are you being impertinent to your cousin again?' asks Marguerite.

'You 'tend to your dinner, Spooky. I have to know what y'all going to choose for your reward before I go.'

'Dinner ain't over yet,' George points out primly. 'And anyways it don't affect you, Viv.'

'You don't know what to ask for, that's what. C'm'ere and I'll help you.'

That purple ghoul's delight round Spooky's eyes is the greatest ever. Bienville hopes it's there for keeps. He brings his head down to his cousin's and whispers: 'Go on and ask for that.'

'O, no, I will not ever,' George calls out, pushing him away. He is crimson to his ears.

'Then you're a punk,' his cousin teases him. 'A punk and a bore.'

'What is he blushing for?' Marguerite wants to know. 'What did you tell him to ask for, Viv?'

'Viv, you are not to say,' George calls out. 'Viv.'

Bienville says promptly: 'Plus de panpan.'

George calls out furiously: 'O, you are stinking for me. O, if you died I would just be bored.'

Pourquoi? Bienville thinks it is a splendid idea. Plus de panpan, or, alternatively, long sleeves on all Marie's blouses and Tante is to take off her rings.

'Like that she can slap you to her heart's content and you won't feel a thing.'

Marguerite laughs. 'Well, why don't you take your cousin's advice, you silly thing? Papa and Uncle Benoir would be delighted.'

Benoir says abruptly: 'The joke's over. Are you going, Bienville, or what?'

'George, I am speaking to you,' says Marguerite.

'You have managed to be exactly one hour late for your appointment. Congratulations,' says Benoir.

Marguerite says: 'You can answer or go upstairs.'

He answers in a muffled voice: 'No, I don't want to choose what Viv said, mama.'

Soit. Since that is his decision. Though if he continues to make a face like that he may soon have reason to regret it.

Bienville calls out immediately: 'I must go. I must fly. Au 'voir, ma petite tante-chérie.'

It is imperative to take Tante's mind off the Dauphin quickly or she will slap him, and then Benoir will surely slap her down and the Punk will start reading the Punksville Address and life will be hideous for ever and ever.

'Au 'voir mon Viv, mon chéri.' She draws his face down fondly. She thinks: he grows more like Georges every day. It's as well she isn't like that idiot Benoir with moumou or she would find it impossible to kiss him, the likeness, especially round the eyes, is so fantastic. 'Au 'voir, mon chéri. We shall see you before Sunday, I hope? We shall be at the Georges V apartment.'

'Of course. Au 'voir, papa.' He kisses his father affectionately. 'Try to think kindly of your wayward child. Remember he's going to leave you in peace for one whole year.'

Thank God for that.

Benoir says: 'Leave me breathe, will you? And see you don't get booked for speeding in that crazy new machine of yours. Hear me? You're not in Paris here. The cops here won't be satisfied just to collect the fine.'

'Okay, papa.'

'You're getting married on Sunday, and I don't mean perhaps. It would just about kill this family to have you on their hands again.'

'Okay, okay,' promises Bienville, kissing his father's hand.

Nap looks out of sight tonight. The relief of being able to hand Mimi and li'l Marie, the well-known duo act, back to the Punk again has made him look about eighteen.

Bienville thinks proudly: the Sioux are a splendid-looking lot. They will look magnificent at his wedding and rubbish the de Greniers in a most satisfying way. The Punk they can leave standing quietly in a corner somewheres like a Victorian sideboard.

Benoir is saying: 'Be good to your maman, Viv, hear me? She will be sad at parting with you, though Christ knows why. Caress her tenderly for me.'

'Pour moi, aussi,' pipes up the Dauphin. 'Caress her tenderly.' That li'l Marie. That mouth is far too much. That small meek mouth which is like white coral and, like white coral, is deliciously disappointing only because it isn't pink.

'You keep your nose in your patates, boy. Hey, I'm comin' up to tell you g'night when I get back.'

'O, Viv. O, promise,' screeches King Nutty, who is ejaculating in a strictly predictable way. 'O, Viv. Whatever time it is. O, promise, Viv.'

'You will do nothing of the kind, Bienville,' says Marguerite. 'I will not have you disturbing your cousin at some ridiculous hour.'

'You will know nothing about it,' Bienville tells her. 'You will be safe in the arms of le bon Oncle Vince. Bai, bai, oeld chearp,' he says to Castleton. 'Bye, Ouisti, you are invited to the wedding too. You must bring him to the ceremony, papa, as well as to the reception. Mummy de Grenier will never dare to breathe a word because she'll think she's the only one who sees him. She'll think our poor Ouisti is her first fit of D.T.s since her cure. Ouh! I was trying to kiss your beast, papa, and he is biting me!'

'Are you surprised? You tease the poor thing all his life and suddenly you expect him to love you.

'Start to move, Viv,' commands Benoir, who is laughing in spite of himself. 'It is disgusting to keep Monique waiting like this. I hope she will be furious with you.'

It will have its advantages. 'If she hates me she won't try to make me all the way to the Boulangers.' He sees superb asparagus. Is it from Ezes les Roches? Already? 'That man of yours down there is a wizard, Tante Mi. He can make anything grow.' Oh, they are good. And this mousseline is divine. He will take two up with him to eat while he is dressing. 'Be chic and lend me Hippo, Benoir. That brute of mine is inconceivably slow. Hey, and lend me five hundred bucks. I left my wallet at the Courcelles this afternoon. Lili is bringing it with her when she joins us at the Cajun, but she is sure to have pinched half.'

'So you went to bed with Lili Courcelle this afternoon.' Benoir is handing the five one-hundred-dollar bills across the table. 'On the eve of your wedding. Felicitations.'

Well, that is where he is wrong.

Oh, Benoir is killing when he goes moral like this. Who but Benoir would even dream of saying 'felicitations'?

'I didn't go to bed with her,' Bienville declares. 'I haven't slept with anyone since my engagement. Except with Elaine. Of course,' says Bienville.

'Eh bien, Viv,' says Benoir, looking meaningly at the Dauphin who is dreaming his life away as usual at the end of the salad queue.

Pas devant les Spooks.

Bienville announces: 'I have promised Elaine to follow your example, papa. I shall remain faithful to her until we're married.'

Touché. From the menacing look Nap is darting at him it looks like the chapeau fits.

As to this afternoon, Lili and he went for a swim. The Courcelles have made a splendid new swimming pool by covering over their courtyard. They have done away with all that palm-and-fountain jazz. The Courcelles are far out. Unlike the Sioux who are under the impression they are still living in pre-secession and are happy to spend the rest of their lives up to the eyebrows in spanish moss.

The Dauphin is being served with his salad by Tante who is giving him all the tenderest leaves of lettuce and 'shampooing' him briskly for dreaming at the same time. 'If you intend to fall asleep at table you may make your goodnights. We will all be delighted to dispense with your company. Là, mange moi ça. I have made a special dressing for you with very little vinegar. You may not leave one single leaf. Now take your fork in your hand and start to eat. Be quick. You are always last.'

Tante is really the greatest. She can make everybody's salad dressing, look absolutely fab, and give li'l Marie hell with the greatest relish in the world.

That hexed-up li'l Marie. I like it all.

Bienville is pocketing the money and observing coolly: 'It was not a dirty date, papa. Like we wore swimsuits, even, for instance. I know you won't believe me, but we did. Lili's brother came with us and I borrowed a pair of drawers from him and I undressed in his room. That's where I left my wallet. Incidentally, and if it interests you, as the Dauphin would say, and also just in case you think you know it all. So while you were with your mistress, your son was disporting himself chastely in cold water with Freddy and Lili Courcelle. And the Courcelles weren't even surprised because the Courcelles don't think I am a libertine and a sex maniac and under compulsion to screw everything in sight, which is obviously what *you* think, papa.'

And in conclusion, Bienville would like to say he finds it bizarre that Benoir should invariably think the worst of him. Bienville says without smiling: 'This is an ugly trait. You are a beautiful creature, papa, but you have a mediocre soul, and I prefer Tante Mi who has no use for chastity at all.'

'Whom are you speaking of?' snarls Nap, who is famous for not permitting one breath of criticism to cloud the bright shield of his ever loving sister's name.

He is talking about his Auntie. 'My beautiful little Auntie.'

'Auntie' is another British word Bienville is kinky for.

'Move.' Nap is making his celebrated feudal gesture with his right hand. 'Move before you feel my hand in your face.'

Nap has been making this gesture ever since anyone can remember, and even li'l Marie, whose natural habitat is the firing line, and whose nerves in consequence are one delicious quaking jelly, is only half impressed.

'O, he is only funning, Vivi,' calls out pale puss. 'I think.' He isn't quite certain. His head is a little to one side. He is pale puss. He has more names than Jehovah. He is beautiful all right.

''Bye, feller.' Bienville drops a careless kiss on to his cousin's head and gets the full scent of the hair up his nose.

Hey. That was the foolish thing all right.

''Bye, Tante Mi. 'Bye, Tante Mi's child. You may come with Tante to my wedding but don't you dare jump about.'

'O, no, he will not, Vivi,' shrieks out pale puss, who is colonel-in-chief of the blood is thicker than water brigade.

'O, you must kiss him properly. He will be your little cousin, don't you know?'

'Hello, my little cousin,' says Bienville. 'What are your views

285

on chastity? He says he likes asparagus better. Bravo,' says Bienville, kissing Marguerite's waist. 'That was a kiss from your big cousin who likes asparagus too. Hey, Tante Mi,' calls out Bienville. 'Hey, he's a she. She has just told me. She says she will be hideous. Six foot tall and covered in sandy hair. Especially her knees.'

'Ah non, Bienville!' calls out Marguerite. 'I forbid you to speak like that, even in fun!' She aims her roll at him. 'You are a pig! You will ruin my pregnancy for me, you fool.'

He avoids the roll by ducking and rushes to the door, laughing and shouting for his valet and his father's valet and for someone else to get on the phone and tell Mlle de Saussures that Mr Benoir is already on his way.

He is suddenly looking forward to seeing little de Saussures. He hopes she will be furious. She has a kind of dirty temper that is tops. He will kiss her till she slaps his face and then he'll give her a whirl. No serious stuff because that is exactly what he doesn't want before his wedding, whatever that sass-giving Nap may think.

And anyways he can always have him a time with Thingo at factory-to-you prices in that crazy bed of his that always gets in on the act.

He'll bring him a friandise from the Cajun. Anything pink in a paper frill Thingo is kinky for. Except it better be something that don't leave crumbs in the bed on account of Tante has an Eye for crumbs in the bed.

With luck he will arrive just after Li'l Marie has had his first night sweat and Mammy has put him dry so he can sweat so she can put him dry so he can start to sweat again.

He bounds into his dressing room shouting 'Move it!' and frightening the nigras to death.

Everything is coming up roses for him fast on account he can have himself a time and it will still be strictly comme il faut et absolutely pour la patrie!

23

The Sharper

A blast from above tells them that Bienville is dressing to the radio as usual.

Benoir says comfortably: 'That poor Elaine, she will have something to put up with with that trash. This mousseline is admirable, Mi. So delicate and soft. I see Vince prefers butter?'

It might be the better choice for him.

Marguerite says dryly: 'Who knows, it might help to oil his tongue.'

'Viv is a case, ain't he, papa darling?' remarks the Dauphin, slipping a spidery hand into Castleton's, and squeezing it with a spiderish ardour.

'Drop papa's hand at once, moumou.'

Marguerite tells him: 'One doesn't hold hands at table.' She asks impatiently: 'Have you finished your salad?'

'Yes'm, mama.'

At last. She serves him with three asparagus. 'Eat those. And take the mousseline, it will be easier for you to digest than the beurre noir.'

'Yes'm, mama.'

That poor thing, struggling with his three asparagus as if they were tree trunks. She says suddenly: 'You may leave them. You have eaten one so I suppose we must be satisfied with that.' She is thinking about Bienville and his abounding health and remarks bitterly: 'Viv will be completely thrown away on that little tart with her aluminium nails.'

'Eh bien, Mi.' Benoir says reasonably: 'She may not be our choice, but Viv and Elaine seem to hit it off quite well. They are both completely egocentric, so neither will get hurt. They can be safely left to fight it out without any help from either side, my dear.'

'What a prospect!'

Why? By the time a child puts in an appearance they will have sorted themselves out. 'Certainly it's no great love match, all the same it wouldn't in the least surprise me if that marriage turned out quite well.'

It would surprise her. Mightily. Marguerite says the one good thing about the de Grenier marriage is that it has done away with the threat of any more disasters like the one that was hanging over their heads last year when Bienville suddenly announced his intention of marrying an air hostess!

'Can you imagine, Vincent? It was actually being put forward as a proposition by my idiot nephew.' Marguerite declares: 'One has really got to be thankful to the de Greniers for saving us from that.'

'The disaster, as she calls it, was purely in Mi's imagination, Vince. These girls are chosen for their good appearance and their adaptability and I was perfectly satisfied that the young person in question was entirely suitable for my son. The truth is no girl will ever be good enouth for Viv in my sister's eyes. She loves her Viv very much, hein, Mi?' He pats her cheek and says kindly: 'It won't be at all a bad thing, my dear, if the Benoirs start marrying outside the family. There is no question that their tendency to intermarry is already having an effect.'

'Meaning my son, I suppose?'

That too. But chiefly he was thinking of her nerves. 'They are far from good, Marguerite.'

Why should that worry him? The worse her nerves, the more nobly forbearing he and Vincent will appear.

St Benoir and St Castleton.

O, mama is funny!

She tells Gustave: 'Pas de *crêpes Suzette* pour p'tit m'sieu! I ordered some plain strawberries and cream for him. Where are they?'

'They are here, madame.'

'Then tell Victor he may serve him with them while the *crêpes Suzette* are being prepared. But not on a hot plate, one hopes.'

She promises her son: 'I will give you a little of my *crêpes* to taste and I will pinch your biggest strawberry in exchange.'

He won't mind that, of course. She thinks, half proudly, that little idiot would give his last sou to anyone who asked for it.

She says to Castleton: 'He adores *crêpes Suzette*, but if he is going to bed directly after dinner they might be a little heavy for him. What d'you think, papa?'

If Vincent puts in a special plea for *crêpes*, she will let moumou have them.

'I wouldn't know.' After that lobster and the rest of it he hardly thinks it matters.

What an answer!

Marguerite thinks: If Vincent had his way, my son would be a complete invalid by now. In bed every night by seven o'clock with a cup of consommé and two soft boiled eggs in a glass! As if that poor thing hadn't little enough opportunity to take his place in the world!

She can hardly wait to get this dinner over. What a bore! What a frightful bore it has turned out to be! And Armand is being the biggest bore of all with his talk about the Bienvilles visiting the Aunts on their honeymoon! As if the young couple will have nothing better to do than visit those old frumps at the Delta.

Her brother says quietly: 'It won't kill Viv and Elaine to spend a few hours with them while they are down at St Cloud. The Aunts have always adored Viv and it will give them immense pleasure to see his bride. You know very well they will be unable to attend Viv's wedding, Mi. The journey to Paris would be too much for them. Those poor things, Vince,'—he tells his brother-in-law—'that poor Zélie must be at least sixty.'

'Tiens, I had no idea you were sixty, Tante Zélie,' cries Marguerite. She is pretending to scrutinise her son's features. 'You are fantastically well preserved, my dear! Allow me to congratulate you!'

O, she is funny!

Benoir continues smoothly: 'They are my mother's four sur-
viving sisters, Vince.' He is completely ignoring his own sister.
The six Bienville girls were famous beauties in their day ...

'Les Girls,' says Marguerite, giving her boy friend a nudge.
(She and Beau used to call them 'Le Massif Central'!)

  ... And it never fails to astound him that of the six only his
mother and Tante Zélie got married. Benoir says: 'Mimi, you are
behaving badly.'

Et quoi? The Bienville women are like a lot of overgrown kids,
Marguerite says. 'Viv has only to send them a handful of dragées
from his wedding. They will be overjoyed and there will not be
the slightest need for the young marrieds to get covered in poudre
de riz and frangipani.'

So that is the whole hideous business taken care of.

'Mon cher old chap,' says Marguerite, filching a strawberry
from her son to give to her brother.

Benoir says stiffly: 'I have Viv's promise that he will visit them.
Viv has his faults, but going back on his word isn't one of them. I
don't want a strawberry, Marguerite.'

'What a fool,' remarks Marguerite. She is choosing a strawberry for her husband. 'Eat it! It's a present from your lovey-
ducky.' She tells Castleton: 'Georges dragged me down there on
our honeymoon. We did nothing but sit in the Grand Salon for
the entire afternoon surrounded by Soutanes and delta Society,
sipping anisette and nibbling those terrible over-sweet macaroons
that monstrously fat cook of Tante Zélie's has been making for
the last twenty years. And served, of course, by that bony Matu-
rine, that impossible old maid of Tante Rose's who knows everybody's business because she is the only one in that house who
knows how to use the telephone!

'Tante Louise did nothing but praise Georges to his face, and
Tante Berthe seriously advised me to eat plenty of green almonds
if I wished to keep my breasts firm and well pointed for my dear
husband.'

Tante Berthe is unmarried, of course.

Marguerite says one can always rely on a maiden aunt to give
the lewdest advice. She asks her husband pertly: 'Shall I eat more
almonds, Poilu? What d'you think? What is your opinion?'

Benoir says coldly: 'I happen to know Tante Berthe refused
several offers of marriage. She sacrificed her life, Marguerite, in
order to bring up your husband. With a tender care and loving

devotion, I may add, which might well be emulated by certain mothers.'

The great wonder is that Georges managed to survive at all, with those four feather beds on top of him, praising him every time he blew his nose! She pouts: 'Vincent, you haven't answered my question. Obviously, you take no interest in my breasts.'

There is no answer, of course. Only her little silly telling the table at large: 'It isn't always easy for us to make sacrifices, Father Kelly says, but even if it is against our natural inclinations it is the path we have to choose.'

'Is it, old love?'

It's too ridiculous how Vincent always speaks to him as if he were four years old.

'Are you all right, darling?'

So he has noticed it too. Whatever is the matter with that child tonight? He is paler than she has ever seen him, and the fact that he is speaking French without coercion isn't at all a good sign. She pushes the last of her crêpes into his mouth. 'Eat that, old daddy, and stop preaching.'

She tells Gustave: 'We will have coffee on the gallery. And tell them to switch the yellow lights on or we shall all be eaten alive. To bed, Tante Zélie, you look completely drunk you are so tired. Are you coming, you two?'

Hey, not so fast. They haven't had dessert yet. Benoir reminds her: 'You have some business to settle with a client of yours first. In case you thought you could run out on him. Have you finished, puss?'

'Yessir, Uncle Benoir.'

'Then come over here and sit between papa and me. We'll tackle this together. Something tells me you aren't quite up to mama on your own.'

Marguerite laughs. 'If you are going to ask for something abysmal like a favour for Dédé, I shan't grant it, Benoir. So you can both save your breath before you start.'

'No strings, Mimi.'

Benoir informs her: 'There are no conditions to this deal. As I see it, you promised puss he could have anything he likes provided he ate his dinner properly. He has kept his part of the bargain and now he is going to claim his reward. Coming, puss?'

'Yes, sir.'

He has come to stand beside his dearest Mr Castleton. His napkin is still round his neck and he is supporting himself by holding on delicately to anything that comes to hand.

'Hey, hey.'

'Little bold thing, where are you holding papa?' But she is laughing about it, and Benoir is laughing too.

George looks up happily at his dearest friend whom he must now only call papa but whom he will always think of as Mr Castleton.

'Want to come up, darling?'

Castleton lifts the white child on to his knee. He is as light as a biscuit. He seems to be made out of some terrible white meringue tonight. It is frightful to take hold of him in this burning condition.

'Let's have your napkin off, then.'

Poor little sod, the hair at the back of his neck is quite hot and wet. He ought to be in bed. Castleton thinks bad-temperedly, it's like the Sioux keeping him up to play their ruddy games for them.

I hope he buggers it and doesn't ask for anything. He can't win, anyway.

Mim is sure to do him out of whatever he asks for, and Benoir will use him as a pawn in an oblique move to try to insure himself against ever again being lumbered with Mum and Son and who can really blame him?

He can hear Benoir at his creamiest plying the naïve Dauphin with suggestions, every one a bid to secure the vital Franco-British pact.

Bloody Benoir politics.

Benoir, of course, is doing nothing of the kind. He is engaged in expertly peeling a pear, his beautiful profile bent intently over his task, his whole attention given to keeping Ouistiti's acquisitive hands from meddling with his knife. 'Will you look at that case, he's kinky for pears! Hey, wait for it, fella, you'll cut yourself! Here. Here, puss.' He is holding out a piece of pear for George. He is a terribly decent stick. He is incapable of a single underhand action, blast him, however advantageous to himself.

Hey, Vince is smiling. And that's a thing that hasn't happened too often tonight. He fits a fresh cigarette into his holder. 'Ready, puss?'

The pale child turns round, smiling. He has been lying back against Castleton, patiently waiting for the grape his dearest friend has been peeling for him, putting on reading glasses to remove every pip and at last shoving it awkwardly into George's mouth.

'Yessir, I'm ready, Uncle Benoir.'

Good. There's a whole list of glittering suggestions for his consideration. 'How'd this suit you, puss?'

A whole cigarette to himself . . .

'Are you mad, Armand?' Marguerite wants to know.

. . . to be smoked with panache pour épater les grown-ups. 'You may use my holder. How's that strike you, puss?'

No appeal? Could be as well. He looks in pretty bad shape tonight.

Aloud he says: 'I suspect your son prefers to smoke his Gauloises in bed, Mimi. I seem to remember I did at his age. It was the secrecy, of course, that made the whole thing so delicious.'

Marguerite says at once: 'Is that true, moumou, that you smoke in bed?' She is holding out a quarter of her peach for him to eat off her fork.

Sometimes, when Viv is with him.

Then he will stop at once. As from this moment. 'C'est bien compris? And when I see your cousin I shall certainly pull his ears . . . What an idea, to let you smoke!'

'Stick to the point, Mimi,' her brother points out, 'whether puss smokes or not isn't under discussion.' The thing now is to discover what her son wants as his reward for eating his dinner without involving them in the usual ruckus which, he may add, is almost invariably triggered off by her.

'So quit interfering, there's a nice fella. I think I've hit on the very thing for you, puss.'

To go with Viv in his new Ferrari at, shall they say, a conservative eighty-five?

'No, I forbid it!' Marguerite calls out. 'Benoir!'

'Viv can let her out along the shore road for you. First thing tomorrow. Before he leaves. Good idea?'

O, yes. O, he would like it of all things.

Then shall they settle for that? 'Shall we claim that from mama as your reward?'

The pale child says shyly: 'I don't know if mama would like it, Uncle Benoir.' He is wiping his lips on his mother's napkin and smiling at her.

She answers coldly: 'What has that got to with it? You have carte blanche. If I don't like what you ask for, tant pis, I will have to let you do it all the same. Your mouth,' she tells him, 'wash your mouth. The acid in the peach has made your lips crack. Use your finger bowl, stupid. Be quick.'

Armand asks him: 'So do we vote for Viv, or what?'

George shakes his head and smiles.

'Why's that? I thought you wanted it so much?'

George only smiles and smiles.

'What d'you want, then?'

He is finding this modesty, or whatever it is, a little excessive. The way puss is playing this it could get to be a bore.

He says a trifle coolly: 'You may have anything you like, you know. Only I'm afraid you'll have to name it for us. Unhappily we are none of us clairvoyant here.'

Marguerite exclaims: 'Oh, if he is going to make a great mystery and drama out of everything, let's call the whole thing off.'

It's that, beyond all doubt. He wants to come into their bed tonight.

'No, Mi. You make him nervous. Let puss speak.'

'Then speak or go to bed, d'you hear? Don't make us drag the whole thing out of you.' She asks him suddenly: 'What's the matter, old daddy, are you ashamed to tell us what you want?'

'No, ma'am.'

It's that. It couldn't be anything else, but he is smiling at her in such a queer way it is impossible to tell if he knows she has guessed what he wants. It's partly a trick of those eyes in that pale face but there are moments when that child looks downright uncanny. Poor thing, he wants it terribly!

She is quite curious to see how he will set about trying to get it. In point of fact that wasn't bad for a beginning. He probably knows by now that smile can charm the birds off the trees. Vincent, of course, surrenders unconditionally the instant it is switched on!

She notices he is playing now with Vincent's ring. He is probably touching it for luck.

She says almost kindly: 'Eh bien, monsieur, the whole room is waiting for your answer. So far we have had only smiles.'

Those smiles, which are perfect replicas of Maman's and which are incidentally half-killing Benoir. That fool is really neurotic, talking to the child in that controlled voice that deceives exactly no one.

'Yes, puss, you've made us curious. Don't keep us guessing.' He says he will give George a moment longer and then, reluctantly, he must declare the offer closed. 'Let's hear from you, fella.' The tone is unmistakable.

George asks if he may whisper his request.

His face and neck, even his chest, have gone a bright fiery red. She was so right. He's going to ask for it. She hasn't a moment to lose.

She says at once in her most intimidating voice: 'Are you ashamed of what you have chosen, George?'

'No, ma'am.'

'Then say what you have to say out loud and be quick about it.'

She's safe. He won't ask for it after that. She knows him so well. He would rather die than lay himself open to rebuff in front of the men.

The conceit of that brat of hers! But she adores him, her moutard with his overweening pride that must be saved at all costs.

Well, it has saved her too. If he had come out into the open with that request of his she would have fobbed him off and the fuss with those two men would have been inconceivable.

It was the voice that had scared him like that. It had literally shoo'd him off like a bird from a cherry tree! What luck, because she has definitely no intention of having any thievish cherry-gobbling finches in her bed tonight!

Marguerite thinks, it will be perfect tonight. All the better for our separation. Tonight it will be as fresh as the first morning of Creation. That poor little donkey with his fiery ears! He is furiously disappointed, but this was a question of expediency. She will make it up to him. The very first Sunday in Paris after Viv's wedding she will go with him to the Saint Esprit and give thanks for her pregnancy. He will adore that. It is his favourite thing to attend Mass with Mlle Mimi.

She blows him a gay kiss. 'What are you blushing for, stupid thing? You have been very good and everyone is pleased with you. So stop being modest and tell us what you want.' She feels this is a perfectly safe question. 'Tell maman, what would you like, ma souris?'

He says politely: 'I don't want anything.'

There is an incredulous sound from Benoir.

'Oh, leave him alone, Armand,' Marguerite says. 'He thinks he's making himself interesting.'

That insult was directly aimed at her, by the way!

What a kid she has picked for herself! Half the size of a bread-crumb and deals her a slap in the face with all the self-possession in the world!

'Send him to bed, Benoir. He is annoying me.'

No, this intrigues him. 'You don't want anything at all?'

'No, sir.'

Not one single thing in all the world?

'No, sir.'

Not a wish in the world. Tiens, tiens. He can't get over it.

'Hear that, Mi? I'm afraid we have a paragon on our hands. I can't pretend I envy him but I congratulate him all the same.'

He adds suavely: 'Perhaps in that case it isn't necessary to keep puss up any longer?' He has lost interest in the whole thing. 'What d'you say, Mi?'

She says for her part she will be glad to see the back of him. 'You are dull, dull, dull. I am ashamed of you. Bienville will be furious when he hears how you behaved. Make your goodnights and disappear.'

He gets off Castleton's lap without a word. His eyes look very bright. Benoir says kindly: 'Want to hold Ouisti, puss?'

He nods, silently holding out his arms for Ouistiti.

His mother declares: 'My God, he's lost his tongue now as well as his wits.'

She beckons him to her but he won't come. He isn't even look-ing at her. Would you believe it, that sulky brat refusing to budge from Vincent's side!

'Hey, consolation prize,' Armand hands over the tiny ape.

'You, Ouisti, behave yourself, hear me?' If that case takes a notion to pinch puss now, there will be Floods at the Delta. They are pretty near as it is. Christ knows what it was he really wanted. They will never know now. It's a secret and has gone to join all the other secrets puss seems determined to take with him to the grave!

Poor puss.

He is standing there, quite lost in the clouds, feeding Ouistiti who is wrenching grapes out of his hands and dashing them on to the floor. He is moving his scalp up and down at a furious rate, and chattering his teeth at Castleton. His tiny brown eyes with their curious tan lids are fixed jealously on Armand's face.

'He is droll,' observes George, carefully handing him back. He hasn't even smiled.

'Goodnight, mama.'

His mother sweeps him into her arms. 'You are a little fool. You had carte blanche and all you could think of was to take that stupid beast into your arms.' She is stroking his hair back and smiling into his eyes. 'Eh bien, monsieur, the offer is closed now. You had your chance to speak, but it seems you can't open your mouth—tant mieux pour nous, alors,' says Marguerite. 'We really ought to thank you for making it so easy for us.'

He is coming out of his disappointment because he has put his two arms round her neck. He is still a little silent, but that won't last for long.

She whispers into his hair: 'You may take papa's book to bed with you if you like. Only don't take it into your bath.'

O, mama is droll.

She would put nothing past him tonight. 'Why are your eyes so bright, old daddy? Have you got fever, by any chance?'

'No, mama, no.'

She doesn't believe him. When she comes up she will take his temperature. 'Quickly to bed now, moumou, you are really tired. Ne récite pas trop longtemps ton chapelet, ma souris, hein?'

O no, he will not.

'I will look at your knees when I come up. If they are red I shall pull your ears.'

She slips a dragée into his mouth with her last kiss. 'That is for you because you have been so good. Now say goodnight to everybody and take yourself off.'

So bright-eyed puss whose temperature, by the looks of things, is taking its nightly climb, is staggering round saying goodnight and kissing hands which, in Castleton's opinion, should on no account be kissed, but, on the contrary, very smartly rapped across the knuckles. He is tired to death and longing for his bed and should actually be delighted at the prospect of being shut of the lot of them for a few peaceful hours, but obviously isn't, and is only longing for tomorrow to come so that he will be able to see them all again.

He is replete with Iced Melon, *Homard Thermidor*, Happiness, Kisses, *Cailles en Chemise*, Champagne, Love, Filial Piety, Champagne, Colibris and Humming Birds, More Champagne, a little Brother, Ouistiti, *Salade à l'Orange*, *Pommes Duchesse*, Viv's Wedding, *Asperges, Sauce Mousseline*, Shyness, Father Kelly, Putting Oneself Last, *Fraises à la Crème*, two tiny *Petits Fours* shaped like paniers des roses, More Champagne, a taste of maman's *Crêpes Suzette*, Obedience, Nice Fruits from everybody, and an oyster direct from the *Brochette d'huîtres* served as a special attention to Mr Castleton who is the favourite of them all and don't eat desserts much.

This oyster is much prized by George both as a novelty—it is the first cooked oyster he has tasted—and also because it has come to him from the plate of his dearest friend, which makes it count almost as much as the sugared almond from mama's mouth which he is sucking now.

O, if he had only had the courage to ask her for the second time if she would let him call her husband by his given name. Everybody had told him he had carte blanche and he had almost dared, but then she had spoken to him in that bad voice and he had been afraid she would get angry with him again.

'Goodnight, papa.'

O, it is simply farouche how he don't want to call him by that name. Even if he is his dearest friend he still don't want it.

'Goodnight, darling.'

The hollow child is holding up his mouth as usual. He kisses the pale lips gingerly. 'Have a lovely sleep.'

'Moumou!' Marguerite calls out sharply. 'How many times must one tell you not to kiss people on the lips like that?'

She is really annoyed. Not with moumou but with Vincent for holding the child in that ridiculous way as if he were made of glass or something. 'Mon dieu, hold him properly, Vincent! He won't break! He isn't made of sugar, you know!'

That's all she knows about it. He is made of purest meringue. The slightest pressure and all they would have left is a pretty little hill of sparkling white sugar. 'We'll have a good look at your book

298

tomorrow, shall we? See if we can find a picture of your little
nest.'

'O yes. O, I am looking forwards, don't you know? Goodnight,
my own dear darling sweet petit-papa, chéri.'

'Goodnight, pretty. Careful how you go.'

And if she didn't like that she can lump it.

'Goodnight, Uncle Benoir.'

''Night, pussy. Sweet dreams, and pray for France.'

'You idiot, Benoir!' his sister exclaims. 'I specially don't want
him to make a long thing of his devotions tonight.'

Her brother tells her calmly: 'He can leave us out of them.
Vince isn't a Catholic and you are past praying for, anyways.
Hear that, puss? Use the time you save on us to intercede for
France.'

O no, he means to pray for all of them and for France as well.

'Bravo, pussy,' says Benoir.

His sister tells him: 'You are disgusting with your half-baked
patriotism, your boring France. If you are trying to turn my son
into a religious fanatic I shall put a stop to it. Of that you can rest
assured.'

'Goodnight, pussy,' says Benoir.

His mother calls out after him: 'If your knees are red you'll get
a slap, so don't forget.'

'You will not get one,' his uncle assures him. 'Sweet dreams,
puss. Pray for France.'

24

Oil for the Cadeau

When he is out of earshot, Armand remarks: 'That wasn't bad at all for nine years old—he was crazy to go with Viv, but he refused because he didn't want to make Mi nervous. You can be proud of your son.'

What for? She happens to know what he wanted tonight. 'To sleep in our bed between Vincent and me. Only he knew I would never let him, so Monsieur spared himself the ignominy of a refusal by pretending he didn't want anything.'

There is an exclamation of disgust from her brother.

'Ah, penses-tu!' Marguerite calls out. 'Espèce d'un idiot! You don't really imagine I would share my husband simply to honour a stupid debt? Just because you and Marie choose to make love with half the Zoo in your bed, it doesn't mean that Vincent and I need follow your example. On the contrary,' says Marguerite, 'over my dead body.'

Benoir says coldly: 'You are a cheat, Mimi.'

What if she is? 'He won't go short, your puss. I've already thought of something which will more than make up for his disappointment. Don't you want to hear what it is?' asks Marguerite. 'Hé, you two!'

Those brutes aren't listening to her, so she may as well save her breath. That idiot Benoir is talking exclusively to Vincent, his profile turned fastidiously away from her, as if she cared!

'I thought puss looked in pretty poor shape tonight. How'd he strike you, Vince?'

Castleton says rudely: 'He looks an absolute mess. What about those damn things under his eyes?'

'What damn things?' his wife wants to know. She has taken his hand and is kissing it briskly. 'If there are damn things you have only yourself to blame, mon vieux. In case you think you can abandon us just like that without a single thought for the consequences.'

Benoir concedes: 'Could be the excitement of having Vince back has tuckered him out.'

He tells his sister: 'Quickly run up and bless him, Mi. Don't keep him waiting for his kiss tonight.'

This is the latest. Since when has it been fashionable for her to dance attendance on her son?

Benoir says stiffly: 'I have the impression that you are still indebted to your son, Marguerite. Have the goodness not to keep him waiting.'

As she goes, he calls out after her: 'Mi!'

'What?'

'Kiss puss for me.'

'Kiss him yourself,' is all the answer he gets.

'That Mi,' says Armand, smiling. The smile is to make it clear that under no circumstances is he going to discuss his sister. He tells Gustave: 'Serve the coffee in the p'tit salon as usual. The gallery could be too risky for Madame in her present condition, what d'you think, Vince?'

He slips his arm through Castleton's. 'Have you seen the evening papers, by the way?'

'No, why?'

'Gustave will bring them to us in the salon. There is something in them I think might interest you.'

'Really?' Christ, what's he up to?

He tries to get an inkling from his brother-in-law's face, but Benoir is busy complimenting Gustave on the excellence of the dinner.

301

'Champagne for all concerned, my compliments to Madame's chef, and don't forget the papers.' On the way to the salon he says gaily: 'When Mi comes down we must decide where we are going to celebrate your return to servitude. Poor Mi, she hasn't got long to enjoy herself before she is withdrawn from circulation.'

Two months after the announcement of a happy event is the Sioux limit for public appearances.

Benoir says characteristically: 'Poor girl, she will have at least seven months of boredom to face. What a filthy trick of nature's, hein, Vince, to make these poor women pay for our satisfaction.'

He really means it. It's part of his fascination for Castleton that he does. He is incredibly olde worlde even by Sioux standards!

He's a great dear, and wildly funny, and hasn't a clue as to what is making his English brother-in-law laugh.

He contents himself with saying good-temperedly: 'What's funny, fella? Anyway, good to see you laugh.'

They turn into the salon where the papers, hundreds of them it seems to Castleton, are already awaiting their perusal.

'That fellow Gustave is an excellent maître d'hôtel,' Armand says warmly. 'I am delighted for Mi's sake. Take a look, Vince.'

'I say,' says Castleton genially.

He is taking a look and not very much caring for what he sees. English, French and American papers, folded back, Castleton notices, chiefly at the financial section, though there are front page articles too, some of them, noticeably those two inspired knockers the *Cri* and the *Voix Populaire*, sporting headlines an inch tall.

LA BOURSE L'A BAPTISÉ ROI DU TEXAS!

PAPOU A VAINCU ENCORE UN FOIS!

BENOIR AVOUE—L'INCONNU C'EST MOI.

MYSTERY BUYER NAMED IN OIL CONCESSIONS SCOOP—A-M. BENOIR TIPPED.

4 MM OIL BUY FLAPS LONDON, NEW YORK.

S. CALIF. ASPARAGUS WILT AS A-M REVS UP W. TEXAS GAS.

'Very nice.' Castleton straightens up. 'What's it in aid of?'

'What, Vince?'

All this. It's not the first time his brother-in-law has bought the odd oilfield. 'You do it every time you have a bit of loose change. What's special this time?'

'You don't know what is special, Vince?'

'No, I don't.' (I hope.)

'You don't feel there is anything different this time?'

'No, sorry. Ought I to?'

He does, of course. Nobody within a mile of Benoir could possibly fail to get the message that the bloody fool has gone and done something inconceivably awful. He says facetiously: 'I hope you're not thinking of buying me an oilfield, ducky. It's frightfully sweet of you and all that, but it would be cruel to keep it in a Paris apartment.'

Which sounds more than a bit off, but he can't help it. This is the worst moment of his life, bar none.

'No, Vince, you needn't be frightened.'

The silly prick is standing there looking more like the Dauphin than anyone would credit. 'C'est pour ton kid, Vince.'

Oil for the cadeau.

'Don't be a bloody fool, Benoir!'

Oil for the cadeau!

'Pourquoi non, Vince?' His English, like the Dauphin's, goes west with the slightest excitement.

'You know damn well pourquoi. So just don't bloody annoy me.'

'Mais si c'est pour ton kid, alors!' Benoir says quickly. 'It will make them like brothers. Equal in every respect except for what puss will inherit later under my cousin's will.'

'Imagine, Vince, like natural brothers!' calls out Benoir.

'Oh, do give over,' groans his brother-in-law, who is at the window staring at nothing in particular with his fists stuffed in his pockets.

He is furiously touched and still more furious with himself for coming out of this so badly. It's all such absolute and utter hell and not the least of it is knowing he's congenitally incapable of saying thank you decently.

It's a Castleton curse and they all have it. With the exception of Cecil, who is Nature's Toff, they are curmudgeons to a man, and proud of it. They are all terrified of being beholden, and the thought of pocketing their pride for long enough to even appear grateful is the Castleton concept of Hell.

The only person he can ever bear to thank is Mim's chap—

303

and that's not, thank Christ, for oilfields, but for flowers and little bits of stuff he picks up in the courtyard, and anyway he makes it all dead easy by simply holding up his face.

His civilised brother-in-law is showing up the Castletons by saying: 'Don't be that way, fella. It's only natural to want to show a little gratitude for everything you've done.'

It may be natural for you, mate, thinks Castleton. He says as agreeably as he can: 'My dear chap, what utter rot,' and hopes Benoir will let it alone.

But the silly blighter is doing the one about being in Castleton's debt, and going almost as pale as Mim's fellow over it, he is feeling it so much.

'You have no idea what a weight you have lifted from my heart.'

'Oh, come off it, ducky.' He finds the Sioux preoccupation with their tickers a real scream. Even old Mim is threatening to use hers now, to hide the cadeau in or under something.

'You saw tonight how much you mean to my sister and to puss.'

Well, that's all right. 'I still don't want your ruddy oilfield.' He adds unendearingly: 'I suppose it was meant to take the curse off being married to your sister.'

What a thing to say! To Benoir of all people! It was sheer bad temper. He says at once: 'Sorry about that, but I literally can't take it. So don't go on about it, love, because you're giving me the willies.'

It's awful. He's not even looking him decently in the face now. 'It's absolutely marvellous of you and all that, but it just can't be done. Not possibly. I mean you've gone too far, as usual. I mean the whole thing's totally out of focus.'

That must have sounded attractive. Also the follow-up: 'You must try and look at it from my angle.'

Which in any case is *the* completest rot, as well as quite a bit of a liberty.

As Mim's brother he has every right to shower the cadeau with oilfields and never mind the kind permission of the British. A lesser person wouldn't even have bothered to discuss the matter. A less kind, polite, and altogether charming chap would have ridden roughshod over the British Curmudgeon and left him to simmer in his own unattractive juice.

What an aristo that chap Benoir is. He's saying quite gaily: 'Soit. If you are against it, Vince, that is an end of the matter. In any case those two will love each other. So what does money matter?'

Which may be typical, but what a gent.

He is actually saying: 'Thanks. Thanks most awfully,' almost normally.

He can hear the Curmudgeon Within muttering uneasily, I say, steady on. Doin' your block a bit, aren't yer?

'You've been absolutely marvellous about this, my dear fellow. I'm enormously obliged to you.'

He has managed to produce a terrible wooden smile and to lay a large and unpleasantly heavy mitt on the poor little blighter's shoulder. It will none of it do, of course. But for the moment it is all he can manage. Probably too much.

With every word an assisted birth the kindest thing will be to spare the fastidious Benoir further sight of these crimson faced convulsions.

Benoir asks gaily: 'What d'you think of the *Cri*'s new attitude, Vince? What restraint, hein?'

He is changing the subject, of course.

'Bloody rag,' Castleton says. 'I see the *Voix* gives you a rave notice for the new Rabat Clinic. A Glorious Phoenix!' (Praise for the newly opened replacement for the one destroyed by O.A.S. bombs two years ago.) 'The Lot!'

'Naturally, since it is rabidly anti-clerical and the Rabat place will be run on non-denominational lines.'

'Oh, really?'

'It's an experiment,' responds Benoir airily.

Well, well.

He takes a quick look at his strange brother-in-law, who apparently doesn't give a row of beans for the church, yet places the greatest confidence in the prayers of a child.

'On verra,' says Benoir calmly.

Oh, absolutely.

Castleton says amiably: 'I must say I feel a bit let down by the old *Cri* over this oilfield business. Considering how it hates your guts I expected it to be far more lavish with the vitriol.'

Still licking its wounds after the last hiding it got.

Benoir says: 'I imagine it's not exactly eager to repeat the dose.' His eyes are shining like liquid pitch. 'They are all mongrels, Vince. One as rabid as the other. The only way is to beat them to their knees with a massive lawsuit and then to keep them there.' He says quietly: 'One rather wonders about puss at times. One imagines he will have the spirit, but will his health permit him to cope with the whole filthy business?

'Poor puss,' says Benoir.

Poor puss-in-gloves.

Castleton says: 'I hope his hands will be all right by the wedding. The right one's still an awful mess.' It's a pretty crude thing to say after all that kindness, but he has said it.

Benoir continues smoothly: 'It's largely a question of temperament. My brother Baudouin, for instance, isn't robust at all, but he manages these things extremely well.

'Beau adores lawsuits,' Benoir says, smiling. 'But then he is ideally equipped for them. He has the same temperament as Mi, you know. Their characters are practically identical.'

Well, bully for them.

Benoir shrugs philosophically. 'Tant pis, if puss can't manage on his own, Viv will hump the load for him. I know you don't believe it, but Viv is quite good to his little cousin.'

'I know he is,' says Castleton, showing willing. And anyhow it's true, worse luck.

'There is that thing between them,' confides Benoir. 'It was the same with my cousin and me, and between our two fathers. Uncle Georges and Papa were devoted to each other. This is curious,' observes Benoir.

It is an' all.

Benoir says affectionately: 'In any case, you'll have no option, my poor Vince. By the time the real trouble starts for the Dauphin we'll probably neither of us be here any longer. Certainly not I.'

As fifty seems the life expectancy for a Benoir, by thirty-six the grave must be well in sight.

'Don't give me that, Benoir.'

'Why, Vince? What does it matter? Viv will take over. He is quite good, that case of mine. What are you looking at me like that for? I've no intention of dying tomorrow, you know.' He is giggling like Mim's fellow when he's not too sure of himself.

'You'd better not.'

Castleton asks him affably: 'Where's your pal, Ouistiti? You don't look dressed without the little brute. I thought he'd just been popped out into the garden to take his little precaution, as the Dauphin would say.' He couldn't care less where the pesky little blighter has got to, but he is still doggedly determined to show willing.

Ouistiti is upstairs being shampoo'd.

Benoir says, smiling: 'It takes three of them to hold him. He will fight like a mad thing till he's under the drier with his caramel. That is the only part of it he likes. After that they will try and comb him and the whole ruckus will begin again.'

'Oh, fancy,' says Castleton cheerfully. There are others, of course, not a hundred miles from here, who get shampoo'd all the time without so much as a sniff at a caramel.

Benoir is saying: 'I shall make an early start tomorrow, Vince. I want to be in New York by ten o'clock, do an hour's business, and be in Paris for dinner without fail. I don't want my wife to be alone any more before Viv leaves. The days immediately before a wedding must be painful for any mother, but for my poor Marie with her enfeebled health they must be little short of martyrdom.

'It's a thousand pities she hasn't got a daughter to console her for Viv's going away. One does what one can, of course, but one lacks the natural gentleness of a woman.'

This after years of Mim. 'Oh, absolutely,' agrees Castleton stoutly.

Vince is an oddball. He is laughing uncontrollably.

'It's those two ruddy great jars,' roars out Castleton. 'Just look at the buggers!'

'Why, don't they please you, Vince?'

He himself finds the two great Japanese vases of lapis and turquoise cloisonné extremely pleasing. 'It was a good idea of Mi's to have them filled with that strange, almost tan-coloured hibiscus. I find this colour amusing. Don't you agree?'

But absolutely! The whole arrangement is a yell.

Benoir remarks a little stiffly: 'My sister has quite an eye for this sort of thing.'

She has the cool, clear eye of a tiger for it. If her boy friend died in the night she would hold the fort with a few dish-faced roses from the courtyard, exactly right in their almost rustic simplicity, but perhaps a little too exuberant to be white. Then in the morning the flowers ordered from her Paris or New York florist would arrive. White parma violets, exactly right for her dead child. Shy, exclusive, and of course without a single hint of colour because of what he died of. And dry-eyed amidst the loud lamen-

307

tations of her grief-stricken household, Mim in her coolest voice
would direct the disposal, to their utmost advantage, of the white
parma violets.

Cool and composed, and most certainly alone. Because if anything like that ever happened, he'd be tip-toeing through the
oleanders to the nearest airport.

He asks his brother-in-law abruptly: 'Are you letting Bienville
fly you back?'

No. It would be quicker, but he has given his word. 'My wife
has always been terrified of my flying. Now Viv is piloting his own
machine she sees us both dead at every turn.'

She probably has a point.

'I have chartered a plane. Marie has a touching faith in pro-
fessionals. Vince?'

'What?'

A word before Mi comes back. This is actually something he
has been wanting to say for a long time.

Christ. What now?

But Benoir says quietly: 'Vince, my poor cousin would be overjoyed if he could see what a wonderful father his son has found in
you.'

'Oh, rot,' says Castleton, highly relieved. This is easy. You can
just stay put and be cheery about things.

'Believe me, Vince, you are exactly the right man. Mi, perhaps,
could find someone else to suit her, but puss never.'

'Get along.'

'Never,' repeats Benoir. 'You are exactly like a father for him.
It was extraordinary to watch him tonight. He has accepted you
completely.'

He hasn't, you know.

Benoir says slyly: 'So you see, Vince, perhaps Mimi had the
right idea for puss after all. It was only her way of carrying it out
which was a little unfortunate.' That point established, Benoir
assures him: 'You'll see, Vince, now she has you, Mi's nerves will
improve gradually.'

Castleton says nastily: 'They better had, and not too gradually,
either.'

They will. He may depend on it. Meanwhile, the thing he
wanted to say was this: 'If you feel you would like another
opinion, I will do my best to persuade my sister to let your Austrian
fellow have a look at puss.'

'Australian. Not for me, thanks,' says Castleton politely.

'Pourquoi pas?'

Because Mim's a Courvoisier woman. Which rather settles it, Castleton thinks.

Not entirely. Benoir says: 'I will naturally do all I can not to upset Marguerite, but if it comes to a decision over puss it is my word that counts.'

'Yes, she told me,' Castleton says.

'Eh bien, alors?'

'Not for me, thanks all the same.'

'My dear Vincent,' says Armand, 'I find you quite extraordinary at times.'

'And I think you're gorgeous,' Castleton tells him. 'I'm frankly mad about you. Let's have coffee. Mim's being an age.'

Benoir reproves him mildly: 'We will wait for Mi.'

'What for? She doesn't deserve to be waited for. I don't like her,' Castleton says, ungallantly pressing the bell. He is choking with laughter again.

'Eh bien, Vince.'

It's a bit of a scream, all the same. Castleton thinks: I like my brother-in-law, I like my stepson, but I don't like my wife! I even like the cadeau better than I like old Mim. This is a discovery that really makes him laugh.

'Eh bien, calme-toi! Idiot!' Benoir is laughing too.

He had really no idea that Vince was so highly strung. This is exceptional for an Englishman, rather. Tout de même, he is the man for all their needs and he, Benoir, is personally quite satisfied not to understand his English brother-in-law. He sees his sister coming in and says quickly: 'Not now. If you want to tell her about this oil thing, tell her after I've gone.'

He has no intention of telling her. Now or at any other time. She would only send the whole thing up rotten at Armand's expense.

'My God, my brother! He really is the full petit-bourgeois where his family is concerned.

'So why didn't you take it, you fool? Espèce d'un altruiste Anglais?'

'Benoir will only use the money to build another dozen clinics with. Another dozen clinics to be bombed!'

And go rushing round their bedroom in her shift, making the French noise for bombs. 'Boum! Another clinic gone to the devil!

Boum! Rabat! Tangier! Pau! Shreveport! Rambouillet! Boum! Boum!'

And finally collapsing on their bed singing the Marseillaise in a wickedly funny take-off of Benoir at his most patriotic.

'Liberté! Fraternité! Égalité! Schlafensiegutunddeutschland-uberalles!'

And end up by turning a complete somersault and showing her pretty bottom.

By the time she would have him rolling on the bed with her, which was what she probably had in mind for him from the start.

As it is she comes in at a brisk canter, catching them both by their coats. 'Why are we not drinking our good coffee on the gallery, mes amis?'

'Monsieur specially requested that the coffee should be served indoors, Madame.' Philippe is standing beside her with the coffee tray.

'Quel Monsieur?'

'Monsieur votre frère, Madame.'

She might have known such solicitude would not have emanated from Monsieur her husband.

Armand says, kissing her: 'It could still prove a little too early in the season for you out there in your condition, chérie.'

'Ah non, je t'en prie, Armand! Not the Condition!' calls out Marguerite. 'Spare us that sacred Benoir fetish The Condition!'

She tells her husband: 'If Benoir had his way, my whole life would revolve around my unborn child from now up till the moment of delivery.

'What are you hovering for?' she asks Philippe. 'Put the tray down and leave us in peace.' She hands her brother his cup.

'Give it to Vince, chérie,' Armand says. 'How did you leave your son? Here, take it, Vince.'

She left her son asleep. Clutching, she needn't tell them, Vincent's ridiculous book. She tells her brother: 'His temperature was quite high.'

White violets.

'I have told Mammy she must take it again tonight. If it hasn't dropped appreciably by the morning I shall call Paris, Benoir.'

Of course. But naturally. 'Did you give him my kiss?'

Yes. She has given it him .'That fool behaved as if I had given him the Banque de France. Of course he had to give me one to give back to his beloved Uncle.' She declares crisply: 'I've a good mind not to give it to you.'

'It's not yours to withhold.' Armand extends his cheek, laughing. She plants an indifferent peck at random. 'That wasn't his. His was much nicer.'

'Then give it to me.'

'No. You're such a fool, you wouldn't even appreciate it if I did.' Marguerite announces: 'Moumou's kisses are exactly like maman's.'

'Eh bien, Mi.'

'It's true.'

She tells Castleton: 'Maman had quite a special way of kissing. She didn't know it, but it was extremely bold. Moumou has got it too. That meek little thing with his bad kisses,' laughs Marguerite.

'Tu as fini déjà?' enquires her brother.

But she is looking at the scattered newspapers, pretending to see them for the first time. 'My God, but what has happened with this room? Ring for Philippe, Vincent. He must be out of his mind. The whole place looks like a Créole market.'

Armand says smoothly: 'Vince and I were looking up some spot for us to go and we got talking. It's not important, chérie. Viv tells me there's quite a good new place just opened on South Canal, of all places. It might amuse you for an hour. Gustave can ring and make our reservations now. If we don't like it we can always join Viv's party at the Cajun, though the Cajun might be a little noisy for you, as you are now.'

She isn't going anywhere tonight. Tonight, Marguerite informs her brother, she is going to stop at home.

Benoir says instantly: 'Ma pauvre soeurette chérie, you have tired yourself out.'

On the contrary. 'You will be happy to learn that my accoucheur considers I have the constitution of a horse. I am not your wife, mon vieux. I have no intention of making a Bienville pregnancy of it. Vincent will most certainly not be required to assist at the birth of his son.'

This is a Mim-crack directed at her sister-in-law who had been so terrified at her confinement that only the close proximity of Benoir throughout the delivery had been able to pacify her.

She slips her hand affectionately into her brother's. 'I simply want to stay at home with my husband. Voilà tout.' Marguerite says: 'If you can bring yourself to accept such a simple explanation, my dear brother. My dear, dear, complicated brother,' says Marguerite, giving him a kiss.

'Ah, si c'est comme ça, mes enfants,' Benoir says archly, 'je m'en vais.'

25

Darby and Joan

So the Castletons stay at home, sitting together on the magnificent Louis Thing sofa, a Benoir version of Darby and Joan. Mim is being very matey, sipping whisky out of his glass.

'Phoui, c'est caca ça! Poilu?'

'What?'

'I love you.'

He gives her a kiss. What she really needs is a fourpenny one, but he gives her a kiss.

'Are you thinking about your present already, Vincent?'

Of course he's not. He has nothing against the cadeau per se, but he's damned if he's going to start thinking about it already.

'You look so happy, my darling,' murmurs Marguerite.

Well, hooray. He had no idea he looks so happy, but if he's smiling it's because he has just remembered something Armand said in the washroom after dinner on the very first night of his stepson's arrival. Armand had remarked what a pity it was that his wife and his sister couldn't have had each other's sons, and how much better his own bloody son would have suited Mim than her own.

Armand was wrong, of course. For who could possibly suit the ferocious girl better than her own little son? That fancy article, specially bred for the N.O. luxury trade. Just nine years old. Marks easy. Speaks very soft. Property known as Georges-Marie Armand, but will answer to anything. Present owner M-M. M. Castleton!

M-M. has been thinking about her fancy article, too, because she has just had the crust to say: 'He was so good while you were away, Vincent. He didn't once need his smack. Little rubbish, I suppose we'll have to give him two tomorrow to make up!'

Oh, 'we' will? You'll get no answer to that one, matey. As far as I'm concerned you haven't uttered. Actually he's quite glad not to talk for the moment because he has just decided to dig up the old anti-slavery bill again. He hasn't been through it since the failure of the Benoir-Castleton talks, and it might need a bit of tightening up. He wants to get it pushed through as soon as possible. After that last remark, the sooner the better, it would appear.

He appends a clause banning bière de la Meuse and allied nostrums, and appreciably stiffens the existing penalty for les bonnes claques. Apart from that he decides to leave it pretty much as it stands. It's still, worse luck, applicable, and obviously quite as necessary as it ever was. He will let the dear girl have it after lunch tomorrow while the boyfriend is having his nap. His smile broadens as he pictures her surprise, because of course that rugged individualist Mrs Castleton has never heard of Children's Rights, and even if she had she wouldn't care a fig.

He intends to uphold the A.S.B. by every means, even by sleeping in his dressing room if it comes to the push. He hopes for his own sake it won't come to it, but with a hellion like Mim it might be a good thing to keep a trick or two up one's sleeve. He shifts his position to let Mim lie more comfortably in his arms. She's deliciously light. Not with the terrible lightness of the hollow child, but with a blossomy and resilient lightness.

Castleton thinks, good old Dorian Gray Benoir. Commits every enormity under the sun and she's absolutely beautiful.

She opens a shining eye and murmurs sleepily: 'J'ai sommeil, Poilu, tiens, c'est curieux, vous savez?' She kisses him softly on the mouth. 'He is making me into a cabbage already, your son.'

'You pore little dear,' says Castleton, amiably.

So that's the plan. It's dismally inadequate, but it's the best he can manage under existing circs, because Mim will certainly go down with the band playing and he will have to be jolly careful how he twists her arm because of upsetting the boy friend, who bursts into tears if anyone only looks at Mum, let alone gives her the bloody good hiding she deserves. He gives her a huge wink: There is going to be only one winner of this contest: Him.

Oh, Vincent is funny when he shuts one eye like that. He always does it to make moumou laugh. She thinks, he hasn't called me darling yet, but she doesn't think he will be long because he has just taken a pin out of her hair.

'J'adore ta coiffure, Old Duck. C'est formidable, ravissante, et excessivement Mim.'

She adores his fluent, bad, amusing French, and the way he flatly refuses to say 'vous' to her. 'Simply can't be did, Old Duck.' He insists it is positively barbaric to call the woman you sleep with 'vous'. 'One of the barbarisms of the over-civilised French.'

She knows it hurts him to hear moumou calling her 'vous'. He is really extraordinary over certain things, this English husband of hers. Well, when he has his son he can do as he likes about it.

She feels a great upsurge of joy when she thinks what a splendid year this is going to be for all of them. She will have her two beautiful boys, Vincent will have his son, and moumou will have a little brother to play with.

It will do him good to have another interest besides maman and papa.

She thinks, it's amazing how he has taken to calling Vincent that. Since he is back he hasn't once said 'Mr Castleton' or 'your husband'.

Something or someone must have satisfied him that he isn't giving Georges' name away. She thinks, it was terrible, that battle. That little weakling with his indomitable will. I thought I would never break it. She doesn't want to think about it now, it wouldn't be good for the pregnancy, but if it's true what that Normande said—that he had lost control of himself—that would be truly terrible.

That poor moumou, he has had so many smacks for it, here and at Shiloh on Davis's account, and now he is saying it quite naturally and happily. One can tell he is saying it from his heart because he hasn't coloured once. Her little stupid who can't tell the smallest lie without blushing!

She is curious to know who had set his heart at rest. It might even have been Vincent. One thing is certain, it was not Benoir!

She can just hear that fool saying: 'If there are further problems you must go to Monseigneur.' She thinks contemptuously, Benoir has not a vestige of belief left, but that would never prevent him from pushing his responsibilities on to the church.

Whoever it was, she is happy that he is thinking of Vincent as his father at last. It will do more than anything to compensate him for the loss of Georges and to make up for this irrational attitude of Benoir's towards him.

Oh, she loves her brother very much, but for his sick worship of their dead mother she has no patience at all. No wonder Bienville had once explained Benoir's prolonged absence at Mal Choisi to guests by saying: 'Papa's apologies, he will be back tomorrow without fail. He has been taken with a slight case of necrophilia at the Delta.'

She is yawning now, a typical Benoir yawn, with delicate jaws stretched wide and eyes watering pleasurably with the strain.

'Aie! Je m'en vais! J'ai un sommeil fou, vous savez! Venez coucher, mon chéri. Mon homme,' says Marguerite, kissing his hair.

In a minute. He wants to finish his cigar.

Oh, he is funny how he will never smoke in her bedroom, or in moumou's. Funny and sweet.

'Poilu.'

'What?'

'J'ai tellement envie!'

He tips her off his knee quite amiably. 'Push off to bed, darling, you're half asleep.'

Oh, he has called her darling at last!

'Oh, I love you, I love you.' She is kissing his cheeks and his eyes in her relief. 'You can take me, my darling, as much as you wish. We shan't harm your little present, it will only make him glad!'

Well, hooray. He's all for doing the cadeau a good turn. Honestly, the Sioux!

'I shan't annoy you with my pregnancy, my own darling. I promise you, you will hardly notice I am carrying him. I will hide him under my heart.' Marguerite says: 'In France we say that when a child doesn't show. I carried moumou like that, Poilu, nearly up till the hour of his birth.' She confides happily: 'Georges always said I was never so attractive to him as while I was enceinte.'

Well, jolly good.

'I will even feed him, Vincent, if that's what you wish,' Marguerite says. 'Benoir will be against it, but I will do it for you.'

Crikey! Old Mim in Pod! He can't help smiling at her vivid face. The ardent girl is practically radioactive with the pride and the joy and the hell of it!

She catches his smile and says perkily: 'I know you don't think so, but Georges considered me a splendid mother.'

He just says: 'Don't be cheeky, Mim.'

He has pulled her round to him and is undoing her necklace. 'Come on, let's get this off for a start. You've flagellated yourself enough for one night.' He drops the rubies into his pocket. 'Really done your nut tonight, haven't you, chum?'

Oh, she detests it when he uses his horrible London argot.

'Wearin' my 'orrible rubies,' Castleton says. 'You want to watch out, you do, or something's going to bust.'

'Oh, Vincent!' exclaims Marguerite.

'Damn near said you were sorry about George, you did. I almost heard you,' Castleton says.

'I have said I am sorry about George, Vincent,' Marguerite says. 'One can't go on repeating it forever.'

'Oh ah?' Castleton says cheerfully. 'As long as you're satisfied. Push off to bed now, there's a good chap. I've had enough of you.'

'Oh, Vincent, you are being really stupid,' Marguerite tells him. 'Benoir has quite forgiven me.'

More fool him. Castleton says: 'Look, don't go on about it, Mim. I'm a bit anti at the moment, so don't go on.' His eyes are very grey. He isn't smiling at her at all. 'I'm off yer, Mrs Castleton.'

Oh, it's impossible to know how much he means it when he says a thing like that. With Georges their whole relationship would have been at an end.

317

Her eyes are full of tears as she says almost shyly: 'But you will come to me, Vincent, you will come?'

Oh, yes, he'll come all right. When he has finished his cigar. 'Go to bed, Mim. You're being a nuisance.'

She goes at once. She has no wish to hear him say a second time she bores him, out of bed.

So that is rather it. He's going to finish his cigar and then he's going to Mim.

Mim loves him dearly and so does her boy. He is the idol of the fierce and complicated Benoirs. No mistake about that. He is Husband, Father and jolly old Bundle of Myrrh to the lot of them. Because, of course, Benoir goes 'quite enormously' by what he says, and as for Mim and the boy, the sun shines out of his arse for them.

His stepson thanks Heaven for him daily on his little bare knees, and his beautiful young wife is so plainly nuts about him that she is even prepared to suckle his son (he cares for the 'Benoir will be against it' bit!).

All the nice Benoir servants are rooting for him. (Castletonne, le bon type Anglais!) Créole and French alike have accorded him le grand Oui, which is jolly decent of them, and in complete contrast to the staff at Ashwater, to whom he merely represents Extra Work.

The only two dissenters in this Benoir Utopia are Ouistiti, who loathes his guts, and Young Benoir to whom he is a matter of complete and utter indifference. And that's all right because it's mutual.

Except, of course, as far as Young Benoir's relationship with his cousin goes.

But if he wants that dainty little *affaire* nipped in the bud he won't get any help from Mim.

'All boys are filthy, Vincent. If moumou has to learn these things it is better he learns them from his cousin.'

Or from his brother-in-law: 'I never meddle in these things, Vince. I guess Viv knows what he's about and puss seems pretty ripe for it. We mustn't minimise the effects of his illness on puss, fella. It's bound to make him precocious.' Capped by the bland assurance: 'If the thing goes overboard I can always pull Viv's ears.'

He can imagine what Mim's reaction would be when he was out of the room. 'What is he going on about, that fool? You and

318

Georges were the same for each other as Bienville and moumou. What harm can it possibly do?'

And her brother explaining indulgently: 'You mustn't forget that Vince is English, Mimi.'

And Mim saying pertinently: 'As if one could!'

They're probably right. The Benoirs are more intelligent about these things than the Castletons.

They are much more sympathetic towards the purely physical for a start. Take an adult view, neither sentimental or prudish (Castletons please copy). Are all for Mum Nature taking her course and know quite splendidly when to mind their own business. In short they have a sure, light, imaginative grasp of the whole business that is likely to be a sight more help to the ardent-natured little Dauphin than all the rather cheerless counsels of his beloved, but nevertheless misguided, stepfather.

Yes indeed, bright-eyed puss will lap the potent stuff up like a saucer of warm milk and come away happy and relaxed, if a trifle unsteady on his pins. And, of course, simply full as a tic of it all to his beloved stepfather from whom he has, but absolutely, no reticences.

'O, can y'all imagine what he done, that Mr Viv? O, he ain't very polite! O, it is providential for him we are kissing cousins or my Uncle Benoir would pull his ears! O, I do love my cousin Benoir, papa darling. I love him best in the whole world except mama and you.'

And only the happiest consequences. Complete harmony at the luncheon table with everybody smiling except him.

'Bravo, puss. Seems you've worked up quite an appetite. (See what I mean, Vince?) Tell mama I think you've earned a second helping of dessert.'

And Mim helping him lavishly. 'Eat it yourself, stupid. I will give you some more for Dédé.'

So, with everybody so delighted, the real question seems to be who'll take over from the appetite-creating Mr Viv while he is away on his long honeymoon? He can already hear his brother-in-law's characteristic reply. 'We will think of something, Vince,' and turning thoughtfully to his sister: 'It is perhaps a little early for puss to take the initiative, Mimi, but perhaps one might do worse than try the little Dédé.'

And Mim's equally characteristic reply. 'Try who you like, Benoir, but be quick about it or we shall have this boring business of Monsieur not eating again. You and Vincent are the first to complain if I have to force him.'

So up the resourceful Benoirs and sucks to Wilberforce Castleton. Let him keep his reformer's zeal for the jolly old A.S.B.

He steps out on to the gallery and throws his cigar over the rail. Under the palms all is black again. The spurts of silver fire have gone. The night is very still and dark and warm and the frogs have started up the chorus that will go on the whole summer, long after they have left and are living in Paris. He doesn't want to live in Paris but they will have to because of the Clinic. Poor old Mim has got an absolute thing about it. He would like to bring up Crombie again. Armand would back him to the hilt and together they could force her hand, but if anything went wrong while her chap was under Crombie it would be the end of everything for them all. A wicked little picture of life without Mim's fellow projects itself, with Mim in a state of frozen self-control, being very serene with the poor bloody cadeau. 'You must ask papa, Cecil. I have nothing to do with your affairs.' And never once mentioning her dead boy friend or visiting his grave at Chantilly where, at Armand's request, he has been laid with his young father. 'Why should I visit it, Vincent? It will alter nothing.' And turning a cool shoulder on anything that might bring back memories of her little son who has mortally offended her by dying.

He has come out in a sweat at the thought of it. It doesn't bear to think, as his stepson is fond of saying.

He decides he will not mention Crombie's name again, and if Armand brings it up he will remain noncommittal, though how the red, white and blue he's going to manage it, Christ only knows.

He leans backwards over the gallery rail, looking up to where a mild light is spilling out over the upper gallery. Mim, in her scented cave, lying in wait for him! Immediately above, the windows of the Dauphin's apartment are dark except for a light in Mammy's room. He'll have a quick look at the boy before he goes to Mim. Christ, the Sioux. The ruddy habit-forming Sioux to whom he has an addiction. It should be made illegal to marry them. They should be left to marry and reproduce themselves for ever and ever. Though, come to think of it, a spot of incest probably wouldn't come amiss amongst the general bashi bazoukerie.

He can see Mim having a whale of a time dodging from 'tu' to 'vous' and back again according to whether she was speaking to Armand as her husband or her brother!

He lights a cigarette and leans over the gallery rail, smoking it.

The future stretches uninvitingly before him for what seems like a very long time.

He can see himself keeping up a sort of preternatural clock-watching counting the months and years, seeing Mim's fellow through until he is sixteen and getting pretty short-tempered in the process. Because whoever else trial and tribulation ennobles, it isn't shirty Castleton.

On his sixteenth birthday, if he lives to see it, the Dauphin will come of age. It's a purely extralegal event, of course, peculiar to the peculiar Benoirs. At sixteen Benoirs, who the day before had been regarded as mere children with arms to be slapped, come into unimaginable freedoms overnight. At sixteen Benoirs start getting married, come into uncountable wealth. Give each other cadeaux. Sleep au grand lit. Buy fast cars by the half-dozen and have them souped up. Endlessly tour their vast estates. Appear on balconies to show their brides. Take mistresses. Take an amie de coeur. (Quite different, this, from taking mistresses.) Have their little suits made for them (by the fifty) in London by Smythe and Smythe. ('They were my cousin's tailors, Vince, as as well as mine.') Help to populate the Delta and receive (at a special ceremony) their Father's ring. Mim had showed it to him on their honeymoon. Very simply engraved:

'À mon fils de son père. Je t'aime.'

And Benoir will kiss him on each cheek for the first and last time. Roll on sixteen. The cadeau will be about six at the time of his beautiful half-brother's liberation. He will join in the general rejoicing and no doubt enjoy the magnificent feux d'artifice like mad, but he will not be required to take an active part. ('There is no need for Cecil to show himself on the gallery, Vincent, he is not a Benoir.') Lucky, lucky cadeau. It strikes Castleton that this is the first time he has thought of the cadeau as his son. He sees him as looking exactly like Sammy and coming it over Mim's chap something cruel. And that's out for a start, thinks Castleton. At the very first hint of coming it I'll stop it out of your wages, Old Duck (he is amused to find he has already fixed the cadeau's pocket money at five bob a week), because however much he loves the cadeau he couldn't possibly love him half as much as he loves Mim's pale fellow. Not possibly. Absolutely can't be did.

*　　*　　*

He's a Sioux addict all right, but he'll have to try and do something about it. Get a few breathers. Nip over to London now and then. Nip over to Ashwater. Pop and join them all at Antibes for a couple of days. Take more water with his Benoirs or soon he won't be able to cope with even the normal dosage.

He sees himself with Cecil now at Ashwater on a cold clear May evening with a hint of a white frost. The daffs are over but the tulip beds near the south terrace are coming into flower, like great open hearths beginning to glow first at one corner then at the other.

They have grabbed any old coats from the hall and are tramping to the south lodge to inspect the Chinese rhododendrons, roaring their heads off about something or other. Probably the Sioux! Their brother Robin is with them, regaling them with macabre contes from the ICI and gesticulating madly. As usual he needs a haircut and one of his laces is undone. He is the only one without a coat. Cecil and he, softened up by years of Hong Kong and New Orleans, are muffled to the eyes.

Robin has christened them something libellous and alludes to them collectively as 'the Troppos'. The south China rhododendrons are still in their bracken huts and darling old Cecil is looking in at each one like a father, drawing their bracken coverlets higher and tucking them up. 'Poor sweets, if only they could get a bit o' sun.'

''E's orf.'

Robin is screwing his temple with a well-kept finger. His foppish hands never fail to give his brothers a surprise. He is the youngest of the three and quite a bit of a dandy in a boffinish sort of way. He is unpredictable, full of a moody charm and quite terrifyingly brainy, and Castleton thinks how much he and Mim would appreciate each other. He can hear Robin saying after some piece of mayhem: 'Cor, she's a bugger, ain't she?' and cheerfully urging his brother to flog her daily and never heed her boy friend's cries.

'Too fuckin' soft, cock, that's yer trouble,' and adding with affectionate scorn: 'You an' ol' Sissl's a coupla bint-ridden bleeders.'

None of the brothers speaks the Queen's English when they're amongst themselves. It's a Castleton thing. The fonder they are of

322

each other the more colloquial they get, and Irish, Loamshire, North country and Cockney, all very bad, are hot favourites for disguising their affection from each other.

Castleton thinks admiringly how completely unaffected and un-selfconscious Mim's family are in this respect. The Benoirs show their love unashamedly and would never dream of addressing each other in anything but a beautiful limpid French and have set, classic phrases for almost all occasions, some of them very beautiful.

Never mind about that. Just now he'd ditch the lot to be with the colloquial Castletons, just the three of them, tramping down the peaty paths at Ashwater, hearing the blackbirds clucking in the fallen leaves and the minute whine of a sunlit plane high up in the sky where it is still afternoon.

Ideally, Syb would be in Ireland with Bill and Alistair attending to her father's estate. The Debs would be in Paris being finished, and the Littles would be immobilised by heavy colds, with the possible exception of Sammy. Yes, Sammy would be with them, Castleton decides, forging through the leaves by his side, her cold hand in his pocket.

They have fallen behind the others a bit, and now there is nobody else in the misty drive but Sammy and him. It's a treat just to stand and watch the glowing plane ploughing steadily from the sun to the moon where the sky is already the tender solemn blue of early night.

The sun and the moon and the glowing plane all in the sky together. And, best of all, not a Sioux in sight.

But of course there is, because floating towards them, pale as a shade, light as a ping-pong ball, is the terrible snow-white child. He is saying something quite fatuous like 'It is your son-in-law who loves you,' and is holding out for Castleton's inspection a minute thumb in which is embedded a bloody great thorn, and at the first sound of the sweet languid drawl Castleton's Dream of Home goes for a chop!

It's useless, now, to append the tailpiece which was to have been a glorious hot wallow in the giant tub with the giraffe-like taps in the unconverted bathroom at the top of the house and keeping up a shouted conversation (in Loamshire) with Robin, whose room is next to his, and who has as usual undressed in record time by the simple expedient of chucking his clothes on the floor, and who is now perambulating starkers. Because even if the bathroom was locked, which of course it wouldn't be, that would never keep the pale chap out, and all too soon he would be standing by the bath saying: 'You are nice. It is not important that you are old.' So that would have been the end of Castleton's Dream anyway.

26

Mado

He's smoked three cigarettes and got a breath of air and now he's
going in.

The house feels very warm and the salon is full of Mim's clever
scent and the smell of his cigar.

He goes straight up in the lift to the Dauphin's apartment,
through the small salon to the bedroom. The salon was to have
been the Dauphin's schoolroom but, owing to the non-reappear-
ance of Fräulein and Miss, it has never been used.

Both Monseigneur and Father Kelly prefer to use the gallery,
where things of interest like a yellow jack's nest on a jalousie can
be pointed out and admired when lessons begin to pall, which,
with Mim's chap, is precious soon.

Castleton has often seen him, head well on one side, standing
between Father Kelly's fat legs, being fed with scraps of knowledge, or leaning soulfully against Monseigneur's knee, his eyes
raised to his mentor's face with the whole caboosh going in one
ear and out at the other.

He has just reached the bedroom when Mammy comes out,

shutting the door almost in his face. She's in a devil of a state. She must have simply flung herself out of bed because she's in her nightgown without dressing gown or slippers.

He feels himself grow hot. He asks as quietly as he can: 'Is anything wrong with the little boy?'

She seems unable to get anything out.

'Speak French.' He sounds like Mim, but it can't be helped. He would like to shake an answer out of her. He feels appallingly hot.

She starts a long thing about how much she has always loved the little boy. 'P'tit m'sieu' he like mah proper child for me, sir. He special for me, sir, he take mah milk.'

He's dead, of course.

He strides past her into the dark bedroom, with Mammy begging and beseeching him not to put on the light. As soon as he switches it on he can see what has happened.

Cuddled up together on the massive bed are George and Dédé fast asleep, a de luxe edition of the Babes in the Wood, all covered over with tailless ermine! Relief goes through him like a high voltage shock. Mammy calls out in a terrified whisper: 'Oh, please sir, don't you tell on me, please sir!'

But he has begun to laugh so loudly he has had to bolt into the salon and shut the door. He can't get over the Babes! The immensely posh Babes all covered over with tailless ermine! He's mad about them!

Mammy comes in, still imploring him not to let on to Mim: 'She ever get to hear ah put mah Dédé in he bed with p'tit m'sieu', Madame she goin' to kill me!'

She is in her dressing gown now, very modest and discreet, her small milk chocolate coloured feet thrust into slippers. She is a most attractive woman, Castleton thinks, even on the brink of panic. He gets an impression that she is about to throw herself, not only on his mercy, but on her knees. He gets up quickly and brings a chair. 'Won't you sit down?'

She thanks him profusely, apologising at the same time for her previous state of undress.

'Don't know what kin' of opinion Mr Castleton goin' to hol' of me walkin' around without no wrapper on.' He begs her not to give it another thought.

'Bet Mr Castleton think ah clear crazy, slam the do' in he face like that.'

Her colour is gradually coming back. 'Man, that rascal sure 'nough had me in a fix. Ah thought it was Madame comin' back!'

She is laughing now at her fright: 'Ah'd got mah congé straight off! That's for a fac'! Yessir, ain' Sidonie the only one to get throwed out on her ass, excuse me, please, sir,' Mammy adds.

So the putsch is already in operation.

Mammy says: 'Mah feller, he scared to sleep alone.'

'He scared for revenants, mah feller.' Mammy says: 'He dream about um mos' ever' night.' She asks him gently: 'Mr Castleton understan' who ah mean?'

Yes, he does.

'Mr Benoir he explain that for me, 'bout mah feller git right low with she nerves after the papa pass over. But now he got him Mr Castleton for a new pa, he goin' to feel tout à fait, Mr Benoir say.'

Oh, did he?

'Yessir,' Mammy assures him warmly. 'Le patron he think the worlds of Mr Castleton. Got the mos' highest possible, le patron say.'

He probably has, what's more. Though he certainly hasn't been letting it get in the way of his own arrangements.

It now comes out that Benoir is the originator of the Babes in the Bed. Mammy is just telling him so in a mixture of French and Créole. It's a bit difficult to follow but what emerges is a Benoir classic, a little gem that deserves, at the very least, to be called 'L'orphelin de Nouvelle-Orléans, ou les confiances de Madeleine.'

On the very first night of her arrival in New Orleans (Mammy is telling him), Monsieur has made a little moment to follow her to her room, where, after complimenting her on the neatness of her apartment, he had said: 'My brave Madeleine, it is unhappily a well-known fact that p'tit m'sieu' does not enjoy that robust health which one would wish for him, and which one might reasonably expect to find in one of his age. It is therefore possible that he may occasionally suffer a disturbed night, perhaps with some dreams in which he might very easily encounter his dead father.

'The fact that this house is bound to remain strange to him for some little time may serve as a contributory cause, while his recent and abrupt separation from his cousin is certainly another point we must by no means overlook.'

At this point (not before time, it seems to Castleton), his

brother-in-law had begged for a glass of water, and after expressing his pleasure at the freshness of it, had continued smilingly: 'I need not remind you, my good Mado, that everything we have discussed up to this point is a matter of pure conjecture and that there is therefore no need for us to presuppose a predicament of any sort. 'But'—and here Monsieur had possessed himself of both her hands—'if in fact such a crisis does arise, then I want you, my Mado, immediately, and without faltering, to place your Dédé in his bed with p'tit m'sieu'.

'Let them embrace each other nicely, see that they are well covered up, and when he is quite comforted and fast asleep, then you must take your daughter up and put her back into her own little bed.

'P'tit m'sieu' sleeps very warmly, and it could perhaps be prejudicial to the little Madeleine's health to leave her in his bed for longer than is strictly necessary.'

Monsieur had then taken her face between his hands and had said quietly: 'This is between us, hein, Mad? Madame has other preoccupations, at the moment, and it would be mere stupidity on our part to let her know of this. I shall leave the whole business to your discretion, Mad. You have my full authority to act, and I know you will do it with your whole heart as you have always done everything I have asked of you.'

Monsieur had then scolded her a little. 'Cheer up! What are you howling for, you stupid goose? This marriage is the best thing that has happened to p'tit m'sieu' since my cousin died, and you are crying like a water melon. In any case, there is no reason for us to anticipate anything but the best. I am more than optimistic of the good effect of Mr Castleton upon p'tit m'sieu', and if all continues as it has begun, then we have every reason to hope that p'tit m'sieu' will not be troubled by these dreams much longer. Come, Mad, stop making a perfect fright of yourself and let me see you smile. Remember, you are doing this for me and for the sake of all the nice times we had together when we were innocent like those two.'

While speaking of those happy years, a tear had stood in Monsieur's eye, but he had recovered himself almost immediately and, kissing her warmly on both cheeks, had dashed from her apartment without another word.

The End.

Whew! All this before dinner! His admiration for his brother-in-law knows no bounds. While the rest of them had been tamely going about their business this gem from Victor Hugo had been going on above their unsuspecting heads.

How Mim would love it all if he told her about it. She adores jokes against her brother. She and Bienville collect what they call 'Armandisms'. He won't tell her, though, (a) because she wouldn't have the slightest compunction about giving away Mammy's trust in him, and (b) quite simply because she doesn't deserve any fun.

With the main issue even Mim would never dare to meddle. It is an Ordinance Benoir and has passed into law. The Victor Hugo bit was just for window dressing.

Mammy says softly: 'Le patron, he like a saint for us all.'

The tears are running down her cheeks. She loves him very much, but then he probably loves her too.

Castleton is certain there is a place in his weird little brother-in-law's heart for women like her. A warm, exclusive little club where sophisticates like Mim and Liane are not received. Napoleon's words—'I love good, gentle and innocent women'—might have been spoken by Benoir.

Mammy is asking anxiously: 'Hope Mr Castleton ain't mad at me?'

Just the opposite. He thinks it's a splendid idea, and as to Mrs Castleton getting to hear about it, his lips are sealed. Her gratitude is such that he's afraid she is going to kiss his hands. He begs her rather firmly not to mention it, and she contents herself with beaming at him from brimming eyes. They are the best of friends. Their secret is a cosy joke between them. She scolds him warmly for not letting her know in time about the cadeau. 'Ah'd of got me some milk,' she assures him hospitably. 'Hit wouldn't have been a speck of trouble. Hit's all mah ol' man's good for, anyways.'

He says: 'Oh, really?' which sounds a bit inadequate, but Mammy is running on jealously: 'Don't care who all Madame pick, she won't fin' her no French lady with milk lak mine.' She recollects proudly: 'When ah give suck to p'tit m'sieu', man, hit was pretty near runnin' down mah laigs.'

It's difficult to know what answer, if any, she expects to that one. He tries to picture Cecil in a similar conversation with the unmaternal Nanny Pratt and fails.

Mammy bursts out: 'Wisht Mr Castleton had of seen mah

feller before he catched la perle. Ever' body turn they haid to that
chile. I got to hear more compliments for um than Madame, he
was so fine. Sassy, too. Monsieur he spoil um to death. My, he
was like a bob-cat after Monsieur die! Couldn't nobody master
that beggar! He done bit that Governor Davis twicet. Even the
Governor couldn't help but laugh, but Madame she pretty smart
cured um of it. Yessir, she learn um who was boss all right. He got
to tout de suite min' what she say or Madame she hide him good.
Yessir, he quite different now, mah poor feller. He learn respect
all right,' says Mammy, 'but at that Shiloh he catched him a
lickin' pretty near ever' day.

'That Shiloh. That pest hole.' Mammy calls out: 'Even to
think about, ah hates that rotten place.'

A tear splashes on to her hand. 'He so sick, mah feller,' says
Mammy in a loving voice. 'He so terrible sick.'

He says as kindly as he can: 'He'll be all right.'

But she calls out with a kind of exasperation: 'Oh, ah wisht ah
could give him half of mah blood, ah do. I wisht he could suck
mah blood lak he was suck mah milk, that beggar.' Mammy calls
out: 'Sometimes he look to me lak he was gone already. Ever'
time I go to wake him in the morning, ah think what y'all goin'
to fin' this time, Madeleine, what? Then that beggar he call out
"Bonjour, nounou," lak hit ain' nothin' the matter with um. Oh,
I could kill um. I could kill um an' kiss um all at one time. What
he so pale for, that cheat!'

Mammy blows her nose: 'Ain' no use to cry. Maybe hit all be
better now, like Mr Benoir say.'

She seems quite cheerful again, and asks politely: 'Mr Castleton fixin' to take the lif'?'

No, he'll walk down. It's only three flights. She'll come with
him to the stairs. 'Ah got to fetch mah Dédé out now, don't,
she push all the covers off she git warm. Ah done tol' her 'bout
one million time—"You don't lay still,"—ah say—"p'tit m'sieu'
he stan' to catch him a cold".'

Mammy says: 'She only a bébé yet. She too young to know
she gotter put her wishes last.'

As they leave the salon she remarks: 'Sure hope them two
chameaux ain' comin' back.' She's talking about Weber and
Merrick, 'buggin' mah feller with lessons when he ain' up. Leas'
thing them two gone straight off an' tell Madame, make more
trouble for um. Special that Weber, that Boche feller.'

330

Mammy says, giggling: 'Mah beggar ain' pay her no min', anyways. Ah kill mahself laughin' sometimes, see um settin' there with his fingers stuck in his ears on account he ain' never gonna learn Boche! Madame she smack him a few for it, but hit ain' changed him none.' She says admiringly: 'Sure can be a shoat, mah feller, when he want.'

Castleton smiles. 'He's not too keen on lessons.'

'Nossir,' Mammy concedes judicially. 'Certainly ain' too keen, but then he ain' too not keen neither. Bet he learns he studies twicet as good now he got Father Kelly.'

As twice nothing is still nothing, Castleton agrees.

Mammy declares enthusiastically: 'Oh, I could watch um forever sittin' up so pretty with his beautiful white skin, sippin' lemonade with Father.

'Yessir, mah feller he doin' all right he ain't got them two chameaux to bug him. Mr Castleton ever hear what Mr Viv say about them two?' She can hardly speak for laughing. 'Mr Viv say you put them British teeth on top of them Boche laigs you sure gonna have yourself a mighty fine pianner!'

It's very funny.

'Ain' that a fact? Sure is a case, that Mr Viv.' Mammy says simply: 'Me, ah jus' keeps right on praying they drops dead.'

They're on the landing now, standing outside the bedroom door. She asks him in a whisper: 'Mr Castleton care to see a pretty thing before he go?'

He would very much.

She fetches from her room a minute garment which she informs him in a whisper is a camisole for his son. It is exquisitely worked in finest lawn. He praises it enormously, also in a whisper. The thought of the cadeau in a camisole is somehow tickling him pink.

She whispers back proudly: 'Your beggar sure gonna have him a swank trousseau. Madame she order ever'thin' from the Saint Esprit same lak for p'tit m'sieu'! Only except he camisoles,' Mammy says. 'Ah done got special leave from Madame to make he camisoles for you beggar, an' ah gonna pull jus' the gauziest stitches ah know.' She sounds absolutely delighted at this opportunity to ruin her eyes on the cadeau.

She folds the fairy-like vest with loving care. 'Goodnight, sir, Mr Castleton.'

331

'Goodnight, Madeleine. And thanks for everything. I'm most grateful to you.'

'Il n'y a pas de quoi.'

She is watching him go downstairs, showing her pretty teeth at him. 'Y'all be careful now you ain' fall.' Not another word about not telling Mim. Her confidence in him appears to be total.

Well, it's nice to know your wife's a holy terror and everybody's terrified of her, and that tonight his stepson's nurse got into such a flap over her that you thought the bloody kid had kicked the bucket.

Still, it's nicer to know that when you put on the light you didn't see the pale sleeper as you have seen him many times, smiling his sweet mysterious smile as if he had got all their numbers and was killing himself about it, only this would be his last sleep and his nice nurse would have already put his rosary into his gloved hands and covered up all the statues in his little oratory with purple.

'Hullo, ducks.'

She's waiting for him so impatiently she's not even pretending to read *Confessions d'un Abbé de la Cour de Louis XIV*, or whatever it is she's reading.

'What have you been doing, Poilu? You have been quite terribly long.'

'I've been having a look at our chap,' says Castleton. He is pulling off his tie. He isn't watching for her reaction. If she doesn't like it she can do the other thing.

'I hope you didn't wake him, Vincent?'

'No fear,' says Castleton cheerfully. 'Our chap's all right.'

Got his lady friend with him an' all, only he doesn't say so. He goes over to her and takes her in his arms.

'Aren't you coming, Poilu?'

'Yes, all right.' He lies on the bed fully dressed for a long time with her in his arms, kissing her and stroking her beautiful hair. She, poor darling, is kissing him back because of course she has no idea she is being kissed to comfort her for being so nasty and because the A.S.B. is hanging over her and she will hate it quite terribly when he makes her toe the line.

Poor old Mim. Everything is in a shocking mess. A bit of the heat has gone out of it but that doesn't make it any better.

He gets off the bed and begins to undress.

27

The Bluecountry

They are sleeping face to face. Mim has got both his hands and is holding them against the poor old grey-eyed cadeau who will probably turn out to be another black-eyed Benoir, and a girl at that.

A girl with La Perle.

At the dark-grey hour of four he is awakened by the telephone.

'Hullo?'

He hears the pleasant voice say quietly: 'Vince?'

'What's the matter?' He knows, of course, at once. A terrible oppression seizes him as he hears Armand say: 'There has been no response to the treatment so far. Courvoisier is afraid for the heart.'

'What can one do?'

The voice says gently: 'I am not optimistic. They have been working on him since yesterday. I shall give the order to stop. It's a massacre. Puss can't take any more.'

'What about Crombie?'

'Mi is against it,' the pleasant voice says. 'There's someone here wants a word with you.'

'Hullo, ducky, hullo.'

There is only a small clicking sound. His brother-in-law says quietly: 'Don't keep him. He's very tired. Let him go, fella.'

He calls out very loudly: 'Where are you, for Christ's sake?'

'Upstairs. Don't come. You wouldn't know him.'

He throws himself up in the bed shouting: 'Mim, Mim, what's Crombie's number? Get hold of Shuter—it's in my desk. Bloody French doctors. I refuse to let them touch him any more, d'you here?'

She isn't there. Her side of the bed is empty. Christ, what a dream. He is out of bed and up the stairs in a flash. The sweat is pouring off him. He has forgotten about the lift.

The light is shining serenely in the Dauphin's apartment. The lobby is thronged as usual with bright crowds of flowers. She comes out of the bedroom, smiling, and gently shuts the door. 'Mon pauvre chéri, I had hoped you wouldn't be disturbed. That little stupid of mine has taken it into his head to develop varicelle. What possessed Mammy to telephone down instead of sending Albert for me, I can't imagine. I suppose rather than disturb that trash she prefers to wake you. You are not spared much on your first day back, my poor Poilu.'

This will preclude them going to the wedding, of course. Bienville will be furious, but, to be quite candid, for herself she won't mind. At least one will be spared the sight of Marie weeping throughout the ceremony because her son is leaving her! As if he had ever been with her!

Marguerite says: 'Monsieur would have been in mourning too, for his favourite cousin. It would have been impossible to speak to him for at least a week after the wedding without precipitating floods of tears.'

'That child is a perfect nuisance,' says Marguerite. 'Benoir is with him now. He will probably infect half Paris but nothing will deflect Benoir from doing his duty as he sees it.' Marguerite says dryly: 'Happily this doesn't include kissing moumou, so with any luck a few of the wedding guests may still manage to escape.'

She puts her arms round his neck and says: 'I shall make as little fuss as possible, my darling. You will hardly be conscious you have an invalid in the house.' She says: 'We shall not give it to your little grey-eyed present. I have had varicelle as a child

335

and moumou knows he mustn't kiss either of us. He is quite good like that, mon petit singe, he will gladly put his wishes to one side.

'What are you staring at me like that for, Vincent?' Marguerite asks.

'My darling,' says Castleton, taking her in his arms. 'My wonderful, wonderful girl.'

Nothing at all has happened, it is all as finito as ever but he's so grateful she didn't come out of the bedroom saying dreadful things like: 'If you are crying for my son, Vincent, it shows you didn't love him. You have no conception what the end was like,' —or—'You surely wouldn't want him to live for the sake of living?'

Which is exactly what he would want. And if it were twice as bad he would still want it.

Mim is tugging at him gaily. 'Come and tell that nuisance of mine what you think of him, dragging you out of bed like that.'

Before they go, 'Vincent,' says Marguerite.

'What, darling?'

She points silently to her waist and then stands up against him, pretty as the dickens, while he kisses the cadeau for her. They go into the bedroom together and there they all are, the bizarre Benoirs, making a proper do of it, champagne and all.

The lights have all been dimmed because of Mim's chap's eyes, though, knowing the Sioux, it's probably more for his looks. There is quite a burst of applause as Castleton makes his entrance in pyjamas. He'd quite forgotten he's only got his pants on.

'Bis! Bis!'

Benoir is thinking: Vince is a well-made fellow, but all the same it would be a tragedy if Mi's child is a girl.

He has seen pictures of Vince's family. Vast optimistic groups of handsome men and jolly-looking women. He must get puss on to the job without delay. If They listen to anyone up there it will be him.

'Papa looks divine!' shrieks out a frighteningly glittering-eyed and rouged-up looking Dauphin, on whom the idiotically named varicelle is acting like a shot in the arm. He's holding court from his magnificent bed, propped up against a whole Himalayan range of snowy pillows engaged, to Castleton's utter astonishment, not only in playing a left-handed game of chess with his cousin, but beating him at it.

The astounding Sioux! Castleton hasn't yet stopped being

336

astonished by them. Mim on their honeymoon, taking the wheel and driving like Stirling Moss in a mammoth toque of macaque fur. The punctilious, almost puritanical, code of his womanising brother-in-law.

'Viv's mad becaise he ain't winning,' observes the Dauphin, making another devasting move. 'Some types they got to keep winning all of the time. Don't, they get catawampus.'

'Some types ain't tout de suite hold their lip they gonna you betcha get ice down their necks.' Young Benoir is lying on the bed fully dressed, including his shoes, and smoking like a chimney. He's sharing a pillow and a convivial glass with his rowdy little cousin and looks sublimely indifferent to either catching the infection or passing it on to his bride.

He has obviously been recalled from some party and as obviously intends going back to it the moment the doctor arrives, which is what everyone is waiting for. Just now he's eyeing with sulky disfavour the spots which are coming out on his cousin's snowy chest. 'Hey, stop that, will you? Hey, Tante, will you lookit your kid?'

'My God, moumou,' scolds Marguerite as if it was all his fault. She is spotting the spots, too, sitting in Castleton's lap, playing it as a game. All the Benoirs are doing it now, greeting each spot as it comes out with a slow handclap.

'Hey, he looks like a Dalmatian pup!' calls out Bienville, who at this point decides the thing is funny.

'Well, I cain't help it,' returns the Dauphin, on whose long-suffering forehead an egg could now be fried. 'Mama, please may I have a cornichon to suck? I'm so thirsty, mama darling, I could just fancy a cornichon à l'eau.'

Mammy will bring him some orgeat. 'You and your cornichons,' laughs Marguerite, pressing the bell. Benoir says, chuckling: 'We might have guessed puss was enceinte by his appetite at dinner, but when it comes to fancying cornichon à l'eau the thing begins to look grave.'

'Oh, Herman, *please* no corn,' groans Bienville. But Benoir is off. 'Luckily we were able to get him married off in time.' He is giggling so much he can hardly speak, 'there'll be no scandal, Vince.'

'Tante, will you please shoot Herman?' begs Bienville.

'Armand, je t'en prie,' says Marguerite.

'Show papa the ring, pussy.'

337

Hermie and Thingo are having themselves a ball with the kind of repartee that's still waiting for the first shots to be fired on Fort Sumpter.

'It was providential we happened to have the ring handy.'

'O, I am not enceinte, Uncle Benoir.'

'It was a near thing, Vince.'

'O, y'all just being bad to me, Uncle Benoir.'

Chree-ist! Herman and Marie are practically giving each other the eye! That hexed-up li'l Marie!

'Show papa, pussy.'

The burning hand with the ring hanging on it is passed across for Castleton's inspection. It's the ring. À mon fils etc. The gold is very heavy and hot.

Marguerite says: 'It was to have been for his sixteenth birthday, but my fool of a brother has chosen to give it him tonight. He will lose it, Armand, it is far too large for him.'

Benoir returns tranquilly: 'Pussy won't lose his father's ring.'

Pussy won't lose his father's ring. 'Oh no,' groans Bienville, rolling off the bed.

The burning skeleton croaks out in a hoarse whisper: 'He may read what is on it, but he is not to read it out loud.'

'George!' calls out Marguerite.

'Well, it is not for him,' returns the skeleton, unabashed.

'It's beautiful,' says Castleton, giving it back. 'I haven't read it.'

The ring is snatched out of his hand by the skeleton, who remarks in satisfied tones: 'It is my papa's ring for me. It don't affect anyone else. You may put it back if you want. It might amuse you. O, I am thirsty and no error.'

His fever is roughing him up, but he seems very happy in a punch-drunk sort of way and keeps repeating loudly: 'O, it is lovely to see you all. O, I could not half do with a nice cup of tea.'

Mammy glides in with his orgeat, fully dressed for the second time that night.

'Bon soir, Madeleine.' Mim's hiding most of his torso and, anyway, what the hell.

'Bon soir, monsieur.' Of course she's never clapped eyes on him before, let alone shared a secret with him. She goes over to the bed and says softly: 'You gonna lif' you haid let Mammy give y'all a nice li'l drink?'

338

'O, yes. O, I am craving,' calls out George. He doesn't touch a drop.

'You drink now, baby,' says Mammy.

'I'll help you with him,' Castleton says.

'Thank you, sir.' She tells him, smiling: 'This beggar throw all she nice dinner up, Mr Castleton ever hear?'

'No really?'

'Yessir. Ain' wut cookin' fo', this beggar. C'mon, you drink now, baby.'

He tries to drink, and chokes. 'O my throat. O, it hurts me.'

'Dunk his nose in!' commands Bienville. Hell, this yellow cow is getting no place! 'Dunk his nose in it, hear me?' Anxiety always makes him furious.

'Come along, old love.'

That gilt-edged security the British Punk is holding the glass somewheres around the back of Marie's neck and trying to sell it him with a line of Brit. Emp. patois that was possibly in vogue while the *Titanic* was sinking. 'Upsadaisy. That's the stuff. Knock it back.' So what the hell business is it of his, anyways? Also, and on the side, Sweet Fanny Adams is happening.

'Make him drink, papa!' calls out Bienville, stamping his foot. For some reason it has suddenly become vital that his cousin should be made to drink. 'Whyn't you dunk his nose in it!'

'Get yourself together, Viv.'

Benoir suggests soothingly: 'Perhaps a straw, Madeleine. It might be easier for p'tit m'sieur. His glands are possibly a little swollen. Try now, puss.'

'O, I cain't swallow, Uncle Benoir,' complains the pale child, hoarsely. He pushes the straw away.

'What nonsense, of course you can.' His mother steps briskly into the circle round the bed. 'Drink it at once.'

With everybody waiting on him hand and foot, it's not surprising he should try to make himself important. She takes the glass from Castleton's hand. 'Now swallow it without further fuss, d'you hear? I will support your head. Be quick.'

Hey, Tante is the Colosseum. Already Thingo is drinking. Tears are running down his cheeks, his teeth are chattering like castanets but, boy, is he drinking!

'Are you finished?'

'Yes'm, mama.'

339

Then he must stop talking. 'This isn't a social occasion. In case you think you've covered yourself with glory by getting chicken-pox.'

'No'm, I'm sorry.'

Boy, she's the Colosseum all right. Bienville reports from the window: 'Hey, Tante, the medic's here. I'm off, papa. If you want me I'm at the Louisianne.'

'So what happened at the Cajun?' Benoir wants to know.

'It stinks of Jews. We painted it. Be sweet and buzz me, huh? I want to hear the verdict.'

'Okay. Get lost,' his father says.

Bienville calls out from the door: 'You tell that medic he has to let Tante and li'l Marie to my wedding, hear me? I don't get married else. Tell him to shift his butt. Do a rush job on it. Herman, you paying me some mind?'

'Blow, boy, blow,' advises Benoir.

Bienville persists: 'I want to hear the good word. So what the sweet Jesus is there to a case of chicken pox these days?'

'Hit the road, Viv,' returns Benoir. He is rising to meet the doctor, who is bending over Marguerite's hand and who looks extraordinarily like a Benoir to Castleton. At least in this light. An ersatz Benoir, of course. Must be. For his sins he seems to have made a corner in all the real ones.

'Allow me to present my brother-in-law, Mr Vincent Castleton. Vince, this is Doctor Alain Rollin. Doctor Rollin has had the misfortune of bringing puss into the world.' This sally is vastly appreciated by the wild-eyed skeleton in the magnificent bed. Far from being flattened, his fever is making him frightfully chipper and full of beans.

'Enchanté, monsieur.'

'Enchanté de faire votre connaissance, M. le docteur.'

He feels a bit Benoirish himself, come to think of it, stripped to the waist and chatting away in French, one arm carelessly round his brother-in-law's shoulders, regardless of frantic pinches from Ouistiti who is going mad trying to dislodge it by pulling out hanks of hair.

'Ow, stop it, you louse!'

He decides he rather likes the little stinker, whose anti-social and unprepossessing adoration for Benoir is so exactly like Mim's for her wretched chap. 'Stop it or I'll clock you one.'

Castleton takes his arm away. He rather enjoyed feeling like a

Benoir. If he knew what was good for him he'd make a cult of it. A Benoir-Castleton merger would probably be the answer.

Dr Rollin, who seems a nice bloke and only looks like a Benoir because of the light, is ribbing the patient while taking his pulse.

'Eh bien, moumou, I suppose you think it's clever to get chicken pox two days before your cousin's wedding? Of course you could help it. One can always help these things. And what is the matter with that hand? Or is that the latest fad, to go to bed in gloves?'

'I burnt it.' The flames of his fever are cancelling out the flames of his blush.

'Burnt it? Aren't you ashamed to give your poor mother such a fright? Not good, not bad,' he says to Marguerite. 'Perhaps it would be possible, madame, to have the room cleared to facilitate the examination? And if you yourself, madame, would have the extreme goodness to remain, I am certain it will serve to give your little one more confidence.'

It's marvellous to hear the bright-cheeked skeleton imploring: 'O yes, O, mama, stay with me, O, mama darling!' and to see him politely waving him and Benoir away. Blowing kisses and calling out solicitously: 'All the best, O, it is really such a shame you have to go! Until tomorrow, then. All the best! He's quite willing to see them both in hell as long as he has Marguerite.

'Goodnight, old love. Sleep well.'

''Night, puss. Don't bite the doctor. He's not Governor Davis, you know.'

'Oh, get on, Benoir, do,' says Castleton, giving him a shove. 'You going out again, old thing?'

No. He has just time to phone Viv, then he must catch his plane.

'Christ, yes. I'd quite forgotten it's morning.' As they leave the room together, the early sun is striking the Dauphin's rose du Barry curtains to a violent blood red.

He gets into bed and waits for Mim, who has evidently stopped behind to do a spot of bullying.

She's got Mammy and the night sister lined up, as well as the boy friend, whose life, one might reasonably suppose, has already been made miserable enough by the chicken pox.

But not on your nelly. Mim adores the boy friend and will specially go out of her way to tick him off and dress him down and generally settle his hash for him.

'It's not important whether or not you feel uncomfortable. What is important is that you shouldn't be scarred for life. You are on no account to scratch, d'you hear? If I see you even lift your hand to touch your face, I shall take away your book. Don't think because you're ill you can't be punished, my friend.'

And afterwards, when she has left them all for dead, she'll jump up on their bed, light as a cat and absolutely radiant from giving everyone the rounds of the kitchen. 'That lovey ducky of yours is quite impossible. Make room for me, Poilu! Selfish thing! You should have heard the fuss because Rollin wanted him to have a suppository. Make my chair for me, Poilu! He didn't want the sister to give it him! Can you believe it? That was what the whole fuss was about! One might have thought his tutu was sacred from the way he defended it. He's a prude, your lovey ducky. Make my chair for me! Vincent! I want my chair!' cries Marguerite.

She calls it making her chair when he puts his arms round her from the back so that she's practically sitting on his lap in bed.

'Here's your ruddy chair, then. Now sit in it and stop wriggling your bottom about, or I'll clout you.'

'Poilu?'

'What? Look, d'you mind? It's six o'clock.' He wants to get some sleep, if she doesn't.

Yes, she wants to go to sleep too. In her chair. 'Are you happy, Poilu?'

Yes. He's happy because she didn't come out of the bedroom saying: 'He had La Perle, what did you expect?' Or an even worse one. 'I am surprised he survived his seventh year. It is extremely rare with these children,' and so establish beyond all possible doubt what he has been suspecting for a long time, that she had never believed that guff about the boy being better when he was twelve or fourteen or whatever age it was they had promised it for. Or any other guff about him. And that she never had a scrap of faith in Courvoisier or the Clinic or Crombie or God or in anything or anybody at all. And never has had for one single moment. And because he hasn't yet been actually made to hear her say it, this has made him very happy.

'Oh, good Lor', yes. Absolutely,' says Castleton in a loud, cheerful voice.

'What are you talking about, Poilu?'

'Happy,' says Castleton. 'Me.'

Mim's dropping off, but he wants to think about the alternative for a bit.

The alternative is a bright jam-coloured piece of thinking which isn't the answer but is the antidote to Mim's nightshade attitude.

It's about Mim's chap, only for the alternative he is called 'Puss' Benoir and is an International Playboy, a Multimillionaire and the Rave of Paris.

He is eighteen and the jour au colère is over, and all the things that used to get him into a row have now been built up into a great scintillating legend. His drawl, his pallor, his wild bucketing walk, his looks, his gaiety and his sex appeal are all zooming.

He is married to an enfant terrible called Bébé . . .

It wasn't ideal, Vince, but puss was set on marrying his little cousin. Those kids are terribly in love.

. . . and is the father of another terrible enfant also called Bébé.

Bébé and Bébé and a loathly little dog called Toto have tantrums every day, but 'Puss' Benoir can cope.

He hasn't got a lot upstairs, but he is extremely clever at handling Bébé and Bébé, as well as his petite maman-adorée, alias Nightshade Mim.

The loathly Toto he takes in his stride along with being the Rave of Paris.

'Puss' Benoir is also quite brilliant at lawsuits, scoring victory after victory against the *Cri* and the *Voix* and quite frequently against both of them together.

All in all a formidable little guy, but never with his stepfather. That mumpish ancient he adores and will forever revere on account of high-souled magnanimity received during those crummy blue years of the jour au colère before he was voted the Rave of Paris.

He is extremely tender of his creaking friend and is forever

343

exhorting Bébé and Bébé to be tender too. Not being hypocrites they don't want to be, but have a loyal go because 'Puss' Benoir is like a little king for them. The 'Puss' Benoirs are very close and always move as a single unit, and if one of them was to go away for even the shortest time, the others would immediately die of broken tickers; even the repellent Toto!

'Ah, non, Poilu! Vous savez!' exclaims lousy Mim.

But he can't help himself. The 'Puss' Benoirs are making him roar. They were terribly, terribly funny tonight!

Old Nightshade Eyes is hissing: 'Vincent! Je vous en prie!'

Especially Toto! Toto had been sensational! Marguerite protests: 'You fool! You are shaking the bed!'

Well, not sensational, but better than the other thing. Better than going along with Mim to her sable abode.

To the plumey gloomy glade of Midnight Mim.

'It seems I have married some sort of madman!'

'Pipe down, Queenie.' He is stroking her silken sides.

Though the thing that is really making him roar is that thing about the glove.

The first lie the Dauphin has ever told. As old Cecil would say: That's the thing to hang on to.

The Sioux inhabit the grue black forest, the stroppy tundra, but the Castletons must have their bit of bright jam. He is stroking her beautiful hide.